Chap 2 Fractions

Chap 3 B R P

P 65 or 67 Commission Sales or Purchases

P.81 Markup or Markdown %

P 88 Median inventory rate or
Value of average inventory

P/09-6 Find Principle
" Rate
" Time

P. 118 Apply United States Rule

P. 138 Find compound Interest

B x R = P

P ÷ B = R

P ÷ R = B

Steven P. Serafino
M C C (Michiana
College of Commerce)
South Bend Ind or
709 N Michigan St
Elkhart Ind

minuend
− Subtrahend
difference

multiplicant
× Multiplican
Product

divisor ⟌ dividend

College
Business
Mathematics

Fifth Edition

College Business Mathematics

Fifth Edition

A Practical Course in Mathematics for College Students
in Business, Liberal Arts, and Professional Programs

R. ROBERT ROSENBERG, Ed.D., CPA

Educational Consultant
Formerly President of Jersey City Junior College
Jersey City, New Jersey

ROY W. POE, M.S.

Consultant in Business and Continuing Education

GREGG DIVISION/McGRAW-HILL BOOK COMPANY

New York St. Louis Dallas San Francisco
Düsseldorf Johannesburg Kuala Lumpur London Mexico Montreal
New Delhi Panama Rio de Janeiro Singapore Sydney Toronto

Sponsoring Editor: Alix-Marie Hall
Senior Editing Manager: Mary Drouin
Copy Editor: Linda Schaffner
Production Supervisor: Haywood Finder
Art Assistant: Charles Carson

Cover Design: Ralph Castenir
Text Design: Richard Stalzer

Library of Congress Cataloging in Publication Data

Rosenberg, Reuben Robert, date.
  College business mathematics.

  1. Business mathematics. I. Poe, Roy W.,
date.   joint author. II. Title.
HF5691.R612 1973   513'.93   72-10993
ISBN 0-07-053797-6

COLLEGE BUSINESS MATHEMATICS, Fifth Edition

STUDENT PERFORMANCE GOALS

Performance goals are becoming more and more important in business and industry for both planning and evaluation. As education becomes increasingly career-oriented, it also must be evaluated on its success in implementing a specific series of goals. Today's business math student is expected to achieve a satisfactory level of performance in every type of mathematical business problem he encounters. The degree of accuracy needed will vary with the type of problem, and the degree of accuracy achieved will vary with the student's ability. The instructor should set up specific achievement requirements for the performance goals in this course. The student's ability to solve first the Practice Drills, then the Application Problems, and finally the Part Problems will indicate to what extent the various performance goals have been achieved. A summary of the goals for each part of *College Business Mathematics, Fifth Edition*, follows.

PART ONE To compute quickly and accurately, using the fundamental operations of addition, subtraction, multiplication, and division.

PART TWO To convert common fractions to decimal fractions and percents; to compute with fractions and percents.

PART THREE To recognize aliquot parts and use them as a tool in computing rate, base, and percentage.

PART FOUR To compute single trade discounts, trade discount series, single-discount equivalents; to compute cash discounts with ordinary, end-of-month, proximo, receipt-of-goods, and extra dating; to prepare an account sales and an account purchases for commission sales and purchases.

PART FIVE To compute markon based on either cost price or selling price; to compute the value of an average inventory and the merchandise inventory rate, or turnover.

PART SIX To compute simple interest using the 360-day banker's method, the banker's 6%, 60-day method, the accounting method, and the accurate-interest method; to find factors to produce a given yield.

PART SEVEN To compute partial payments on notes based on the United States Rule and the Merchant's Rule; to compute the proceeds of discounted drafts.

PART EIGHT To compute compound interest, carrying charges, and interest on small loans; to compute present worth and true discount.

PART NINE To identify typical payroll deductions; to compute employee compensation based on the hourly-rate plan, the piece-rate plan, the bonus and premium-wage plan, and the commission and profit-sharing plan.

PART TEN To compute depreciation based on the straight-line method, the decreasing-rate method, the declining-balance method, the production-unit method, the sum-of-the-years-digits method; to apply Internal Revenue Service regulations to depreciation computations.

PART ELEVEN To compute overhead distribution; to determine profit and loss; to analyze and compare financial statements; to determine the value of goodwill; to reconcile bank statements.

PART TWELVE To compute sales and excise taxes; to compute premiums and benefits for fire, automobile, and life insurance; to compute net return and percent of return in real estate; to compute mortgage payments.

PART THIRTEEN To distribute partnership profits and corporate dividends; to divide a bankrupt's assets.

PART FOURTEEN To compute periodic payments for a sinking fund and for a debt that is to be amortized.

PART FIFTEEN To compute and interpret the mean, the median, and the mode; to organize, display, and interpret statistical data in the form of bar graphs, broken-line graphs, single-line graphs, rectangle graphs, and circle graphs.

PART SIXTEEN To measure length, area, and volume, angles and circles, liquid and dry capacity using the English system and the metric system; to convert from one of these systems to the other.

PREFACE

College Business Mathematics is one of the most widely used textbooks at the collegiate level. It is used as the core curriculum in business mathematics courses at community colleges, technical institutes, private business schools, and four-year colleges and universities. The fifth edition of this program is designed to meet the needs of at least two groups of students: those who are preparing for business careers and those who want to review basic mathematics and sample the business applications that affect both worker and consumer. Like the previous editions, *College Business Mathematics, Fifth Edition,* is a practical course. This program reinforces the student's understanding of basic concepts in mathematics, improves his skills in the fundamental operations, and provides insight into the types of problems he is most likely to encounter early in his career.

This new edition reflects a careful analysis of current business practices and major trends. Rarely performed computations, such as those for equating due dates for accounts and coding the cost price and the selling price for retail operations, have been omitted so that the student can concentrate on those computations that will be most important to him later on. All other content areas from previous editions have been updated, including those on income and social security taxes. However, because tax rates are likely to change frequently, specific tax rates are cited only for the sake of illustration. The information provided is mainly procedural so that the student can apply the standard methods to new rates.

New topics that reflect modern business practices include an introduction to sampling for business forecasting, commission and profit-sharing compensation plans, and the latest provisions authorized by the Internal Revenue Service for computing depreciation.

A very important change in emphasis is marked by the inclusion of measurement as a part in the text, rather than as a supplement as in earlier editions. The metric system of measurement, long used in scientific and industrial research centers, has been gaining acceptance in business and industry and is soon expected to become the standard of measurement in the United States. Accordingly, the part on measurement provides considerable practice in converting from the English system to the metric system.

The business mathematics applications selected will be helpful to anyone who must manage financial resources either in business or as a consumer, and they are particularly well suited to the needs of the future accountant, business data processing planner, financial analyst, or business manager.

Organization

College Business Mathematics, Fifth Edition, can be used for either a one-term course or a full-year course, depending on the topics selected from this program.

The text contains 16 parts that are divided into a total of 104 units. Each part begins with a statement of why the topics covered in it are pertinent to today's business situations and then provides definitions of key terms.

The unit is the basis of instruction. The concepts of each unit are explained in straightforward language and then illustrated with one or more examples whose solutions are shown in step-by-step format. When the student is satisfied that he can transfer his understanding to similar problems, he proceeds to the Practice Drills. The answers that accompany these exercises provide an immediate self-check for the student. When the student has achieved success on the Practice Drills, he attempts to solve the Application Problems at the end of the unit. These exercises reinforce all the concepts and skills developed in the unit.

In addition to the Practice Drills and the Application Problems, a set of problems, grouped by unit for ready reference, appears at the end of each part. These problems not only reinforce the concepts and skills developed in the part, but also serve as a diagnostic tool so that the student may return to particular units as needed.

The book also includes helpful reference materials. Tables for social security taxes and federal income taxes are provided for use with Part Nine: Wage and Salary Administration. Glossaries of standard business symbols and abbreviations that have been updated to reflect the age of electronic data processing follow the text material.

At the end of the book, a separate section of answers for all the odd-numbered problems in the text is provided as an aid to the student who wishes to check his work. This answer section also contains plotted graphs for the odd-numbered Practice Drills in Unit 102. [A complete answer key with facsimile answers for the narrative problems is provided in the instructor's manual.]

Performance Sequence

The first three parts of the text provide a comprehensive review of the fundamental operations of addition, subtraction, multiplication, and division. Ample instruction is also provided for the conversion of common fractions to decimal fractions and percents and for the use of aliquot parts. This material can serve either as a quick review for students with rusty skills or as a basis for building skills in students who have had insufficient training in basic mathematics. A survey of hundreds of experienced business mathematics instructors who have used previous editions of *College Business Mathematics* supports the practice of placing this refresher material in the text instead of in an appendix. These instructors were overwhelmingly in favor of beginning with the fundamental operations and related topics and following them with the applications of mathematics needed by those working in wholesale or retail operations, banking, accounting, tax law, insurance, statistics, and industrial measurement. Parts Four through Sixteen use the fundamental operations as a vehicle to developing the more complex computations required for various business applications.

Supportive Materials

College Business Mathematics, Fifth Edition, is amply supported by the student's activity guide and the instructor's manual and key.

The *Activity Guide for College Business Mathematics, Fifth Edition,* contains both problem material that reinforces the work of each unit of the text and exercises that provide a constant review of fundamental operations and their business applications. The authors believe that this combination of concept reinforcement and skill review is highly desirable because many students become proficient in business mathematics only after much practice.

The *Instructor's Manual and Key for College Business Mathematics, Fifth Edition,* contains answers to all the problems in the textbook and detailed solutions for the narrative problems. Also included are a facsimile key for the activity guide and a bank of test items that can be used as source material for instructor-prepared examinations.

ACKNOWLEDGMENTS

The authors are grateful to the many men and women from business who made suggestions on topics to be covered and to the instructors who offered constructive criticism on the mode of presentation. *College Business Mathematics, Fifth Edition,* reflects these recommendations.

R. ROBERT ROSENBERG
ROY W. POE

CONTENTS

PART THREE

Aliquot Parts & Percents   41

PART FOUR

Discounts & Commissions   52

PART FIVE

Retail Store Computations   71

PART SIX
Simple-Interest Computations   91

PART SEVEN
Notes & Drafts   109

PART EIGHT
Compound Interest, Present Worth & Installment Interest   129

PART NINE
Wage & Salary Administration   155

PART ONE
Fundamental Operations in Practical Mathematics

How important is mathematical skill? For the accountant, the budget planner, the statistical clerk, the data processor, and the financial analyst, numbers are as meaningful as words; for the supervisor, the manager, and the executive, numbers enter into nearly every major business decision. Numbers are the executive's blueprint—they tell him how his enterprise has grown, how it is doing currently, and how it is likely to fare in the future. For the secretary and administrative assistant, especially an assistant to a controller, a treasurer, or a financial vice-president, mathematical skills can be as important as stenographic skill.

One might argue that today's offices are completely mechanized and that people rarely do computations manually. It is true that mathematical operations are often performed on adding machines, calculators, or even computers. However, the decision-maker doesn't always have a machine available when he needs it; besides, he must know what numbers to enter into a machine in order to get the answers he wants. If he doesn't know how to do percentage, for example, a machine won't help him very much.

All this is said to reassure you that mathematics is not a dead skill that has been replaced by automation. Numbers are more important than ever before in managing an enterprise, and the ambitious business worker must have mathematical skill quite apart from proficiency in machine operation. Thus, a thorough review of the fundamental processes of arithmetic is a good way to start your study of college business mathematics.

1 INCREASING SPEED IN ADDITION

The Larchmont Auto Accessory Store summarizes the daily sales of each of its six departments so that each week the manager can compare the sales of one department with those of another, find out on what days most people shop, compare total sales with those of the previous week to see whether his business is growing, and so on.

Following is a summary, in dollars only, of the sales for the week of July 7.

				SALES SUMMARY FOR WEEK OF July 7			
Date	Day	Dept. A	Dept. B	Dept. C	Dept. D	Dept. E	Dept. F
7	Monday	$811	$ 354	$ 759	$430	$257	$ 342
8	Tuesday	774	833	941	555	527	242
9	Wednesday	227	177	458	287	144	677
10	Thursday	466	463	398	333	582	452
11	Friday	511	933	926	743	631	321
12	Saturday	933	1,215	1,214	987	800	1,007

How would you total the columns as rapidly (and accurately) as possible? Here are four methods that will increase your speed.

METHOD 1
As you add, combine two or more numbers and state the result.

Example | In adding 8, 6, 3, 9, and 5, it is better to say, "14, 17, 26, 31" rather than "8 and 6 are 14, and 3 are 17, and 9 are 26, and 5 are 31."

METHOD 2
When adding two numbers of two digits each, first add the tens numbers, and then add one of the units numbers to that sum. To this second sum add the other units number.

Example | **PROBLEM**   Add 78 and 39.

SOLUTION   First add 70 to 30 = 100
                      To 100 add 8   = 108
                      To 108 add 9   = 117

METHOD 3
When adding more than two numbers of two digits each, add the tens numbers first, multiply by ten, and add the units numbers in sequence.

Example

PROBLEM   Add 83, 47, 52, and 96.

SOLUTION   To the sum of 8, 4, 5, 9 multiplied by 10, add 3, then 7, then 2, and then 6.

$$
\begin{array}{r}
8\,3 \\
4\,7 \\
5\,2 \\
9\,6 \\
\hline
\end{array}
$$

26 × 10 = 260

260 + 3 + 7 + 2 + 6 = 278

or

$$
\begin{array}{r}
80 \\
40 \\
50 \\
90 \\
\hline
260
\end{array}
$$

260 + 3 + 7 + 2 + 6 = 278

Practice Drills

Find the sum of each of the following by adding the tens numbers before the units numbers.

1. 86	2. 92	3. 25	4. 77	5. 82
74	83	64	56	37
160	*175*	*89*	*133*	*119*

6. 37	7. 51	8. 92	9. 32	10. 84
28	67	56	85	27
84	32	87	47	91
56	48	28	76	56
205	*198*	*263*		

ANSWERS   1. 160   2. 175   3. 89   4. 133   5. 119   6. 205
7. 198   8. 263   9. 240   10. 258

METHOD 4

Another suggestion for increasing speed in addition is to look for groups of two or more numbers in each column that total 10.

Examples

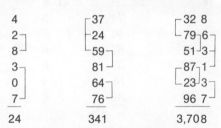

Practice Drills | Find groups that total 10 in each of the following problems and add.

1. 37	2. 86	3. 27	4. 56	5. 48
64	74	89	87	52
23	39	53	43	23
19	78	48	92	67
86	27	76	65	49
25	95	27	58	18
			401	

ANSWERS   1. 254   2. 399   3. 320   4. 401   5. 257

APPLICATION PROBLEMS

P. 4
odd 1-29   Find the sum in each of the following problems by adding the tens numbers before the units numbers.

1. 76	2. 89	3. 65	4. 88	5. 96	6. 54
54	63	97	49	47	68
130		*162*		*143*	

7. 85	8. 36	9. 79	10. 83	11. 76	12. 78
32	36	28	92	84	36
97	75	56	87	76	74
45	49	78	93	82	91
259		*241*	*~~355~~*	*318*	*~~279~~*

13. 23	14. 39	15. 82	16. 74	17. 53	18. 26
47	84	84	39	77	24
65	26	56	84	65	53
81	53	74	74	52	86
97	31	31	63	39	67
64	87	86	93	32	49
377		*413*		*318*	

Find the sum in each of the following problems by recognizing the groups that total 10.

19. 5	20. 38	21. 8	22. 6	23. 9	24. 76
4	74	3	4	2	47
6	46	5	5	1	21
3	87	9	7	8	84
8	53	6	9	3	57
2	68	4	1	4	93
7	32	2	3	6	46
35		*37*		*33*	

25. 8	26. 89	27. 4̂8̂3 ⁵⁵	28. $128.68	29. $ 96.58 ⁵⁴⁵
3	57	642	714.24	812.32
7	96	286	658.82	574.51
4	13	263	852.41	8.83
2	54	658	276.14	36.58
9	85	516	416.24	900.07
1	26	319	431.28	74.46
8	27	875	114.96	893.18
6	18	186	715.86	7.07
5	47	532	293.33	136.64
5̄1̄		4,7̄6̄0		3̄5̄.4̄9̄2̄ 4̄

2 CHECKING ACCURACY OF ADDITION

Quotations are frequently given by suppliers to their customers without the benefit of an adding machine or a calculator. Contractors, landscapers, upholsterers, drapery consultants, and others go into people's homes to estimate the cost of jobs. They sometimes compute the costs on note pads or on the backs of envelopes. Once a quotation is given to the potential buyer, the seller is usually committed to it.

There is no such thing as being "almost right" when a salesman gives a buyer a quotation: it is either entirely right or entirely wrong; and no businessman should commit himself without rechecking his computations.

The simplest and most common method of checking the accuracy of addition is the *reverse-order check*. After finding the sum downward do the following.
1. Add each column upward.
2. Write the sums to the right of the problem.
3. If the sums obtained by both checks agree, check off each answer.

Example

74,653	25 √
82,091	31 √
58,784	28 √
93,438	26 √
27,849	33 √
336,815	

There is another reverse-order check which is similar to the one just given. After finding the sum downward do the following.
1. Add each column upward.
2. Write the sum above the problem.
3. If the two sums agree, the answer is probably correct.

Example

$10,881.86 √

$ 8,618.32

295.18

1,037.44

846.53

84.39

─────────

$10,881.86

Practice
Drills

Add, and check the accuracy of the addition by the reverse-order check.

1. 817	2. 3,218	3. 54,819	4. $563.28
642	5,094	87,384	458.93
361	8,275	43,726	247.85
954	4,735	94,353	639.49
768	9,467	21,267	976.27
291	2,881	89,986	481.63
309	5,326	76,743	709.91

ANSWERS   1. 4,142   2. 38,996   3. 468,278   4. $4,077.36

APPLICATION PROBLEMS

Add, and check the accuracy of the addition by the reverse-order check.

1. 325	2. 7,217	3. 96,582	4. $586.45	5. $4,516.83
874	9,814	73,598	254.78	9,519.68
235	7,983	39,715	349.43	2,674.26
283	2,488	43,386	874.86	8,436.97
684	1,625	97,453	635.82	3,876.32
795	7,429	62,597	381.56	7,324.85
320	3,671	19,764	877.22	3,125.49
986	5,938	82,848	233.18	7,987.55

   In certain types of addition problems, the proof of accuracy is found
when the grand total of horizontal addition is the same as the grand
total of vertical addition. Complete the following table, which shows
the commissions earned by the salesmen of the Colorvision Company
for the week ending August 8. Find the total weekly commissions for
each salesman, the total of the commissions for each day, and the total
of the commissions for the week. Make certain that the sum of the
Totals *column* is the same as that of the Totals *row*. That is your check.

P. 7
Home work
Thur

Salesman	Monday	Tuesday	Wednesday	Thursday	Friday	Totals
6. Alber, H.	$11.35	$12.15	$ 8.70	$ 9.60	$14.50	$ 56.30
7. Burke, L.	8.65	9.20	9.15	7.85	8.95	43.80
8. Cook, B.	6.85	6.75	8.65	9.90	9.35	41.50
9. Hand, C.	7.65	9.80	8.85	8.75	8.80	43.85
10. Hill, R.	10.25	8.40	8.95	12.60	9.85	49.45
11. Lutz, A.	9.15	10.10	9.70	10.25	11.35	50.55
12. Tull, J.	10.55	9.75	13.80	11.25	10.95	56.30

Totals   13. $ 64.45 14. $ 66.15 15. $67.80 16. $ 78.20 17. $ 73.75 18. $ 342.35

3 CHECKING ACCURACY OF SUBTRACTION

In checking the accuracy of subtraction, the sum of the subtrahend and the difference must equal the minuend.

Example | **PROBLEM** From 8,429 subtract 3,592 and check the accuracy of the computation.

SOLUTION

8,429, minuend	Check:	3,592, subtrahend
− 3,592, subtrahend		+4,837, difference
4,837, difference		8,429, minuend

Practice Drills | Subtract, and check the accuracy of the subtraction by adding the subtrahend and the difference to get the minuend.

1. 8,025
   3,996

2. 4,817
   3,098

3. $186.93
   76.99

4. $3,679.18
   1,693.19

ANSWERS 1. 4,029   2. 1,719   3. $109.94   4. $1,985.99

APPLICATION PROBLEMS

Subtract, and check the accuracy of the subtraction by adding the subtrahend and the difference to get the minuend.

1. 6,213
   3,849

2. 7,295
   4,898

3. 6,394
   4,588

4. 5,692
   3,673
   2,019

5. 9,485
   4,528

6. 5,879
   2,695

7. 6,470
   2,971

8. 8,734
   4,896
   3,838

9. 4,863
   2,986

10. 5,894
    3,976

4 − 8 − 12

11. 5,478
2,896

12. 6,406
3,464

2942

13. 7,741
1,868

14. 7,494
4,986

15. 5,495
2,586

4 SHORT METHODS OF MULTIPLICATION

The following short methods will help you multiply quickly and easily without sacrificing accuracy.

Multiplying by 10 or a Multiple of 10

Here is a tip that will increase your multiplication speed when you are multiplying by 10 or by a multiple of 10. Move the decimal point in the multiplicand as many places to the right as there are zeros in the multiplier; then multiply by the *significant digit* or digits. (All digits except zero are significant in a number like 52,000. But in a number like 502 or 5.02, the zero is also significant because it tells the number of tens or tenths, respectively.)

Examples

1. $5,964 \times 10 = 5,964.0.\ = 59,640$, product
2. $832 \times 100 = 832.00.\ = 83,200$, product
3. $77 \times 1,000 = 77.000.\ = 77,000$, product

4. 468×300:

$468 \times 100 = 468.00.\ = 46,800$

46,800
×3

140,400, product

5. $\$236.54 \times 600$:

$\$236.54 \times 100 = \$236.54.\ = \$23,654$

$23,654
×6

$141,924, product

Practice Drills

Using short methods, find the product in each of the following problems.

1. $2,164 \times 10$
2. 594×50
3. 916×10
4. $84 \times 1,000$
5. $\$216 \times 300$
6. $712 \times 4,000$
7. 348×600
8. $\$18.76 \times 70$
9. $355 \times 10,000$

ANSWERS 1. 21,640   2. 29,700   3. 9,160   4. 84,000   5. $64,800
6. 2,848,000   7. 208,800   8. $1,313.20   9. 3,550,000

Multiplying by 25

Another short method in multiplication may be used when multiplying by 25. Multiply by 100; then divide the product by 4 (25 is $\frac{1}{4}$ of 100).

Example | PROBLEM   Multiply 14,592 by 25.

SOLUTION $14,592 \times 100 = 1,459,200$

$$4)\overline{1,459,200}$$
$$364,800$$

Multiplying by 50 and 75

The same method used for multiplying by 25 also works when multiplying by 50 and 75. In multiplying by 50, multiply first by 100; then divide by 2. In multiplying by 75, multiply first by 100, then by $\frac{3}{4}$ (divide the product by 4 and multiply that quotient by 3).

Example | PROBLEMS   Multiply 7,385 by 50 and $265.60 by 75.

SOLUTIONS $7,385 \times 100 = 738,500$ $265.60 \times 100 = $26,560$

$$2)\overline{738,500}$$ $$4)\overline{$26,560}$$
$$369,250$$ $$\$\ 6,640$$
$$\times 3$$
$$\$19,920$$

Practice Drills | Using short methods, find the product in each of the following problems.

1. $9,284 \times 25$
2. 613.32×75
3. 786×50
4. $5,354 \times 25$

5. $2,351 \times 50$
6. 376.84×75
7. 697.60×25
8. 346.48×50

9. 489.75×50
10. 637.87×25
11. $8,024.46 \times 25$
12. $4,687 \times 75$

ANSWERS   1. 232,100   2. $45,999   3. 39,300   4. 133,850
5. 117,550   6. $28,263   7. $17,440   8. $17,324
9. $24,487.50   10. $15,946.75   11. $200,611.50   12. 351,525

Multiplying Any Two Numbers of Two Digits Each

This is one of the most useful of the short methods. Every step in the multiplication process is the same as in ordinary multiplication, except that the total of the second step is *carried*.

Example | **PROBLEM**   Multiply 63 × 48.

SOLUTION

$$8 \times 3 = (2)4$$
$$8 \times 6 = 48, +2 = (50), \text{ carry}$$
$$4 \times 3 = 12, +50 = (6)2$$
$$4 \times 6 = 24, +6 = 30$$

Practice Drills | Find the product by carrying the total of the second step.

1. 36	2. 51	3. 84	4. 93	5. 75
42	76	57	28	36

ANSWERS   1. 1,512   2. 3,876   3. 4,788   4. 2,604   5. 2,700

APPLICATION PROBLEMS

Using short methods, find the product in each of the following problems.

1. $945 × 70
2. 8,527 × 300
3. 836 × 5,000
4. 4,832 × 10
5. $5.80 × 60

6. 746 × 50
7. 3,618 × 40
8. 2,816 × 100
9. 568 × 700
10. 9,284 × 25

11. $613.32 × 75
12. $376.84 × 75
13. $489.75 × 50
14. $8,024.46 × 25
15. 4,687 × 75

16. $441.42 × 50
17. 54 × 27
18. 58 × 39
19. 87 × 24
20. 71 × 43

5 CHECKING ACCURACY OF MULTIPLICATION

Several methods may be used to check the accuracy of multiplication. One of the most useful is to interchange the multiplier and the multiplicand and remultiply.

Example | **PROBLEM**   Multiply 834 by 627, and check the accuracy of the multiplication.

SOLUTION

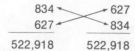

834	627
627	834
522,918	522,918

Practice Drills | Multiply, and check the accuracy of the multiplication by interchanging the multiplier and the multiplicand and again finding the product.

1. 372	2. 509	3. 2,064	4. 3,862
416	276	318	507

ANSWERS   1. 154,752   2. 140,484   3. 656,352   4. 1,958,034

A second method of checking the accuracy of multiplication is the *factor-division check.* Divide the product by either of the two factors (multiplier or multiplicand). The quotient should equal the other factor.

Example

PROBLEM Multiply 568 by 346, and check the accuracy of the product by the factor-division check.

SOLUTION

$$
\begin{array}{r}
568 \\
\times\,346 \\
\hline
196{,}528
\end{array}
$$

Check: $346\overline{)196{,}528}$ = 568

$568\overline{)196{,}528}$ = 346

Practice Drills

Multiply, and check the accuracy of the multiplication by the factor-division check.

1. 826	2. 506	3. 2,574	4. 6,482
235	307	680	745

ANSWERS   1. 194,110   2. 155,342   3. 1,750,320   4. 4,829,090

$\int_0^0$

APPLICATION PROBLEMS

1-2°
odd

Find the product, checking each answer by interchanging the multiplier and the multiplicand and again finding the product.

1. 542	3. 492	5. 3,406	7. 3,771
209	176	2,514	4,059

2. 638	4. 928	6. 40,605	8. 8,216
415	76	817	435

Find the product, checking each answer by the factor-division check.

9. 825	12. 6,623	15. 31,284	18. 116,308
362	5,595	4,497	1,214

10. 368	13. 1,077	16. 36,246	19. 43,796
259	420	9,751	$2.29

11. 4,501	14. 18,822	17. 234,422	20. 81,077
329	564	795	$5.70

SHORT METHODS OF DIVISION

Division can be done quickly and easily by the following short methods.

Dividing by 10 or a Multiple of 10

Here is a short method that will increase your speed in division when dividing by 10 or by a multiple of 10. Move the decimal point in the dividend as many places to the left as there are zeros in the divisor; then divide by the significant digit or digits in the divisor.

Examples

1. $3,850 \div 10 = 385.0. = 385$, quotient
2. $5,670 \div 1,000 = 5.670. = 5.67$, quotient
3. $2,700 \div 300$:
   $$2,700 \div 100 = 27.00. = 27$$
   $$27 \div 3 = 9, \text{ quotient}$$

Practice Drills

Using short methods, find the quotient in each of the following problems.

1. $8,670 \div 10$
2. $3,296 \div 50$
3. $\$16.25 \div 100$
4. $\$397.36 \div 600$
5. $16,350 \div 1,000$
6. $7,816 \div 400$

ANSWERS   1. 867   2. 65.92   3. $.1625   4. $.6622⅔   5. 16.35   6. 19.54

Dividing by 25

Another short method in division may be used when dividing by 25. When you need to divide by 25, first divide by 100, as shown above. Since dividing by 100 results in a quotient 4 times smaller than dividing by 25, multiply the quotient by 4.

Example

PROBLEM   Divide $32,600 by 25.

SOLUTION
$$\$32,600 \div 100 = \$326.00$$
$$\$326.00 \times 4 = \$1,304.00$$

Dividing by 50 and 75

The same method used for dividing by 25 may also be used when dividing by 50 or 75. In dividing by 50, first divide by 100; then multiply the quotient by 2. In dividing by 75, first divide by 100; then divide by ¾ (multiply the quotient by 4 and divide the product by 3).

Examples | **PROBLEMS** Divide $6,800 by 50 and $2,550 by 75.

SOLUTIONS $6,800 ÷ 100 = $68.00 $2,550 ÷ 100 = $25.50
$68.00 × 2 = $136.00 $25.50 × 4 = $102.00
$102.00 ÷ 3 = $34.00

Practice Drills | Using short methods, find the quotient in each of the following.

1. 3,590 ÷ 25   4. $313.60 ÷ 50   7. 6,250 ÷ 25
2. 7,816 ÷ 50   5. 9,775 ÷ 25   8. $724.80 ÷ 75
3. 984 ÷ 75   6. 488 ÷ 75   9. 245.30 ÷ 50

ANSWERS   1. 143.6   2. 156.32   3. 13.12   4. $6.272   5. 391
6. 6.506⅔   7. 250   8. $9.664

APPLICATION PROBLEMS

Using short methods, find the quotient in each of the following.

1. $93.40 ÷ 40   6. 4,270 ÷ 100   11. $325.50 ÷ 75
2. 6,864 ÷ 300   7. $630 ÷ 400   12. 890 ÷ 50
3. 9,300 ÷ 6,000   8. 58,300 ÷ 1,000   13. 7,280 ÷ 25
4. 7,260 ÷ 10   9. 47,700 ÷ 4,000   14. $6,240 ÷ 50
5. 3,820 ÷ 60   10. 6,375 ÷ 25   15. 180 ÷ 75

7 CHECKING ACCURACY OF DIVISION

The most common and effective method of checking accuracy in division is the factor-multiplication check. Multiply the factors (the divisor, or the factor given, and the quotient, or the required factor you must find). The product must equal the dividend. If there is a remainder in the division operation, add the remainder to the product. The sum must equal the dividend.

Example | **PROBLEM** Divide 28,763 by 538, and check the accuracy of the division.

SOLUTION

```
            53                Check:      538
  538)28,763                            × 53
       2690                             1614
       1863                             2690
       1614                            28,514
        249                           + 249
                                      28,763
```

Practice | Divide; then check the accuracy of the division by the factor-multipli-
Drills | cation check.

1. $36\overline{)1,098}$ 2. $85\overline{)10,764}$ 3. $108\overline{)24,709}$ 4. $246\overline{)31,815}$

ANSWERS 1. 30.5   2. $126\frac{54}{85}$ 3. $228\frac{85}{108}$ 4. $129\frac{27}{82}$

APPLICATION PROBLEMS

Find the following quotients, checking each answer by the factor-multiplication check.

1. $89\overline{)32,192}$ 3. $93\overline{)91,875}$ 5. $37,968 \div 218$

2. $58\overline{)392,530}$ 4. $8,709 \div 64$ 6. $83,076 \div 924$

8 ROUNDING OFF NUMBERS

In many business situations it is not necessary to use actual numbers.
For example, assume you are presenting your department's budget for
the coming year to management. The audience will not be interested in
the actual amount of a quotation, like "four thousand seven hundred
forty-eight dollars and sixty cents," but they will be interested in a
rounded number, like "about forty-seven hundred dollars," and are
likely to remember it longer. Other expenses, as well as income, assets,
and liabilities, are similarly estimated in small discussion groups and
general planning sessions.

Rounding off numbers is also helpful in judging whether actual numbers are reasonable. It acts as a check on exact quotations. For example,
a retailer is told that 28 coats are selling at $42.50 each, totaling $1,190.
In order to decide whether $1,190 is a reasonable answer, you can
round off 28 to 30, and $42.50 to $40. When multiplied, the product,
$1,200, is close to the actual amount.

How much an actual number is rounded off depends on the use the
number is to serve. An actual number can be rounded to the nearest
tens, hundreds, thousands, etc. For instance, if the number of acres on
a ranch is 5,889, an estimate for general purposes would be 6,000. If a
house sells for $31,750, an estimate would be $32,000. If a car is
priced at $3,025.75, an estimate would be $3,000.

Examples

811,501	becomes 812,000 when rounded off to thousands
53,499	becomes 53,000
819	becomes 800 when rounded off to hundreds
995	becomes 1,000
63	becomes 60 when rounded off to tens
15.053	becomes 15.1 when rounded off to tenths
.679	becomes .7
126.225	becomes 126.23 when rounded off to hundredths
8.6949	becomes 8.69
.08057	becomes .081 when rounded off to thousandths

396	is rounded off to	400
412		400
809		800
775		800
2,392, actual		2,400, estimated

If the actual answer were 3,392 after being estimated at 2,400, the actual addition would have to be rechecked.

Practice Drills

Round off the following numbers as indicated.

1. To tens
a. 64
b. 23.59

2. To hundreds
a. 449.5
b. 960

3. To thousands
a. 71,501
b. 83,298

4. To tenths
a. 3.250
b. 62.0049

5. To hundredths
a. 18.095
b. 326.6495

6. To thousandths
a. 6.2905
b. 94.005

Estimate the answers in the following problems by rounding off the addends as indicated. Then add the actual numbers and check whether your sums are reasonable by comparing them with the estimated answers.

7. To tens
86
95
32
87
64

8. To hundreds
315
774
289
846
537

9. To thousands
5,803
2,649
3,291
8,082
9,499

ANSWERS 1a. 60 1b. 20 2a. 400 2b. 1,000 3a. 72,000 3b. 83,000
4a. 3.3 4b. 62.0 5a. 18.10 5b. 326.65 6a. 6.291 6b. 94.005
7. $90 + 100 + 30 + 90 + 60 = 370$, actual $= 364$
8. $300 + 800 + 300 + 800 + 500 = 2,700$, actual $= 2,761$
9. $6,000 + 3,000 + 3,000 + 8,000 + 9,000 = 29,000$, actual $= 29,324$

APPLICATION PROBLEMS

Round off the following numbers as indicated.

1. To tens	3. To hundreds	5. To tenths
355.1	548.55	6.454
58.25	3,261	39.048
866.65	994.95	8.076
9.13	12,672	219.937
84.49	459	.049

2. To hundredths	4. To thousands	6. To thousandths
372.5	4,601.50	36.3609
96.2821	37,399.49	8.9673
9.0387	216,500.88	.0054
582.899	6,824	211.4688
.4769	80,555.55	51,106.8249

Estimate the answer in each of the following problems by rounding off the addends as indicated. Then add the actual numbers and check whether your sum is reasonable by comparing it with the estimated answer.

7. To tens	10. To hundreds	13. To thousands
37	332	5,501
85	819	8,499
96	754	3,264
49	681	7,985
32	948	9,595

8. To thousands	11. To hundreds	14. To thousands
3,262	447	1,099
9,108	593	9,185
2,527	814	7,800
8,493	735	3,425
7,645	922	8,674

9. To tens	12. To hundreds	15. To thousands
93	629	3,459
47	387	2,949
56	542	6,378
84	975	5,501
75	463	8,849

PROBLEMS FOR PART ONE

Fundamental Operations in Practical Mathematics

1 Find the sum by adding the tens numbers before the units numbers.

1. 37	2. 48	3. 99	4. 63
28	79	77	97

5. 46	6. 52	7. 62	8. 28
51	46	88	64
29	34	91	83
63	55	58	88

9. 43	10. 26	11. 99	12. 37
21	35	52	87
46	89	53	29
63	69	27	61
94	94	49	53
25	31	46	39

Find the sum by recognizing the groups that total 10.

13. 4	14. 9	15. 78	16. 36
3	2	21	23
8	8	78	38
4	3	34	86
2	7	56	47
8	5	47	23
6	5	23	32

17. 589	18. 4,392	19. $28,648.52	20. $16,444.18
517	4,217	629.58	4,246.22
453	6,596	8,914.87	1,377.19
768	1,863	2.37	143.21
942	7,985	59,108.96	8,644.12
153	2,789	1,281.54	17,387.70
619	6,817	59.84	12.65
319	4,976	852.12	717.75
875	5,762	8,068.93	6,414.14
215	9,184	4,987.46	377.76

2 Add, and check the accuracy of the addition by the reverse-order check.

1. 4,596	2. 243	3. 43,219	4. $784.56	5. $5,286.43
7,588	857	37,684	818.24	861.48
3,243	492	59,694	557.91	9,095.66
4,869	678	83,228	646.88	37.63
3,583	916	67,514	414.39	59.79
5,678	569	32,816	376.47	7,081.35
8,585	844	68,249	218.85	4,529.68
3,877	221	42,851	122.66	1,640.44

Complete the following departmental sales schedule of the Fairchild Automotive Equipment Company for the year ending December 31.

Dept.	Cash Sales	Credit Sales	C.O.D. Sales	On-Approval Sales	Consign-ment Sales	Totals
6. Bumpers	$4,094	$2,413	$1,948	$6,284	$7,453	$ ____
7. Carburetors	642	1,889	753	5,293	5,364	____
8. Fenders	2,967	814	3,967	6,768	6,758	____
9. Luggage carriers	564	596	655	3,346	2,564	____
10. Mirrors	1,087	917	899	1,571	5,236	____
11. Seat covers	438	731	349	2,086	7,474	____
12. Speedometers	695	553	764	1,257	3,682	____
13. Tires	2,643	4,592	1,296	3,242	5,463	____
Totals	14. $____	15. $____	16. $____	17. $____	18. $____	19. $____

3 Find the difference in each of the following, checking each answer by adding it to the subtrahend to get the minuend.

1. 5,304	3. 5,876	5. 5,376	7. 5,980	9. 11,877
2,675	3,587	1,849	1,981	6,964

2. 8,296	4. 4,673	6. 4,876	8. 7,645	10. 213,851
3,897	2,674	2,695	3,798	194,616

Determine the increase or decrease in the earnings of four employees of Malden and Company. The total of the Earnings Last Year column, minus the total of the Increase column, plus the total of the Decrease column must equal the total of the Earnings Previous Year column.

Employees	Earnings Last Year	Earnings Previous Year	Increase	Decrease
11. Fields, C.	$ 9,725	$ 7,880	$ _____	$ _____
12. Gilroy, H.	10,550	8,465	_____	_____
13. Jones, W.	8,275	10,090	_____	_____
14. Otis, B.	12,690	9,865	_____	_____
Totals 15. $ _____		16. $ _____	17. $ _____	18. $ _____

4

Multiply by short methods.

1. 476 × 10
2. $317 × 25
3. 320 × 250

4. 28 × 20
5. 574 × 300
6. 1,068 × 50

7. 648 × 500
8. 43 × 40
9. 408 × 4,000

10. 840 × 75
11. 48 × 750
12. 5,643 × 100

5

Find the product in each of the following, and check by reversing the multiplier and the multiplicand.

1.   363
       274

3. 21,357
       924

5.   6,824
       357

7. 82,460
     5,793

2.   936
       648

4. 92,745
     2,468

6.   8,462
     5,137

8. 24,357
     1,689

Find the product, and check the accuracy by the factor-division check.

9.   825
       362

11. 18,822
        564

13. 3,501
       329

15. 36,246
      9,751

10.   368
        259

12. 31,284
      4,497

14. 6,623
      5,595

16. 94,257
      9,348

Using short methods, find the quotient.

1. 4,370 ÷ 10
2. $87.60 ÷ 40
3. 5,820 ÷ 60
4. 5,250 ÷ 100

5. 3,867 ÷ 300
6. $340 ÷ 400
7. 46,300 ÷ 1,000
8. 56,700 ÷ 3,000

9. 3,280 ÷ 25
10. 9,748 ÷ 50
11. $60 ÷ 75
12. $32,000 ÷ 50

7 Work the following problems, and check the accuracy by the factor-multiplication check.

1. $423\overline{)72,654}$ 3. $681\overline{)70,132}$ 5. $467\overline{)341,965}$ 7. $3,582\overline{)796,842}$

2. $574\overline{)87,891}$ 4. $835\overline{)562,684}$ 6. $294\overline{)881,793}$ 8. $4,276\overline{)635,897}$

8 Round off the following numbers.

1. To tens	3. To thousands	5. To hundredths
a. 37	a. 26,607	a. 27.065
b. 17.79	b. 77,777	b. 447.3333
2. To hundreds	4. To tenths	6. To thousandths
a. 327.4	a. 4.150	a. 5.9202
b. 670	b. 73.9957	b. 31.005

Estimate the answers in the following problems by rounding off the addends as indicated. Then add the actual numbers, and check whether your sums are reasonable by comparing them with the estimated answers.

7. To tens	8. To hundreds	9. To thousands
77	916	4,777
43	732	9,211
27	116	6,328
81	396	7,062
66	239	1,007

PART TWO
Fractions & Decimal Fractions

If everything were measured in whole numbers, we would not have to worry about fractions. The fact is, however, that fractions and decimal fractions are very much with us and always will be, because things are not always whole. We still deal with parts of wholes, such as $\frac{1}{2}$ bushel, $2\frac{2}{3}$ yards, $5\frac{13}{16}$ inches, $1\frac{1}{4}$ pounds, $16\frac{2}{3}$¢ a dozen, 9.5 gallons, and so on.

Following are basic terms in the study of fractions and decimal fractions. An understanding of terms is essential to a successful review.

Common fraction — A fraction expressed by a numerator and a denominator separated by either a diagonal or a horizontal line: $3/4$, $\frac{1}{2}$.

Proper fraction — A fraction whose denominator is larger than its numerator: $\frac{3}{8}$, $\frac{1}{4}$, $\frac{7}{16}$.

Improper fraction — A fraction whose denominator is equal to or less than its numerator: $\frac{5}{5}$, $\frac{16}{2}$, $\frac{8}{3}$.

Mixed number — A number made up of a whole number and a fraction: $7\frac{5}{8}$, $66\frac{2}{3}$, $3\frac{1}{3}$.

Decimal fraction — A fraction written in whole numbers after a decimal point: 1.75, 6.50, 8.39. (Decimal fractions can also be expressed as mixed numbers with denominators such as 10, 100, or 1,000.)

Complex fraction — A fraction whose numerator or denominator or both are either fractions or mixed numbers: $\frac{\frac{3}{4}}{31}$, $\frac{3}{8\frac{1}{4}}$, $\frac{\frac{4}{31}}{\frac{7}{9}}$, $\frac{8\frac{1}{4}}{12\frac{1}{2}}$.

Simple fraction — A fraction whose numerator and denominator cannot both be divided by the same number. Such a fraction is said to be in *simplest form,* or in *lowest terms.*

Renaming fractions — The process of changing the numerator and the denominator of a fraction without altering the value. Fractions can be renamed in *higher terms* ($\frac{3}{4}$ expressed as $\frac{6}{8}$ or $\frac{12}{16}$) or in *lower terms* ($\frac{45}{240}$ expressed as $\frac{15}{80}$ or $\frac{3}{16}$) without changing their value.

Cancellation — The process of dividing numerator and denominator by a common factor.

9 CHANGING IMPROPER FRACTIONS TO WHOLE OR MIXED NUMBERS

Because an improper fraction is greater than or equal to a whole number, it can be changed to a whole number or a mixed number.

Example | **PROBLEM** Change the improper fraction $\frac{45}{8}$ to a mixed number.

SOLUTION Divide the numerator by the denominator. The improper fraction $\frac{45}{8}$ is equal to $5\frac{5}{8}$. The form of the fraction is changed, but not the value.

$$\frac{45}{8} = 8\overline{)45} = 5\frac{5}{8} \qquad \text{or} \qquad \frac{45}{8} = 45 \div 8 = 5\frac{5}{8}$$
$$\phantom{\frac{45}{8} = 8)}\frac{40}{5}$$

Practice Drills | The following improper fractions are the sums that were obtained by adding columns of fractions on inventory sheets. Change each improper fraction to a whole or a mixed number.

1. $\frac{32}{3}$ 3. $\frac{84}{7}$ 5. $\frac{125}{15}$ 7. $\frac{219}{11}$

2. $\frac{97}{8}$ 4. $\frac{59}{6}$ 6. $\frac{416}{12}$ 8. $\frac{580}{75}$

ANSWERS 1. $10\frac{2}{3}$ 3. 12   5. $8\frac{1}{3}$ 7. $19\frac{10}{11}$
 2. $12\frac{1}{8}$ 4. $9\frac{5}{6}$ 6. $34\frac{2}{3}$ 8. $7\frac{11}{15}$

 APPLICATION PROBLEMS

Change each of the following improper fractions to a whole or mixed number.

1. $\frac{59}{7}$ 3. $\frac{747}{12}$ 5. $\frac{968}{20}$ 7. $\frac{493}{25}$ 9. $\frac{32}{5}$

2. $\frac{87}{6}$ 4. $\frac{596}{9}$ 6. $\frac{347}{8}$ 8. $\frac{509}{18}$ 10. $\frac{782}{7}$

10 CHANGING MIXED NUMBERS TO IMPROPER FRACTIONS

To change a mixed number to an improper fraction, use the following procedure.
1. Multiply the whole number by the denominator of the fraction.
2. Add the numerator of the fraction to the product.
3. Write the sum over the given denominator.

Example | **PROBLEM**   Change the mixed number $8\frac{3}{4}$ to an improper fraction.

SOLUTION   The denominator of the fraction shows that the mixed number is to be changed to fourths. Since there are $\frac{4}{4}$ in one unit, in eight units there are $\frac{32}{4}$.

$$8\frac{3}{4} = \frac{32}{4} + \frac{3}{4} = \frac{35}{4}$$

or

$$8\frac{3}{4} = \frac{(8 \times 4) + 3}{4} = \frac{32 + 3}{4} = \frac{35}{4}$$

Practice Drills | To facilitate the preparation of a bill, very often a quantity or price that is in the form of a mixed number is changed to an improper fraction before multiplying. Change the following mixed numbers to improper fractions.

1. $46\frac{1}{2}$ 2. $23\frac{3}{4}$ 3. $18\frac{5}{6}$ 4. $59\frac{4}{5}$

ANSWERS 1. $\frac{93}{2}$ 2. $\frac{95}{4}$ 3. $\frac{113}{6}$ 4. $\frac{299}{5}$

APPLICATION PROBLEMS

Change each of the following mixed numbers to improper fractions.

1. $34\frac{1}{3}$ 3. $82\frac{3}{4}$ 5. $67\frac{2}{3}$ 7. $68\frac{4}{5}$ 9. $93\frac{3}{8}$
2. $46\frac{1}{4}$ 4. $95\frac{2}{5}$ 6. $74\frac{1}{6}$ 8. $54\frac{5}{6}$ 10. $56\frac{7}{8}$

11 CHANGING COMPLEX FRACTIONS TO SIMPLE FRACTIONS

To change a complex fraction (or one whose numerator or denominator is itself a fraction or mixed number) to a simple fraction, do the following.
1. Change the fractions in the numerator and the denominator to fractions with a common denominator.
2. Multiply both the numerator and the denominator of the complex fraction by the common denominator of the fractions.
3. Express the results in lowest terms.

Examples | **PROBLEM 1**   Change $\dfrac{8\frac{3}{4}}{12\frac{1}{2}}$ to a simple fraction.

SOLUTION   A common denominator is found.

$$\frac{8\frac{3}{4}}{12\frac{1}{2}} = \frac{8\frac{3}{4}}{12\frac{2}{4}}$$

Both the numerator and the denominator of the complex fraction are multiplied by the common denominator of the fraction.

$$\frac{4 \times 8\frac{3}{4}}{4 \times 12\frac{2}{4}} = \frac{35}{50}$$

The fraction is expressed in lowest terms.

$$\frac{35}{50} = \frac{7}{10}$$

$$\frac{8\frac{3}{4}}{12\frac{1}{2}} = \frac{7}{10}$$

PROBLEM 2   Change $\dfrac{3}{4\frac{1}{2}}$ to a simple fraction.

SOLUTION   3 is expressed as a fraction having a denominator of 2.

$$\frac{3}{4\frac{1}{2}} = \frac{\frac{6}{2}}{4\frac{1}{2}}$$

Both the numerator and the denominator of the complex fraction are multiplied by the common denominator of the fraction. The fraction is then expressed in lowest terms.

$$\frac{2 \times \frac{6}{2}}{2 \times \frac{9}{2}} = \frac{\frac{12}{2}}{\frac{18}{2}} = \frac{12}{18}$$

The fraction is then expressed in lowest terms.

$$\frac{12}{18} = \frac{2}{3}$$

Practice Drills

1. $2\frac{3}{4}$ yards of material were sold from a bolt that contained $16\frac{1}{2}$ yards. What part of the material on the bolt was sold?

2. Change each of the following complex fractions to a simple fraction.

a. $\dfrac{\frac{1}{2}}{\frac{1}{3}}$ b. $\dfrac{\frac{2}{3}}{5\frac{4}{5}}$ c. $\dfrac{4}{3\frac{5}{6}}$ d. $\dfrac{8\frac{1}{2}}{11\frac{1}{4}}$

ANSWERS 1. $\frac{1}{6}$ 2a. $\frac{1}{6}$ 2b. $\frac{10}{87}$ 2c. $\frac{24}{23}$ 2d. $\frac{34}{45}$

APPLICATION PROBLEMS

Change each of the following complex fractions to a simple fraction.

1. $\dfrac{\frac{2}{3}}{\frac{1}{6}}$ 3. $\dfrac{\frac{3}{4}}{\frac{1}{2}}$ 5. $\dfrac{\frac{4}{5}}{6\frac{5}{6}}$ 7. $\dfrac{\frac{5}{6}}{8\frac{1}{3}}$ 9. $\dfrac{6}{4\frac{3}{4}}$

2. $\dfrac{4\frac{1}{3}}{6\frac{1}{4}}$ 4. $\dfrac{\frac{5}{6}}{\frac{3}{4}}$ 6. $\dfrac{\frac{2}{3}}{9\frac{3}{4}}$ 8. $\dfrac{5}{8\frac{1}{4}}$ 10. $\dfrac{3}{6\frac{1}{3}}$

12 CHANGING FRACTIONS TO HIGHER TERMS

To change a fraction to higher terms, multiply both the numerator and the denominator by the same number.

Example | **PROBLEM** Change $\frac{5}{6}$ to 48ths.

SOLUTION   Since 6 is contained 8 times in 48, to change the fraction $\frac{5}{6}$ to 48ths, it is necessary to multiply both the numerator (5) and the denominator (6) by 8.

$$48 \div 6 = 8$$

$$\frac{5}{6} = \frac{5 \times 8}{6 \times 8} = \tfrac{40}{48}$$

$$\frac{5}{6} = \tfrac{40}{48}$$

or

$$\frac{5}{6} = \frac{(48 \div 6) \times 5}{48} = \frac{8 \times 5}{48} = \tfrac{40}{48}$$

Practice Drills | Fractions must have a common denominator before they can be added or subtracted. Change $\frac{3}{4}$ and $\frac{2}{3}$ to 12ths so that they can be added or subtracted.

ANSWERS $\frac{9}{12}$, $\frac{8}{12}$

APPLICATION PROBLEMS

Change each of the following fractions to the higher term indicated.

1. $\frac{5}{6} = \frac{?}{42}$ 3. $\frac{7}{8} = \frac{?}{64}$ 5. $\frac{5}{8} = \frac{?}{32}$ 7. $\frac{5}{7} = \frac{?}{35}$ 9. $\frac{7}{9} = \frac{?}{27}$

2. $\frac{3}{4} = \frac{?}{36}$ 4. $\frac{7}{12} = \frac{?}{60}$ 6. $\frac{2}{3} = \frac{?}{21}$ 8. $\frac{5}{12} = \frac{?}{48}$ 10. $\frac{5}{6} = \frac{?}{54}$

13 CHANGING COMMON FRACTIONS TO DECIMAL FRACTIONS

To change a common fraction to a decimal fraction, express the numerator as hundredths by adding two zeros after the decimal point. Then divide the numerator by the denominator of the fraction.

Example | **PROBLEM** Change $\frac{15}{16}$ to a decimal fraction.

SOLUTION If possible, express the common fraction in the result as a decimal fraction, as shown in this example.

$$\frac{15}{16} = 16\overline{)15.00}^{\;.93\frac{3}{4}}$$

$$\frac{15}{16} = .93\frac{3}{4} = .9375$$

Practice Drills | Before working the following problems, change each common fraction to its decimal-fraction equivalent.

1.	.93	2.	68.097	3.	$83\frac{7}{8}$	4.	$83\frac{3}{8}\overline{)589.125}$
	$\frac{11}{16}$		$-19\frac{5}{16}$		$\times 38.937$		
	$\frac{5}{8}$						
	$+.8716$						

ANSWERS 1. 3.1141   2. 48.7845   3. 3,265.840875   4. 7.066

APPLICATION PROBLEMS

Change each of the following common fractions to a decimal fraction.

1. $\frac{1}{6}$	4. $\frac{5}{12}$	7. $\frac{3}{8}$	10. $\frac{7}{16}$	13. $\frac{7}{12}$
2. $\frac{5}{8}$	5. $\frac{5}{6}$	8. $\frac{11}{12}$	11. $\frac{4}{9}$	14. $\frac{9}{16}$
3. $\frac{1}{12}$	6. $\frac{7}{8}$	9. $\frac{3}{16}$	12. $\frac{13}{16}$	15. $\frac{8}{15}$

14 CHANGING DECIMAL FRACTIONS TO COMMON FRACTIONS

In changing a decimal fraction to a common fraction, count the decimal places in the number. If there are two places, the fraction is expressed in hundredths; if there are three places, the fraction is expressed in thousandths; and so on.

Examples

PROBLEM 1   Change the decimal fraction .209 to a common fraction.

SOLUTION   The decimal fraction .209 is expressed in thousandths, so the denominator of the fraction is 1,000.

$$.209 = \frac{209}{1,000}$$

PROBLEM 2   Change .0064 to a common fraction.

SOLUTION   The decimal fraction .0064 is expressed in ten thousandths (four decimal places), so the denominator of the fraction is 10,000.

$$.0064 = \frac{64}{10,000} = \frac{16}{2,500} = \frac{4}{625}$$

PROBLEM 3   Change .43$\frac{3}{4}$ to a simple fraction.

SOLUTION   The decimal .43$\frac{3}{4}$ is a two-place decimal; hence it is expressed as hundredths.

$$.43\tfrac{3}{4} = \frac{43\frac{3}{4}}{100} \qquad \frac{4 \times 43\frac{3}{4}}{4 \times 100} = \frac{175}{400} = \frac{7}{16}$$

Practice Drills

Before working the following problems, change each decimal fraction to a common fraction.

1. $\frac{7}{12}$
    .85
    .625
    $+ .08\frac{1}{3}$

2.   .9375
    $- \frac{11}{12}$

3. $35\frac{1}{8}$
    $\times 8.8125$

4. $\frac{15}{16} \div .08\frac{1}{3}$

ANSWERS   1. $2\frac{17}{120}$ 2. $\frac{1}{48}$ 3. $309\frac{69}{128}$ 4. $11\frac{1}{4}$

APPLICATION PROBLEMS

Change each of the following to a common fraction.

1. .65
2. $87\frac{1}{2}$
3. .09
4. .005
5. .0105
6. .725
7. .00125
8. $.62\frac{1}{2}$
9. $.08\frac{1}{3}$
10. $.83\frac{1}{3}$

15 ADDING COMMON FRACTIONS AND MIXED NUMBERS

In adding fractions, remember that only like numbers can be added. Thus, when the denominators of the fractions to be added are not the same, you have to change the fractions to fractions having a common denominator.

Usually you can find the common denominator simply by looking for the smallest number into which the denominators can be divided without a remainder. This number is called the *lowest common denominator.*

Examples

PROBLEM 1 Find the sum of $\frac{1}{2}$, $\frac{2}{3}$, and $\frac{3}{4}$.

SOLUTION The smallest number into which 2, 3, and 4 can be equally divided is the number 12, so the lowest common denominator is 12.

$$\frac{1}{2} = \frac{6}{12}$$
$$\frac{2}{3} = \frac{8}{12}$$
$$\frac{3}{4} = \frac{9}{12}$$
$$\frac{23}{12} = 1\frac{11}{12}$$

PROBLEM 2 Find the sum of $6\frac{7}{8}$, $7\frac{3}{4}$, $8\frac{5}{6}$, and $5\frac{2}{3}$.

SOLUTION If a larger group of fractions is to be added and the lowest common denominator cannot be determined by inspection, select the largest denominator given. Here it is 8. Multiply 8 by 2 or 3 or the like until you find the lowest common denominator—in this case, 24 (8 × 3).

$$6\frac{7}{8} = 6\frac{21}{24}$$
$$7\frac{3}{4} = 7\frac{18}{24}$$
$$8\frac{5}{6} = 8\frac{20}{24}$$
$$5\frac{2}{3} = 5\frac{16}{24}$$
$$26\frac{75}{24} = 26 + 3\frac{3}{24} = 29\frac{1}{8}$$

Practice Drills

Find the sums.

1. $\frac{1}{2}$ 2. $8\frac{3}{4}$ 3. $37\frac{5}{6}$ 4. $84\frac{5}{8}$
   $\frac{1}{3}$ $6\frac{2}{5}$ $64\frac{3}{8}$ $36\frac{7}{16}$
   $\frac{1}{4}$ $9\frac{7}{10}$ $28\frac{1}{4}$ $59\frac{11}{12}$
   $\frac{1}{6}$ $4\frac{1}{2}$ $91\frac{2}{3}$ $73\frac{1}{6}$

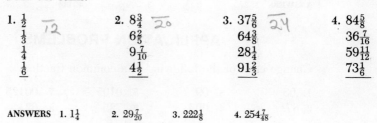

ANSWERS 1. $1\frac{1}{4}$ 2. $29\frac{7}{20}$ 3. $222\frac{1}{8}$ 4. $254\frac{7}{48}$

APPLICATION PROBLEMS

Add each of the following fractions and mixed numbers.

1. $\frac{1}{4}$ 2. $\frac{2}{3}$ 3. $\frac{1}{6}$ 4. $\frac{7}{8}$
   $\frac{1}{2}$ $\frac{3}{4}$ $\frac{3}{8}$ $\frac{2}{3}$
   $\frac{1}{5}$ $\frac{4}{5}$ $\frac{1}{4}$ $\frac{5}{6}$

5. $\frac{3}{4}$ $\frac{4}{5}$ $\frac{7}{8}$ $\frac{5}{6}$

6. $\frac{3}{8}$ $\frac{11}{12}$ $\frac{3}{4}$ $\frac{1}{3}$ $\frac{5}{6}$

7. $\frac{5}{16}$ $\frac{2}{3}$ $\frac{1}{6}$ $\frac{7}{12}$ $\frac{5}{8}$

8. $\frac{1}{12}$ $\frac{1}{8}$ $\frac{2}{3}$ $\frac{1}{4}$ $\frac{1}{16}$

---

9. $4\frac{1}{4}$ $6\frac{5}{12}$ $2\frac{5}{6}$ $8\frac{2}{5}$ $6\frac{1}{2}$ $5\frac{3}{4}$

10. $3\frac{7}{10}$ $7\frac{1}{6}$ $4\frac{1}{2}$ $6\frac{2}{3}$ $4\frac{1}{4}$ $3\frac{2}{5}$

11. $13\frac{5}{8}$ $64\frac{1}{3}$ $46\frac{3}{4}$ $27\frac{1}{2}$ $38\frac{5}{6}$ $54\frac{7}{8}$

12. $73\frac{1}{3}$ $38\frac{1}{6}$ $85\frac{2}{5}$ $36\frac{2}{3}$ $28\frac{4}{15}$ $72\frac{5}{6}$

16   SHORT METHOD OF ADDING TWO FRACTIONS

Here is a short method of adding two fractions, which can save you time as well as serve as an accuracy check.

1. Multiply the denominator of each fraction by the numerator of the other fraction. The sum of the two products is the required numerator.
2. Multiply the denominators. The product is the required denominator.
3. Express the result in lowest terms.

Examples

PROBLEM 1   Find the sum of $\frac{1}{3} + \frac{1}{4}$.

SOLUTION $\dfrac{(1 \times 4) + (1 \times 3)}{3 \times 4} = \dfrac{4 + 3}{12} = \frac{7}{12}$

PROBLEM 2   Find the sum of $\frac{1}{2}$ and $\frac{2}{3}$.

SOLUTION $\dfrac{(1 \times 3) + (2 \times 2)}{2 \times 3} = \dfrac{3 + 4}{6} = \frac{7}{6} = 1\frac{1}{6}$

Practice Drills

Add, using the short method.

1. $\frac{2}{3} + \frac{3}{5}$ 2. $\frac{1}{4} + \frac{5}{6}$ 3. $\frac{3}{8} + \frac{1}{6}$

ANSWERS   1. $1\frac{4}{15}$ 2. $1\frac{1}{12}$ 3. $\frac{13}{24}$

APPLICATION PROBLEMS

Add each of the following fractions, using the short method. Express each sum in lowest terms. If a sum is an improper fraction, express it as a mixed number.

1. $\frac{2}{3} + \frac{1}{4}$ 3. $\frac{1}{5} + \frac{1}{2}$ 5. $\frac{5}{6} + \frac{3}{8}$ 7. $\frac{7}{8} + \frac{8}{9}$ 9. $\frac{6}{7} + \frac{4}{5}$

2. $\frac{1}{3} + \frac{1}{5}$ 4. $\frac{3}{4} + \frac{1}{3}$ 6. $\frac{4}{5} + \frac{1}{6}$ 8. $\frac{5}{6} + \frac{3}{4}$ 10. $\frac{7}{8} + \frac{1}{6}$

17 SUBTRACTING FRACTIONS AND MIXED NUMBERS

As you know, fractions must have the same denominator before they can be added; the same is true when fractions are to be subtracted. It is a very simple process to subtract fractions when the subtrahend is less than the minuend — for example, subtracting $\frac{1}{4}$ from $\frac{3}{4}$. Often, however, the fraction in the subtrahend is greater than the fraction in the minuend. In this case, use the following method.

1. Take one unit from the minuend whole number and add it to the minuend fraction.

2. Subtract both fractions and whole numbers.

Example

PROBLEM From $86\frac{5}{6}$ take $47\frac{7}{8}$.

SOLUTION The lowest common denominator of 6 and 8 is 24. $\frac{5}{6} = \frac{20}{24}$ and $\frac{7}{8} = \frac{21}{24}$. Since $\frac{21}{24}$ is greater than $\frac{20}{24}$, take 1 unit, or $\frac{24}{24}$, from the whole number 86, adding it to $\frac{20}{24}$.

$$86\frac{5}{6} = 86\frac{20}{24} = 85\frac{44}{24}$$
$$47\frac{7}{8} = 47\frac{21}{24} = 47\frac{21}{24}$$
$$\overline{38\frac{23}{24}}$$

Practice Drills

Find the difference between the fractions or mixed numbers in each of the following.

1. $\frac{13}{16}$ and $\frac{7}{12}$ 3. $8\frac{3}{4}$ and $5\frac{2}{3}$ 5. $69\frac{1}{6}$ and $32\frac{5}{16}$

2. $\frac{6}{7}$ and $\frac{8}{21}$ 4. $24\frac{4}{5}$ and $11\frac{7}{8}$ 6. $48\frac{3}{16}$ and $29\frac{1}{3}$

ANSWERS 1. $\frac{11}{48}$ 2. $\frac{10}{21}$ 3. $3\frac{1}{12}$ 4. $12\frac{37}{40}$ 5. $36\frac{41}{48}$ 6. $18\frac{41}{48}$

APPLICATION PROBLEMS

Find the difference in each of the following.

1. $53\frac{1}{4} - 28\frac{2}{3}$ 4. $47\frac{3}{8} - 32\frac{5}{6}$ 7. $432\frac{5}{12} - 238\frac{7}{8}$

2. $63\frac{2}{3} - 48\frac{3}{4}$ 5. $95\frac{1}{2} - 77\frac{3}{5}$ 8. $848\frac{4}{7} - 129\frac{5}{6}$

3. $82\frac{5}{6} - 38\frac{7}{8}$ 6. $38\frac{7}{12} - 19\frac{5}{16}$ 9. $582\frac{1}{6} - 493\frac{11}{16}$

18 SHORT METHOD OF SUBTRACTING FRACTIONS

Here is a method of subtracting fractions that can save you time; it is similar to the short method used in adding fractions, which was reviewed in Unit 16.

1. Multiply the denominator of the subtrahend by the numerator of the minuend.

2. From this product subtract the product of the denominator of the minuend and the numerator of the subtrahend. The difference is the required numerator.

3. Multiply the denominators. The product is the required denominator.

4. Express the result in lowest terms.

Examples

PROBLEM 1   From $\frac{4}{5}$ subtract $\frac{3}{4}$.

SOLUTION $\frac{4}{5} - \frac{3}{4} = \dfrac{(4 \times 4) - (3 \times 5)}{5 \times 4} = \dfrac{16 - 15}{20} = \frac{1}{20}$

PROBLEM 2   Subtract $\frac{7}{6}$ from $\frac{9}{4}$.

SOLUTION $\frac{9}{4} - \frac{7}{6} = \dfrac{(9 \times 6) - (7 \times 4)}{4 \times 6} = \dfrac{54 - 28}{24}$

$= \frac{26}{24} = 1\frac{2}{24} = 1\frac{1}{12}$

Practice Drills

Subtract, using the short method. Show the details of the work.

1. From $\frac{5}{8}$ subtract $\frac{1}{6}$.
2. $\frac{11}{12} - \frac{5}{16}$

3. From $3\frac{3}{4}$ take $\frac{6}{7}$.
4. $6\frac{2}{5} - 2\frac{7}{8}$

ANSWERS 1. $\frac{11}{24}$ 2. $\frac{29}{48}$ 3. $2\frac{25}{28}$ 4. $3\frac{21}{40}$

APPLICATION PROBLEMS

Subtract each of the following fractions, using the short method. Express each difference in lowest terms.

1. $\frac{5}{6} - \frac{2}{3}$
2. $4\frac{1}{2} - 2\frac{6}{7}$
3. $\frac{2}{3} - \frac{5}{16}$
4. $\frac{3}{4} - \frac{5}{9}$
5. $\frac{7}{12} - \frac{5}{9}$
6. $\frac{11}{15} - \frac{5}{8}$
7. $\frac{8}{9} - \frac{7}{8}$
8. $1\frac{5}{6} - \frac{7}{9}$
9. $4\frac{1}{3} - 2\frac{7}{8}$
10. $5\frac{11}{16} - 4\frac{15}{16}$

19 SUBTRACTING DECIMAL FRACTIONS

The subtraction of decimal fractions is the same as for common fractions. The important thing is to remember to place the decimal point in the subtrahend directly under the decimal point in the minuend.

Examples

1. $485.81\frac{1}{8} = 485.81\frac{3}{24} = 485.80\frac{27}{24}$
    $\underline{239.83\frac{1}{3}} = \underline{239.83\frac{8}{24}} = \underline{239.83\frac{8}{24}}$
    $245.97\frac{19}{24}$

2. $73.375\frac{1}{4} = 73.375\frac{1}{4} = 73.375\frac{3}{12} = 73.374\frac{15}{12}$
    $\underline{51.9\frac{1}{6}} = \underline{51.916\frac{2}{3}} = \underline{51.916\frac{8}{12}} = \underline{51.916\frac{8}{12}}$
    $21.458\frac{7}{12}$

Practice
Drills

Subtract the following decimal fractions.

1. $43.8\frac{3}{4}$
    $\underline{13.9\frac{1}{3}}$

2. $96\frac{5}{6}$
    $\underline{28.37\frac{1}{2}}$ 28 3/8

3. 208.9375
    $\underline{182\frac{7}{12}}$

ANSWERS 1. $29.9\frac{5}{12}$ 2. $68\frac{11}{24}$ 3. $26\frac{17}{48}$

 .975

APPLICATION PROBLEMS

Subtract each of the following.

1. $84.68\frac{3}{4}$
    $\underline{37\frac{7}{8}}$ 87 1/2
    46.81 1/4

3. $36.78\frac{3}{4}$
    $\underline{24.99\frac{5}{6}}$

5. $361.91\frac{2}{3}$
    $\underline{280.93\frac{3}{4}}$

7. $51.81\frac{1}{4}$
    $\underline{29\frac{5}{8}}$

9. $472.15\frac{1}{8}$
    $\underline{333.33\frac{1}{3}}$

2. $3.13\frac{1}{3}$
    $\underline{.666\frac{2}{3}}$

4. $136\frac{4}{5}$
    $\underline{93.625}$

6. 82.25
    $\underline{47.06\frac{2}{3}}$

8. $547\frac{7}{12}$
    $\underline{268\frac{13}{16}}$

10. $6.38\frac{7}{16}$
    $\underline{.47\frac{9}{16}}$

20 MULTIPLYING A FRACTION BY A FRACTION

When fractions are multiplied, the denominators need not be the same, as they do in adding or subtracting fractions. To multiply one fraction by another, find the product of the numerators to determine the new numerator; then find the product of the denominators to determine the new denominator.

Example

PROBLEM An investor who held $\frac{2}{3}$ of the stock of a corporation sold $\frac{1}{4}$ of it. What part of the total stock was the amount sold?

SOLUTION

$\frac{1}{4}$ of $\frac{2}{3} = \frac{1}{4} \times \frac{2}{3} = \frac{2}{12} = \frac{1}{6}$, part of the total stock sold

An easier method of solving the problem in the previous example is to divide the terms of the fraction by a common fraction before multiplying—that is, to use cancellation.

Example | $\frac{1}{\cancel{4}} \times \frac{\cancel{2}}{3} = \frac{1}{6}$
^{2}

Practice Drill | Hull and Cane were equal partners. With Cane's consent, Hull sold $\frac{3}{8}$ of his interest to Barnes. What share did Hull retain in the business?

ANSWER $\frac{5}{16}$

APPLICATION PROBLEMS

Find the value of each of the following.

1. $\frac{3}{4}$ of $\frac{1}{6}$ 3. $\frac{7}{8}$ of $\frac{4}{5}$ 5. $\frac{1}{2}$ of $\frac{4}{5}$ 7. $\frac{6}{7}$ of $\frac{1}{3}$ 9. $\frac{5}{8}$ of $\frac{6}{7}$
2. $\frac{2}{3}$ of $\frac{6}{7}$ 4. $\frac{3}{8}$ of $\frac{5}{6}$ 6. $\frac{1}{4}$ of $\frac{1}{6}$ 8. $\frac{2}{3}$ of $\frac{4}{5}$ 10. $\frac{1}{4}$ of $\frac{5}{6}$

21 MULTIPLYING A MIXED NUMBER BY A MIXED NUMBER

To multiply a mixed number by another mixed number, use the following steps.

1. Multiply the fraction in the multiplicand by the fraction in the multiplier.
2. Multiply the whole number in the multiplicand by the fraction in the multiplier.
3. Multiply the fraction in the multiplicand by the whole number in the multiplier.
4. Multiply the whole number in the multiplicand by the whole number in the multiplier.
5. Add all the products.

Example | **PROBLEM** $73\frac{4}{5} \times 48\frac{3}{4} = ?$ ($73\frac{4}{5}$ is the multiplier, and $48\frac{3}{4}$ is the multiplicand.)

SOLUTION

$$\frac{4}{5} \times \frac{3}{4} = \quad \frac{3}{5}$$
$$\frac{4}{5} \times 48 = \quad 38\frac{2}{5}$$
$$73 \times \frac{3}{4} = \quad 54\frac{3}{4}$$
$$73 \times 48 = 3{,}504$$
$$\overline{\quad\quad\quad 3{,}597\frac{3}{4}}$$

Mixed numbers may also be multiplied by changing the common fractions to decimal fractions.

Example | **PROBLEM** $73\frac{4}{5} \times 48\frac{3}{4} = ?$

SOLUTION

$$73\frac{4}{5} \times 48\frac{3}{4} = 3{,}597.75$$

$$
\begin{array}{r}
48.75 \\
\times\, 73.8 \\
\hline
39{,}000 \\
14{,}625 \\
34{,}125 \\
\hline
3{,}597.750
\end{array}
$$

A third way of multiplying mixed numbers is by changing the mixed numbers to improper fractions and finding the product by cancellation.

Example | **PROBLEM** $73\frac{4}{5} \times 48\frac{3}{4} = ?$

SOLUTION

$$73\frac{4}{5} \times 48\frac{3}{4} = \frac{369}{5} \times \frac{\overset{39}{\cancel{195}}}{4} = \frac{369 \times 39}{4} = \frac{14{,}391}{4} = 3{,}597\frac{3}{4}$$

Practice Drills | Find the product. Check by changing the mixed numbers to either decimal fractions or improper fractions. Then multiply again.

1. $28\frac{1}{8} \times 16\frac{1}{4}$ 2. $64\frac{1}{2} \times 35\frac{1}{6}$ 3. $49\frac{3}{5} \times 85\frac{6}{7}$ 4. $16\frac{2}{3} \times 48\frac{5}{6}$

ANSWERS   1. $457\frac{1}{32}$ 2. $2{,}268\frac{1}{4}$ 3. $4{,}258\frac{18}{35}$ 4. $813\frac{8}{9}$

APPLICATION PROBLEMS

Find the product in each of the following problems.

1. $36\frac{1}{3} \times \$.24\frac{1}{4}$
2. $81\frac{5}{6} \times 48\frac{2}{3}$
3. $69\frac{1}{2} \times 57\frac{1}{6}$
4. $84\frac{3}{8} \times 56\frac{4}{7}$
5. $51\frac{3}{4} \times 52\frac{5}{9}$

6. $78\frac{7}{8} \times 96\frac{7}{12}$
7. $132\frac{7}{9} \times 72\frac{11}{12}$
8. $104\frac{4}{7} \times 8\frac{5}{8}$
9. $28\frac{2}{3} \times 5\frac{5}{12}$
10. $402\frac{1}{2} \times 23\frac{1}{6}$

22 MULTIPLYING DECIMAL FRACTIONS

To multiply decimals, proceed as in the multiplication of whole numbers. The product contains as many decimal places as there are decimal places in the multiplier and in the multiplicand.

Example | **PROBLEM** Multiply 8.82 by 6.87.

SOLUTION

$$\begin{array}{r} 8.82 \\ \times\,6.87 \\ \hline 60.5934 \end{array}$$

The answer is sensible because it must be more than 8 × 6, or 48; and it must be less than 9 × 7, or 63.

Practice Drill | Multiply the following decimal fractions.

1. 84.3	2. 9.34	3. 4.062	4. 82.9
6.72	86.1	.084	2.0032

ANSWERS 1. 566.496   2. 804.174   3. .341208   4. 166.06528

APPLICATION PROBLEMS

Multiply the following decimal fractions.

1. 73.5 by 3.96
2. 42.3 by 82.8
3. 5,964 by 8.07
4. 207.1 by .3001
5. 721 by .93

6. 4.23 by .072
7. 58.64 by 32.05
8. 4.078 by 6.50
9. 416.3 by 414.03
10. 81.8 by 7.167

23 DIVIDING A FRACTION BY A FRACTION

To divide a fraction by a fraction, change the division sign to a multiplication sign, invert the divisor, and multiply. You may use cancellation to help you give the simplest answer.

Example | **PROBLEM** Divide $\frac{3}{4}$ by $\frac{5}{6}$.

SOLUTION $\frac{3}{4} \div \frac{5}{6} = \frac{3}{4} \times \frac{6}{5} = \frac{18}{20} = \frac{9}{10}$ or $\frac{3}{4} \times \frac{\overset{3}{\cancel{6}}}{5} = \frac{9}{10}$

Practice Drills | Find the quotients.

1. $\frac{1}{2} \div \frac{5}{6}$ 2. $\frac{1}{8} \div \frac{2}{3}$ 3. $\frac{11}{12} \div \frac{2}{5}$ 4. $\frac{7}{16} \div \frac{7}{8}$

ANSWERS 1. $\frac{3}{5}$ 2. $\frac{3}{16}$ 3. $2\frac{7}{24}$ 4. $\frac{1}{2}$

APPLICATION PROBLEMS

Divide the following fractions.

1. $\frac{2}{3} \div \frac{1}{6}$
2. $\frac{5}{6} \div \frac{7}{8}$
3. $\frac{3}{8} \div \frac{5}{16}$

4. $\frac{7}{12} \div \frac{1}{4}$
5. $\frac{1}{4} \div \frac{3}{8}$
6. $\frac{7}{8} \div \frac{3}{4}$

7. $\frac{5}{16} \div \frac{4}{5}$
8. $\frac{1}{3} \div \frac{1}{4}$
9. $\frac{1}{2} \div \frac{3}{5}$

24 DIVIDING A MIXED NUMBER BY A MIXED NUMBER

To divide one mixed number by another, use the following procedure.
1. Change the mixed numbers to improper fractions.
2. Change the division sign to a multiplication sign.
3. Invert the improper fraction following this sign.
4. Multiply by cancellation.
5. Change the product to a mixed number.

Example

PROBLEM   Divide $36\frac{3}{4}$ by $21\frac{5}{6}$.

SOLUTION $36\frac{3}{4} \div 21\frac{5}{6} = \frac{147}{4} \div \frac{131}{6} = \frac{147}{\overset{}{\underset{2}{4}}} \times \frac{\overset{3}{6}}{131} = \frac{441}{262} = 1\frac{179}{262}$

Practice Drills

Divide the following mixed numbers.

1. $8\frac{1}{2} \div 5\frac{3}{4}$ 2. $6\frac{4}{5} \div 9\frac{2}{3}$ 3. $16\frac{5}{8} \div 7\frac{1}{6}$ 4. $32\frac{3}{7} \div 15\frac{9}{14}$

ANSWERS   1. $1\frac{11}{23}$ 2. $\frac{102}{145}$ 3. $2\frac{55}{172}$ 4. $2\frac{16}{219}$

APPLICATION PROBLEMS

Find the quotients.

1. $56\frac{1}{2} \div 18\frac{3}{4}$
2. $98\frac{5}{6} \div 54\frac{6}{7}$
3. $56\frac{2}{3} \div 39\frac{7}{8}$

4. $84\frac{3}{4} \div 52\frac{1}{6}$
5. $72\frac{4}{5} \div 35\frac{11}{12}$
6. $64\frac{5}{8} \div 48\frac{2}{3}$

7. $96\frac{7}{8} \div 36\frac{5}{12}$
8. $49\frac{5}{6} \div 24\frac{6}{7}$
9. $81\frac{5}{8} \div 46\frac{4}{9}$

25 DIVIDING DECIMAL FRACTIONS

When the divisor is a decimal fraction, make it a whole number by multiplying it by a number such as 10, 100, or 1,000. To do this, move the decimal point as many places to the right as there are decimal places. To keep from changing the relative values, multiply the dividend by the same number: $.6.\overline{)1.5.}$ $=$ $6\overline{)1.5}$

Example

PROBLEM Divide 21.888 by .64.

SOLUTION Both divisor and dividend are multiplied by 100, which is the same as moving the decimal point two places to the right.

$$\begin{array}{r} 34.2 \\ .64.\overline{)21.88.8} \end{array}$$

Practice Drills

Divide the following decimal fractions.

1. 31.62 by .9   2. 597.3 by .64   3. 8.973 ÷ 16.7   4. 348.1 ÷ 9.006

ANSWERS 1. $35.1\frac{1}{3}$ 2. $933\frac{9}{32}$ 3. $.53\frac{122}{167}$ 4. $38\frac{2,936}{4,503}$

APPLICATION PROBLEMS

Divide the following decimal fractions.

1. 753.80 by .38
2. 52.724 by 3.12
3. 809.1 by .86

4. 3.245 by 43.7
5. 9.841 by 34.2
6. 52.73 by 12.31

7. 834.52 by .013
8. 508.201 by 5.05
9. 1,204.5 by .335

PROBLEMS FOR PART TWO

Fractions & Decimal Fractions

9

Change each of the following improper fractions to a whole or mixed number.

1. $\frac{43}{4}$ 4. $\frac{88}{12}$ 7. $\frac{259}{5}$ 10. $\frac{824}{16}$ 13. $\frac{487}{25}$

2. $\frac{59}{3}$ 5. $\frac{95}{5}$ 8. $\frac{468}{9}$ 11. $\frac{911}{12}$ 14. $\frac{1,170}{12}$

3. $\frac{67}{7}$ 6. $\frac{133}{6}$ 9. $\frac{616}{25}$ 12. $\frac{336}{11}$ 15. $\frac{717}{7}$

10

Change each of the following mixed numbers to an improper fraction.

1. $28\frac{2}{3}$ 4. $86\frac{5}{6}$ 7. $64\frac{1}{4}$ 10. $42\frac{2}{3}$ 13. $51\frac{3}{8}$

2. $58\frac{3}{4}$ 5. $99\frac{7}{8}$ 8. $84\frac{3}{5}$ 11. $21\frac{4}{5}$ 14. $46\frac{1}{4}$

3. $79\frac{2}{5}$ 6. $72\frac{2}{3}$ 9. $31\frac{1}{6}$ 12. $67\frac{3}{4}$ 15. $72\frac{2}{5}$

11

Change each of the following complex fractions to a simple fraction.

1. $\dfrac{\frac{5}{6}}{\frac{3}{4}}$ 3. $\dfrac{\frac{1}{3}}{\frac{3}{4}}$ 5. $\dfrac{\frac{4}{5}}{8\frac{2}{3}}$ 7. $\dfrac{2\frac{1}{2}}{3\frac{1}{4}}$ 9. $\dfrac{4\frac{2}{3}}{5\frac{1}{6}}$ 11. $\dfrac{24\frac{1}{4}}{37\frac{2}{3}}$

2. $\dfrac{\frac{2}{3}}{\frac{1}{6}}$ 4. $\dfrac{\frac{3}{8}}{5\frac{1}{6}}$ 6. $\dfrac{\frac{3}{8}}{7\frac{1}{4}}$ 8. $\dfrac{5\frac{1}{3}}{6\frac{1}{2}}$ 10. $\dfrac{12\frac{2}{3}}{15\frac{5}{6}}$ 12. $\dfrac{36\frac{1}{2}}{84\frac{2}{3}}$

12 | Change each of the following fractions to higher terms.

1. $\frac{3}{4}$ to 48ths   4. $\frac{4}{5}$ to 65ths   7. $\frac{5}{9}$ to 36ths   10. $\frac{2}{9}$ to 45ths
2. $\frac{1}{6}$ to 78ths   5. $\frac{11}{12}$ to 84ths   8. $\frac{7}{12}$ to 96ths   11. $\frac{7}{8}$ to 72ds
3. $\frac{5}{8}$ to 56ths   6. $\frac{9}{10}$ to 90ths   9. $\frac{6}{7}$ to 21sts   12. $\frac{7}{15}$ to 75ths

13 | Change each of the following common fractions to a decimal fraction.

1. $\frac{2}{3}$ 5. $\frac{6}{7}$ 9. $\frac{5}{8}$ 13. $\frac{9}{16}$ 17. $\frac{3}{7}$ 21. $\frac{7}{12}$
2. $\frac{5}{6}$ 6. $\frac{15}{16}$ 10. $\frac{3}{16}$ 14. $\frac{1}{6}$ 18. $\frac{7}{16}$ 22. $\frac{11}{16}$
3. $\frac{11}{12}$ 7. $\frac{2}{15}$ 11. $\frac{3}{8}$ 15. $\frac{5}{16}$ 19. $\frac{4}{9}$ 23. $\frac{5}{7}$
4. $\frac{7}{8}$ 8. $\frac{7}{9}$ 12. $\frac{1}{12}$ 16. $\frac{13}{16}$ 20. $\frac{1}{8}$ 24. $\frac{1}{16}$

14 | Change each of the following decimal fractions to a common fraction.

1. .83   4. .007   7. $.31\frac{1}{4}$ 10. $.41\frac{2}{3}$ 13. $.18\frac{3}{4}$
2. .095   5. $.93\frac{3}{4}$ 8. $.93\frac{1}{3}$ 11. $.06\frac{1}{4}$ 14. $.43\frac{3}{4}$
3. .0101   6. $.42\frac{6}{7}$ 9. $.28\frac{4}{7}$ 12. $.44\frac{4}{9}$ 15. $.26\frac{2}{3}$

15 | Add the following.

1. $\frac{1}{2}$ 4. $\frac{1}{6}$ 7. $\frac{1}{2}$ 10. $\frac{3}{4}$ 13. $\frac{5}{8}$
$\frac{1}{3}$ $\frac{5}{8}$ $\frac{2}{7}$ $\frac{5}{6}$ $\frac{11}{16}$
$\frac{1}{4}$ $\frac{1}{3}$ $\frac{13}{14}$ $\frac{7}{8}$ $\frac{5}{6}$
        $\frac{2}{3}$
        $\frac{1}{2}$

2. $\frac{1}{2}$ 5. $\frac{4}{5}$ 8. $\frac{5}{9}$ 11. $\frac{2}{3}$ 14. $\frac{1}{7}$
$\frac{2}{3}$ $\frac{1}{4}$ $\frac{1}{3}$ $\frac{1}{2}$ $\frac{5}{8}$
$\frac{5}{6}$ $\frac{11}{12}$ $\frac{1}{6}$ $\frac{11}{12}$ $\frac{1}{2}$
      $\frac{5}{8}$ $\frac{3}{4}$
      $\frac{11}{15}$ $\frac{2}{3}$

3. $\frac{5}{6}$ 6. $\frac{5}{6}$ 9. $\frac{1}{3}$ 12. $\frac{5}{6}$ 15. $\frac{3}{5}$
$\frac{2}{3}$ $\frac{7}{8}$ $\frac{1}{4}$ $\frac{1}{3}$ $\frac{5}{12}$
$\frac{3}{4}$ $\frac{5}{12}$ $\frac{5}{6}$ $\frac{1}{8}$ $\frac{1}{4}$
        $\frac{1}{4}$ $\frac{2}{15}$
        $\frac{11}{12}$ $\frac{5}{6}$

16 | Add each of the following fractions, using the short method.

1. $\frac{2}{3} + \frac{4}{5}$ 3. $\frac{1}{4} + \frac{5}{6}$ 5. $\frac{7}{16} + \frac{7}{8}$ 7. $3\frac{3}{4} + 5\frac{7}{8}$
2. $\frac{3}{8} + \frac{11}{16}$ 4. $\frac{7}{8} + \frac{5}{12}$ 6. $\frac{7}{8} + \frac{5}{6}$ 8. $7\frac{1}{4} + 5\frac{3}{5}$

17 Find the difference.

1. $32\frac{1}{2} - 17\frac{2}{3}$ 6. $58\frac{3}{5} - 37\frac{2}{3}$ 11. $787\frac{3}{4} - 564\frac{7}{16}$

2. $46\frac{2}{3} - 23\frac{5}{6}$ 7. $64\frac{5}{9} - 28\frac{5}{6}$ 12. $653\frac{1}{7} - 291\frac{5}{12}$

3. $97\frac{1}{6} - 38\frac{3}{4}$ 8. $99\frac{1}{2} - 31\frac{3}{4}$ 13. $488\frac{3}{8} - 189\frac{3}{5}$

4. $64\frac{5}{8} - 39\frac{5}{6}$ 9. $28\frac{1}{3} - 13\frac{5}{8}$ 14. $516\frac{1}{5} - 432\frac{1}{2}$

5. $85\frac{4}{5} - 45\frac{6}{7}$ 10. $47\frac{1}{9} - 25\frac{1}{7}$ 15. $862\frac{5}{7} - 351\frac{8}{9}$

18 Subtract, using the short method. Express each difference in lowest terms.

1. $\frac{5}{8} - \frac{1}{3}$ 3. $\frac{11}{15} - \frac{1}{6}$ 5. $\frac{6}{5} - \frac{5}{6}$ 7. $19\frac{1}{4} - 12\frac{1}{3}$

2. $\frac{5}{6} - \frac{3}{5}$ 4. $\frac{6}{7} - \frac{1}{12}$ 6. $1\frac{3}{8} - \frac{5}{6}$ 8. $8\frac{3}{8} - 4\frac{5}{6}$

19 Subtract.

1. $27.86\frac{1}{3}$ 3. $813\frac{7}{16}$ 5. $512.41\frac{2}{3}$ 7. $9.87\frac{1}{2}$ 9. $48.43\frac{3}{4}$
   $18.97\frac{1}{2}$ $97.87\frac{1}{2}$ $386.43\frac{3}{4}$ $3.66\frac{2}{3}$ $47\frac{11}{12}$

2. $56.37\frac{1}{2}$ 4. $243\frac{5}{8}$ 6. $18.3\frac{3}{4}$ 8. $38.67\frac{3}{4}$ 10. $83.6\frac{1}{4}$
   $28\frac{11}{16}$ $.58\frac{1}{3}$ $12.83\frac{1}{3}$ $19\frac{5}{6}$ $44.3\frac{2}{3}$

20 Find the value of each of the following.

1. $\frac{2}{3}$ of $\frac{7}{8}$ 3. $\frac{2}{5}$ of $\frac{5}{8}$ 5. $\frac{5}{8}$ of $\frac{11}{12}$ 7. $\frac{2}{3}$ of $\frac{5}{7}$

2. $\frac{5}{6}$ of $\frac{3}{4}$ 4. $\frac{1}{2}$ of $\frac{4}{7}$ 6. $\frac{1}{3}$ of $\frac{1}{6}$ 8. $\frac{3}{8}$ of $\frac{4}{5}$

21 Find the product.

1. $32\frac{1}{2} \times 48\frac{3}{4}$ 5. $48\frac{5}{9} \times 81\frac{1}{2}$ 9. $172\frac{2}{3} \times 105\frac{15}{16}$

2. $56\frac{5}{6} \times 84\frac{3}{7}$ 6. $72\frac{2}{3} \times 57\frac{5}{6}$ 10. $132\frac{5}{6} \times 246\frac{11}{12}$

3. $84\frac{3}{4} \times 42\frac{2}{3}$ 7. $124\frac{5}{6} \times 240\frac{1}{4}$ 11. $108\frac{4}{5} \times 145\frac{1}{6}$

4. $64\frac{11}{12} \times 24\frac{7}{8}$ 8. $144\frac{1}{4} \times 112\frac{7}{12}$ 12. $226\frac{4}{11} \times 352\frac{1}{2}$

22 Multiply.

1. 4.72 by 83.4   3. 108.2 by 35.6   5. 6.005 by .807   7. 4.74 by .913

2. 596 by 3.28   4. 7.414 by 7.8   6. 52.1 by .007   8. 583.9 by .048

23 Divide.

1. $\frac{5}{16} \div \frac{3}{5}$ 3. $\frac{4}{9} \div \frac{8}{11}$ 5. $\frac{15}{16} \div \frac{5}{6}$ 7. $\frac{5}{8} \div \frac{1}{2}$

2. $\frac{3}{7} \div \frac{9}{10}$ 4. $\frac{5}{11} \div \frac{15}{16}$ 6. $\frac{3}{8} \div \frac{3}{4}$ 8. $\frac{1}{2} \div \frac{2}{3}$

24 Divide.

1. $12\frac{3}{4} \div 7\frac{1}{2}$
2. $24\frac{2}{3} \div 16\frac{3}{4}$
3. $32\frac{5}{6} \div 24\frac{7}{8}$
4. $64\frac{7}{8} \div 32\frac{2}{3}$

5. $42\frac{6}{7} \div 28\frac{1}{2}$
6. $36\frac{1}{2} \div 16\frac{5}{6}$
7. $54\frac{11}{12} \div 36\frac{4}{5}$
8. $37\frac{4}{5} \div 42\frac{3}{5}$

9. $46\frac{7}{16} \div 16\frac{11}{12}$
10. $28\frac{1}{2} \div 24\frac{5}{6}$
11. $35\frac{5}{8} \div 32\frac{11}{12}$
12. $12\frac{7}{8} \div 34\frac{11}{16}$

25 Divide the following decimal fractions.

1. 807.6 by .53
2. 745.46 by .084
3. 9.0081 by .0072

4. 32.76 by 4.009
5. 3.388 by 246.6
6. 83.4 by 4.72

7. 6.005 by .807
8. 27.75 by 5.25
9. 81.81 by 3.03

PART THREE
Aliquot Parts & Percents

Aliquot parts and their fractional equivalents are used extensively in computations involving fractions, percentages, interest, discounts, and so on. Any number that is contained in any other number a whole number of times is referred to as an *aliquot part* of that number. In speaking of an aliquot part of $1, we mean the fractional part of $1 which represents that number. For example, if 25¢ is $\frac{1}{4}$ of $1, $\frac{1}{4}$ is the aliquot part. Multiples of aliquot parts— such as $66\frac{2}{3}$ ($\frac{2}{3}$ of 100), $31\frac{1}{4}$% ($\frac{5}{16}$ of 100%), and $87\frac{1}{2}$¢ ($\frac{7}{8}$ of $1)— will also be referred to as aliquot parts.

Like aliquot parts, percentage is also the expression of an amount in relation to a total amount, or base. The relationship is expressed in hundredths, or as a percent—50¢ (percentage) is 25 percent (%) of $2.00 (base). Percentage applies the principles of common and decimal fractions to the solution of business problems. For example, if a new business projects a weekly income of $1,000 and weekly expenses of $900, are its income and expenses in proportion to those of a similar established business with a weekly income of $1,400 and weekly expenses of $1,120? The expenses of the two companies cannot be compared unless the various dollar amounts are viewed as percentages. When we do this, we see that $900 is 90% of $1,000, and $1,120 is 80% of $1,400. Thus the new business's projected weekly expenses of $900 are *higher* than those of the established business ($1,120). Using the established business's figures as percentage guides, the new business must cut its expenses to $800 or raise its income to $1,125. ($800 = 80% of $1,000; $900 = 80% of $1,125.)

The following are terms used in percentage. When any two of them are known, the third can be found.

Base The number from which the percentage is taken.

Rate The rate of percent or rate percent.

Percentage The amount that results from taking a given percent of the base.

26 ALIQUOT PARTS OF $1

To find any aliquot part, place the amount over the base and reduce the fraction to a common fraction in lowest terms.

Examples

PROBLEM 1 What part of $1 is $12\frac{1}{2}$¢?

SOLUTION Place $12\frac{1}{2}$ cents over 100 cents and change the fraction to a common fraction in lowest terms.

$$\frac{12\frac{1}{2}}{100} = \frac{2 \times 12 + 1}{2 \times 100} = \frac{25}{200} = \frac{1}{8}$$

PROBLEM 2 What part of $1 is $8\frac{1}{3}$¢?

SOLUTION Place $8\frac{1}{3}$ cents over 100 cents and reduce the fraction to a common fraction in its lowest terms.

$$\frac{8\frac{1}{3}}{100} = \frac{3 \times 8 + 1}{3 \times 100} = \frac{25}{300} = \frac{1}{12}$$

PROBLEM 3 What part of $1 is $6\frac{1}{4}$¢?

SOLUTION $$\frac{6\frac{1}{4}}{100} = \frac{4 \times 6 + 1}{4 \times 100} = \frac{25}{400} = \frac{1}{16}$$

PROBLEM 4 What part of $1 is $16\frac{2}{3}$¢?

SOLUTION $$\frac{16\frac{2}{3}}{100} = \frac{3 \times 16 + 2}{3 \times 100} = \frac{50}{300} = \frac{1}{6}$$

Practice Drills

What aliquot part of $1 is represented by each of the following amounts?

1. $33\frac{1}{3}$¢
2. $87\frac{1}{2}$¢
3. $31\frac{1}{4}$¢

4. $6\frac{2}{3}$¢
5. $14\frac{2}{7}$¢
6. $11\frac{1}{9}$¢

7. $43\frac{3}{4}$¢
8. $66\frac{2}{3}$¢
9. $91\frac{2}{3}$¢

ANSWERS 1. $\frac{1}{3}$ 2. $\frac{7}{8}$ 3. $\frac{5}{16}$ 4. $\frac{1}{15}$ 5. $\frac{1}{7}$ 6. $\frac{1}{9}$ 7. $\frac{7}{16}$ 8. $\frac{2}{3}$ 9. $\frac{11}{12}$

APPLICATION PROBLEMS

What aliquot part of $1 does each of the following amounts represent?

1. $6\frac{1}{4}$¢
2. $8\frac{1}{3}$¢
3. $12\frac{1}{2}$¢

4. $16\frac{2}{3}$¢
5. $83\frac{1}{3}$¢
6. $18\frac{3}{4}$¢

7. $31\frac{1}{4}$¢
8. $37\frac{1}{2}$¢
9. $58\frac{1}{3}$¢

10. $66\frac{2}{3}$¢
11. $41\frac{2}{3}$¢
12. $56\frac{1}{4}$¢

13. $87\frac{1}{2}$¢
14. $93\frac{3}{4}$¢
15. $43\frac{3}{4}$¢

27 EQUATING FRACTIONS AND ALIQUOT PARTS

It is important to know the fractions that represent aliquot parts of $1 or 100 and also to what amounts such aliquot parts and the fractions that represent them are equal. For example we must know that $83\frac{1}{3}$¢ is equal to $\frac{5}{6}$ of $1 and, vice versa, that $\frac{5}{6}$ of $1 is equal to $83\frac{1}{3}$¢. To find what amount of $1, or 100, a fraction equals, change the numerator to a decimal fraction; then divide it by the denominator. The example below illustrates this procedure.

Example

PROBLEM   To what is $\frac{5}{6}$ of $1 equal?

SOLUTION

$$\frac{5}{6} \times \$1 = \$\frac{5}{6} = 6\overline{)\$5.00} \quad \$ .83\tfrac{1}{3}$$

Practice Drills

The following fractions represent aliquot parts of $1. To what amount is each equal?

1. $\frac{1}{3}$ 2. $\frac{1}{4}$ 3. $\frac{1}{8}$ 4. $\frac{7}{16}$ 5. $\frac{2}{7}$ 6. $\frac{5}{6}$ 7. $\frac{7}{8}$ 8. $\frac{5}{9}$ 9. $\frac{15}{16}$

ANSWERS   1. $33\frac{1}{3}$¢   2. 25¢   3. $12\frac{1}{2}$¢   4. $43\frac{3}{4}$¢   5. $28\frac{4}{7}$¢
6. $83\frac{1}{3}$¢   7. $87\frac{1}{2}$¢   8. $55\frac{5}{9}$¢   9. $93\frac{3}{4}$¢

APPLICATION PROBLEMS

Each of the following fractions represents an aliquot part of $1. What is its dollar equivalent?

1. $\frac{3}{8}$ 4. $\frac{2}{3}$ 7. $\frac{11}{12}$ 10. $\frac{3}{7}$ 13. $\frac{7}{12}$
2. $\frac{1}{6}$ 5. $\frac{5}{12}$ 8. $\frac{5}{8}$ 11. $\frac{5}{11}$ 14. $\frac{5}{16}$
3. $\frac{3}{16}$ 6. $\frac{9}{16}$ 9. $\frac{11}{16}$ 12. $\frac{13}{16}$ 15. $\frac{4}{9}$

28 DETERMINING THE TOTAL COST WHEN THE UNIT PRICE IS EXPRESSED AS AN ALIQUOT PART

When the price of a unit is an aliquot part of $1, multiply the number of units that were purchased by that aliquot part. Find the total cost by the cancellation process.

Examples | **PROBLEM 1**   Find the cost of 72 articles @ $62\frac{1}{2}$¢.

SOLUTION

$$62\frac{1}{2}¢ = \frac{62\frac{1}{2}}{100} = \frac{125}{200} = \frac{5}{8} \text{ of \$1, or } \$\frac{5}{8}$$

$$\overset{9}{\cancel{72}} \times \$\frac{5}{\cancel{8}} = \$45.00$$

PROBLEM 2   Find the cost of 42 articles @ $58\frac{1}{3}$¢.

SOLUTION

$$58\frac{1}{3}¢ = \frac{58\frac{1}{3}}{100} = \frac{175}{300} = \frac{7}{12} \text{ of \$1, or } \$\frac{7}{12}$$

$$\overset{7}{\cancel{42}} \times \$\frac{7}{\underset{2}{\cancel{12}}} = \$\frac{49}{2} = \$24.50$$

Practice Drills | How much will each of the following purchases cost?

1. 96 articles @ $87\frac{1}{2}$¢

2. 42 articles @ $58\frac{1}{3}$¢

3. 56 articles @ $31\frac{1}{4}$¢

4. 33 articles @ $83\frac{1}{3}$¢

ANSWERS   1. $84   2. $24.50   3. $17.50   4. $27.50

APPLICATION PROBLEMS

Each of the following two groups represents the items on a purchase invoice. Find the cost of the items. Then add the cost of all items in each group to obtain the total cost on each invoice.

1. a. 318 pk. @ $8\frac{1}{3}$¢
    b. 404 pk. @ $6\frac{1}{4}$¢
    c. 296 pk. @ $43\frac{3}{4}$¢
    d. 176 pk. @ $91\frac{2}{3}$¢
    e. 604 pk. @ $81\frac{1}{4}$¢
    f. *Total* _____

2. a. 144 doz. @ $56\frac{1}{4}$¢
    b. 252 doz. @ $16\frac{2}{3}$¢
    c. 198 doz. @ $41\frac{2}{3}$¢
    d. 174 doz. @ $58\frac{1}{3}$¢
    e. 105 doz. @ $28\frac{4}{7}$¢
    f. *Total* _____

29 DETERMINING THE TOTAL NUMBER OF UNITS BY EXPRESSING THE UNIT PRICE AS AN ALIQUOT PART

To use aliquot parts to determine the number of units that may be purchased for a given amount, first reduce the unit price to its fractional equivalent based on $1. Then divide the amount by this result.

Example | **PROBLEM**   How many articles can be purchased for $65 if they cost $62\frac{1}{2}$ cents each?

SOLUTION $62\frac{1}{2}$ cents $= \frac{\$62.5}{100} = \frac{5}{8}$ of $1, or $\frac{5}{8}$

$$\$65 \div \$.62\frac{1}{2} = 65 \div \frac{5}{8} = \overset{13}{\cancel{65}} \times \frac{8}{\cancel{5}} = 104, \text{ total number}$$
$$\text{of units}$$

Practice Drill | A school supplier sells educational toys for $87\frac{1}{2}$ cents each. The Fairfax Elementary School has $238 in its budget for toys for the current year. How many toys can be purchased?

ANSWER   272

APPLICATION PROBLEMS

Determine the number of units that would be received for each of the following amounts.

1. $504 @ $37\frac{1}{2}$¢ each   4. $805 @ $43\frac{3}{4}$¢ each   7. $440 @ $68\frac{3}{4}$¢ each
2. $660 @ $91\frac{2}{3}$¢ each   5. $234 @ $81\frac{1}{4}$¢ each   8. $195 @ $62\frac{1}{2}$¢ each
3. $399 @ $87\frac{1}{2}$¢ each   6. $210 @ $93\frac{3}{4}$¢ each   9. $215 @ $41\frac{2}{3}$¢ each

30 REPRESENTING FRACTIONS AS PERCENTS

Common fractions may be expressed as either decimal fractions or percents. For example, $\frac{7}{8} = \frac{87.5}{100} = .875$ and $\frac{87.5}{100} = 87.5\%$. To express a decimal fraction as a percent, move the decimal point two places to the *right* and add the percent sign: $.875 = 87.5\%$.

Conversely, to express a percent as a decimal fraction, drop the percent sign and move the decimal point two places to the *left:* $87.5\% = .875$.

Examples | **PROBLEM 1**   Express the following decimal fractions as percents: $.17, .45, .65\frac{1}{2}$.

SOLUTION
$$.17 = 17\%$$
$$.45 = 45\%$$
$$.65\frac{1}{2} = 65\frac{1}{2}\%$$

PROBLEM 2   Express the following percents as decimal fractions: 54%, 39%, 176%.

SOLUTION
$$54\% = .54 \left(\tfrac{54}{100}\right)$$
$$39\% = .39$$
$$176\% = 1.76$$

Practice Drills

Change each of the following to hundredths, decimals, and percents.

1. $\frac{4}{5}$ 2. $\frac{3}{10}$ 3. $\frac{1}{6}$ 4. $\frac{7}{12}$ 5. $\frac{7}{8}$ 6. $\frac{5}{16}$

ANSWERS 1. $\frac{80}{100}$, .80, 80%   2. $\frac{30}{100}$, .30, 30%   3. $\frac{16\frac{2}{3}}{100}$, .16$\frac{2}{3}$, 16$\frac{2}{3}$%

4. $\frac{58\frac{1}{3}}{100}$, .58$\frac{1}{3}$, 58$\frac{1}{3}$%   5. $\frac{87\frac{1}{2}}{100}$, .87$\frac{1}{2}$, 87$\frac{1}{2}$%   6. $\frac{31\frac{1}{4}}{100}$, .31$\frac{1}{4}$, 31$\frac{1}{4}$%

APPLICATION PROBLEMS

Change each of the following common fractions to hundredths, its decimal form, and its percent form. (Use this form: $\frac{1}{4} = \frac{25}{100} = .25 = 25\%$.)

1. $\frac{2}{5}$ 4. $\frac{2}{3}$ 7. $\frac{5}{6}$ 10. $\frac{3}{5}$
2. $\frac{3}{4}$ 5. $\frac{5}{12}$ 8. $\frac{9}{16}$ 11. $\frac{11}{12}$
3. $\frac{3}{8}$ 6. $\frac{1}{12}$ 9. $\frac{3}{16}$ 12. $\frac{5}{8}$

31 COMPUTING PERCENTAGE

To find the percentage, or amount, multiply the rate by the base $(R \times B = P)$.

Examples

PROBLEM 1   What is 36% of $845?

SOLUTION $845, base
                            .36, rate
                          $304.20, percentage

Note: The rate percent was expressed as a decimal fraction because the fractional equivalent of 36% is awkward to use.

PROBLEM 2   What is 62$\frac{1}{2}$% of $920?

SOLUTION $62\frac{1}{2}\% = .62\frac{1}{2} = \frac{5}{8}$

                    Rate $\times$ Base = Percentage

                              115
                $62\frac{1}{2}\%$, or $\frac{5}{8} \times \$920 = \$575$

Note: The rate percent was expressed as a fraction because it is similar to an aliquot part of $1 (62$\frac{1}{2}$¢ = $\frac{5}{8}$ of $1).

Practice
Drills

Find the percentage in each of the following.

1. 35% of $756
2. $16\frac{2}{3}$% of $204

3. $87\frac{1}{2}$% of $596
4. $\frac{1}{2}$% of $117

5. $112\frac{1}{2}$% of $48
6. 150% of $150

ANSWERS   1. $264.60   2. $34   3. $521.50   4. $.58$\frac{1}{2}$ 5. $54   6. $225

Po

APPLICATION PROBLEMS

1. Find the percentage, and round off your answer to the nearest cent.
a. 40% of $805
b. $12\frac{1}{2}$% of $564
c. 36% of $726

d. $108\frac{1}{3}$% of $984
e. $41\frac{2}{3}$% of $408
f. $6\frac{1}{2}$% of $920

g. $\frac{1}{4}$% of 4,398
h. $\frac{5}{6}$% of $522

2. R. H. Cox, a hardware dealer, sells merchandise at $37\frac{1}{2}$% more than it cost him. If a power mower cost him $68, at what price must he sell it to realize his usual profit margin?   68 + 25

3. Approximately $17\frac{1}{2}$% of all novelty goods sold by Tifton Wholesalers are returned to the company for credit by its dealers. Tifton's total sales during a 3-month period amounted to $628,712.
a. By how much did the returns reduce sales?
b. What was the net amount of the sales?

4. A bank charges $7\frac{3}{4}$% on all secured loans and $8\frac{7}{8}$% on personal notes of borrowers. Find the total amount received by the bank on an $8,750 secured loan and a $1,380 personal loan.

5. Myra Kauffman sells on commission, receiving $7\frac{1}{2}$% on sales up to and including $25,000, $12\frac{1}{2}$% on the next $20,000, and 15% on all sales above $45,000. If Myra's sales last year amounted to $83,860 and she drew $520 a month to be charged against her commission, what was the balance due her?

68 × 3/8 = 25.50

17 35 x 7/40
2   200
34

32 COMPUTING RATE

To find the rate percent, divide the percentage by the base $(P \div B = R)$.

Examples

PROBLEM 1   A man who received $72 from a friend who had borrowed it spent $10.80 for a dozen golf balls. What percent of his money did he spend?

.08
12)1.00

SOLUTION $10.80 = percentage; $72 = base

10.80 ÷ 72 = rate

$$.15 = 15\%, \text{ percent spent}$$
$$10.80 \div 72 = 72\overline{)10.80}$$

PROBLEM 2   Cato and Martin, law partners, pay an annual rental of $6,300 for the building they occupy. They have been told by the owner of the building, however, that when the lease expires they will have to sign a new lease at $715 a month. What percent of increase is being asked by the owner?

SOLUTION $715 a month = $8,580 a year

$8,580 - $6,300 = $2,280, increase in rental

?% of $6,300 = $2,280

$2,280 ÷ $6,300 = .3619 = 36%, percent of increase*

Practice Drills

1. During a 7-year period, the Swan Lake Community College football team played 66 games and won 47 of them. What percent of the games did the team win?

2. A carpenter's average income during the 3-year period before his retirement was $560 a month. When he retired, he received an income from an annuity of $165 monthly. What percent of decrease in his monthly income was this?

ANSWERS   1. $71\frac{7}{33}\%$ 2. $70\frac{15}{28}\%$

APPLICATION PROBLEMS

1. Find the rate, rounding off your answer to the nearest whole number percent value.

a. ___% of $360 = $65

b. ___% of $656 = $82

c. ___% of $224 = $38

d. 99 is what percent of 132?

e. 292 is what percent of 438?

f. 125 is what percent of 300?

2. Herschel Mingus is paying $103.04 a month on an improvement loan on his home. If his monthly salary is $850, what percent of his salary is the payment?

3. The enrollment in the data processing department of the Lofton Business University this year is 1,054 students. Last year the enrollment was 692 students. What percent greater is this year's enrollment?

*Percent of increase or percent of decrease is always based on the original quantity.

4. Kenwood Country Club sold a set of golf clubs for $137.50 in its Pro Shop. The Pro Shop made $60 on the sale.
a. What percent of the retail price was the profit?
b. What was the cost?
c. What percent of the cost was the profit?

5. Van Ness Mail Order, Inc., has 1,018 employees. Of this total, 845 are in sales, 97 in accounting and clerical, and the remaining employees in administration. What percent of the total employees is represented by each group?

33 COMPUTING BASE

To find the base, divide the percentage by the rate percent *(P ÷ R = B):*

Example | **PROBLEM**   John Williams spent $360 to rent a cottage in Maine for the month of August. This amount was $6\frac{1}{4}$% of his earnings for the past six months. Find his semiannual earnings.

SOLUTION $6\frac{1}{4}$% of what amount = $360?

Percentage ÷ Rate = Base
$360 ÷ $6\frac{1}{4}$% (or $\frac{1}{16}$) = $360 × $\frac{16}{1}$ = $5,760, semiannual earnings

Practice | 1. A restaurant did 17% more business last year than the year before.
Drills | Last year the total business amounted to $99,801. How much less did the restaurant take in the year before?

2. A textile factory produced 42,486 yards of linen cloth during October. This was 27% less than the September production. How much was produced in September?

ANSWERS 1. $14,501   2. 58,200 yards

APPLICATION PROBLEMS

1. Find the base (the percentage and the rate percent are given).

a. $16\frac{2}{3}$% of $____ = $84
b. $16\frac{2}{3}$% of $____ = $132
c. $31\frac{1}{4}$% of $____ = $180
d. 250% of $____ = $475
e. 9% of $____ = $711

f. $62\frac{1}{2}$% of $____ = $315
g. $45 is 18% of what amount?
h. $378 is 42% of what amount?
i. $21 is 7% of what amount?
j. $270 is $11\frac{1}{4}$% of what amount?

2. Transportation workers negotiated a new contract in which they received, in addition to fringe benefits, an hourly raise of 27 cents. This raise was 6% of the wages they had been receiving. What was their hourly wage before the new contract?

3. A vacuum cleaner cost $137.98, including a 4% city sales tax based on the price of the cleaner. What was the price of the cleaner not including the tax?

4. A portable TV set was sold for $160.25. This price included a city sales tax of 4% and a state tax of 3%.
a. What was the actual selling price of the set, not including the taxes?
b. What was the amount of the tax that had to be turned over to the city? to the state?

PROBLEMS FOR PART THREE

Aliquot Parts & Percents

Each part 1 & 3

26 What aliquot part of $1 is represented by each of the following amounts?

1. 25¢   3. $62\frac{1}{2}$¢   5. $91\frac{2}{3}$¢   7. $6\frac{2}{3}$¢   9. $28\frac{4}{7}$¢
2. $33\frac{1}{3}$¢   4. $81\frac{1}{4}$¢   6. $68\frac{3}{4}$¢   8. $22\frac{2}{9}$¢   10. $26\frac{2}{3}$¢

27 What is the dollar equivalent of each of the following aliquot parts of $1?

1. $\frac{2}{5}$ 3. $\frac{3}{4}$ 5. $\frac{1}{3}$ 7. $\frac{1}{11}$ 9. $\frac{7}{11}$ 11. $\frac{8}{9}$
2. $\frac{1}{7}$ 4. $\frac{4}{5}$ 6. $\frac{5}{6}$ 8. $\frac{7}{9}$ 10. $\frac{5}{7}$ 12. $\frac{14}{15}$

28 Each of the four groups below represents sections on a purchase order. Find the cost of the items; then add the cost of all items in each group to obtain the total amount on the purchase order.

1. a. 264 qts. @ $8\frac{1}{3}$¢   2. a. 312 parts @ $58\frac{1}{3}$¢   3. a. 132 doz. @ $8\frac{1}{3}$¢
   b. 528 qts. @ $41\frac{2}{3}$¢   b. 750 parts @ $66\frac{2}{3}$¢   b. 372 doz. @ $33\frac{1}{3}$¢
   c. 750 qts. @ $16\frac{2}{3}$¢   c. 102 parts @ $83\frac{1}{3}$¢   c. 630 doz. @ $16\frac{2}{3}$¢
   d. 594 qts. @ $33\frac{1}{3}$¢   d. 264 parts @ $33\frac{1}{3}$¢   d. 168 doz. @ $91\frac{2}{3}$¢
   e. 348 qts. @ $91\frac{2}{3}$¢   e. 246 parts @ $16\frac{2}{3}$¢   e. 336 doz. @ $41\frac{2}{3}$¢
   f. *Total* _____   f. *Total* _____   f. *Total* _____

29 Determine the number of units that would be received for each of the following.

1. $104 @ $12\frac{1}{2}$¢ each
2. $313 @ $16\frac{2}{3}$¢ each
3. $83 @ $6\frac{1}{4}$¢ each
4. $75 @ $8\frac{1}{3}$¢ each
5. $115 @ $14\frac{2}{7}$¢ each
6. $429 @ $68\frac{3}{4}$¢ each
7. $238 @ $43\frac{3}{4}$¢ each
8. $1,810 @ $41\frac{2}{3}$¢ each
9. $2,300 @ $91\frac{2}{3}$¢ each

30 Change to decimal fractions.

1. 50%
2. $33\frac{1}{3}$%
3. 80%
4. $7\frac{1}{2}$%
5. 100%
6. 68.75%
7. .16%
8. $.8\frac{1}{4}$%
9. $.\frac{1}{2}$%
10. 150%

Change to fractions.

11. $37\frac{1}{2}$%
12. $66\frac{2}{3}$%
13. $87\frac{1}{2}$%
14. 85%
15. $12\frac{1}{2}$%
16. $8\frac{1}{3}$%
17. $14\frac{2}{7}$%
18. $3\frac{1}{2}$%
19. 750%
20. .5%

Change to percents.

21. .75
22. .08
23. $.62\frac{1}{2}$
24. 1.15
25. $1.12\frac{1}{2}$
26. $\frac{3}{5}$
27. $\frac{2}{3}$
28. $\frac{3}{4}$
29. .003
30. .0065

31 Find the percentage.

1. 20% of 375
2. 25% of 1,764
3. $33\frac{1}{3}$% of 183
4. $12\frac{1}{2}$% of 296
5. $8\frac{1}{3}$% of 372
6. $87\frac{1}{2}$% of 168
7. $16\frac{2}{3}$% of 258
8. $62\frac{1}{2}$% of 416
9. $6\frac{1}{4}$% of 912
10. 35% of 189
11. $41\frac{2}{3}$% of 564
12. $18\frac{3}{4}$% of 368
13. $91\frac{2}{3}$% of $198
14. $43\frac{3}{4}$% of 224
15. 150% of $76.50
16. $108\frac{1}{3}$% of 432
17. $237\frac{1}{2}$% of 120
18. $\frac{1}{4}$% of 296
19. $\frac{3}{5}$% of $125
20. .5% of $86
21. 120% of $180

32 Find the rate.

1. ___% of $780 = $130
2. ___% of $328 = $41
3. ___% of $114 = $19
4. ___% of $156 = $13
5. ___% of $660 = $495
6. ___% of $427 = $61
7. ___% of $255 = $51
8. ___% of $248 = $93

33 Find the base.

1. $12\frac{1}{2}$% of $___ = $70
2. $31\frac{1}{4}$% of $___ = $90
3. 150% of $___ = $36
4. 7% of $___ = $63
5. $37\frac{1}{2}$% of $___ = $81
6. $62\frac{1}{2}$% of $___ = $95
7. $43\frac{3}{4}$% of $___ = $91
8. 28% of $___ = $84

PART FOUR
Discounts & Commissions

A discount is a reduction in an amount. In business it is offered to encourage buying in higher quantities or paying a bill promptly. Most businesses, whether they sell products or services, offer discounts of one kind or another to their customers.

A *trade discount* is offered by one business to another. For example, a wholesale grocer offers a retail supermarket a reduction of $33\frac{1}{3}$% of the price of canned goods listed in the wholesaler's catalog. A trade discount, then, is a deduction the buyer may take from the catalog (or *list*) price.

A *cash discount,* on the other hand, is usually offered to encourage the customer to order in larger quantities or to pay for his purchase promptly. For example, a firm buys $370 worth of stationery from an office supply house. If the firm pays the amount within a certain period, it will be allowed to deduct a discount of 2% or more.

Some manufacturers do not have salesmen to sell their products. They find it less expensive and more convenient to market their goods through commission merchants or through factors (agents who buy or sell goods for others on commission).

Following are terms that you need to be familiar with in commission buying and selling.

Consignment	Merchandise shipped with the understanding that the agent may return anything left unsold. The agent agrees to remit all proceeds, less his commission, to the shipper.
Consignor	Shipper of goods.
Consignee	Commission merchant or person to whom goods are shipped.
Gross proceeds	Amount for which goods are sold by the consignee to the consignor.
Net proceeds	Sum remitted by the commission merchant to the consignor after the commission, freight, insurance, storage, and similar charges have been deducted.
Prime cost	Sum of the cost of labor and materials directly traceable to production of merchandise. This is the cost of merchandise purchased by the commission merchant and on which his commission is based.
Gross cost	Prime cost plus the commission and other expenses connected with the purchase of goods by a commission merchant.

34 SINGLE TRADE DISCOUNTS

The amount of the discount and the net price (the list price less the discount) can be computed in three ways.

METHOD 1

The first method of computing a trade discount is to multiply the list price by the discount rate.

Example | **PROBLEM**   Find the discount and the net price of an invoice that totals $900 with a discount of 25%.

SOLUTION $900 X .25 = $225, discount
$900
−225
$675, net price

METHOD 2

The second method of computing a discount is to deduct the discount rate from 100% and multiply the list price by the remaining rate.

Example | 100% − 25% = 75%
75% of $900 = $675, net price

METHOD 3

A third method of computing a discount is to change the discount rate to its common-fraction equivalent and then multiply the list price by this fraction.

Example | 100% − 25% = 75% = $\frac{3}{4}$
$\frac{3}{4}$ X $900 = $675

Practice | Find the discount and net price of the following purchases, using one of
Drills | the three different methods explained. Then check your answer using one of the other methods.

1. $1,740, less 20%
2. $240, less $33\frac{1}{3}$%
3. $876, less $16\frac{2}{3}$%

ANSWERS 1. $1,392   2. $160   3. $730

APPLICATION PROBLEMS

1. A department store purchased 40 double-grill hibachis from a manufacturer at a list price of $12 each. The trade discount was computed at the rate of 25%. Find the net price of the invoice by three different methods.

2. The Carlton Book Store placed the following order with the Reformation Publishing Company. Find the net amount of the order.

60 trade books @ $6.50, less 40%
50 professional and reference books @ $11.75, less 33⅓%
20 high school textbooks @ $5.60, less 25%
100 college textbooks @ $8.00, less 20%

112.—
28.—
84.—

35 TRADE DISCOUNT SERIES

Very often a series of two or more discounts, known as a *trade discount series,* is allowed by a manufacturer in order to increase his business. He may issue a discount sheet announcing that the buyer may take his usual 20% discount but that he will also receive an additional 10% discount on certain items. If the price of an article listed at $150, less 20%, is reduced, an additional discount of 10% might be offered, making the new price $150, less 20% and 10%. If the price goes up, the 10% might be reduced to 5% or eliminated entirely.

It is important to remember that a 20% and 10% discount is not equivalent to a 30% discount. The rate of 20% is applied to the list price, but the second discount of 10% is applied to the list price less the first discount.

The same three methods for computing single discounts can be used for computing a series of discounts.

METHOD 1
One method of computing a series of discounts is to multiply the list price by the first discount, and then to multiply that product by the second discount.

Example | **PROBLEM** Find the deduction allowed and the amount due on a purchase totaling $360, less 20% and 16⅔%.

SOLUTION

$360.00 = list price
−72.00 = 20%, or ⅕, of $360
$288.00
−48.00 = 16⅔%, or ⅙, of $288
$240.00 = net price
$360 − $240 = $120, trade discount

In the example, the first discount (20%) was deducted from the list price ($360), and the second discount (16⅔%) was deducted from the balance remaining after the first discount was taken ($288). Whenever a series of discounts is offered, the net price and the trade discount are found by subtracting each discount in the discount series from the cost remaining after the preceding discount has been deducted. After all discounts have been deducted, the balance is the amount due, or the net price. The difference between this price and the list price is the trade discount.

Changing the order in which the discounts are taken does not change the net price. A simple check on the accuracy of the net price can be obtained by the following way.

Example

$$\$360.00 = \text{list price}$$
$$\underline{-60.00} = 16\tfrac{2}{3}\%, \text{ or } \tfrac{1}{6}, \text{ of } \$360$$
$$\$300.00$$
$$\underline{-60.00} = 20\%, \text{ or } \tfrac{1}{5}, \text{ of } \$300$$
$$\$240.00 = \text{net price}$$

METHOD 2

In this method, 100% is used as the basis of each discount. The percent remaining after the discount has been deducted from 100% is applied to the price remaining after the preceding discount has been taken.

Example

100% − 20% = 80%, percent remaining after first discount is deducted
80% of $360 = $288, price after first discount is deducted
100% − 16$\tfrac{2}{3}$% = 83$\tfrac{1}{3}$%, percent remaining after second discount is deducted
83$\tfrac{1}{3}$% of $288 = $240, net price

METHOD 3

This is a shorter method of finding the net price of an invoice on which trade discount is allowed. Subtract each discount from 100%. In each case, reduce the remainder to a fraction in its lowest terms. Then find the product of the fractions. You may use the cancellation process to compute the net price.

Example

$$100\% - 20\% = 80\% = \tfrac{4}{5}$$
$$100\% - 16\tfrac{2}{3}\% = 83\tfrac{1}{3}\% = \tfrac{5}{6}$$
$$60$$
$$\tfrac{4}{5} \times \tfrac{5}{6} \times \cancel{\$360} = \$240, \text{ net price}$$

Practice Drill

A meat market proprietor purchased from a wholesaler a refrigerator listed at $270, less discounts of 25% and 12$\tfrac{1}{2}$%. Find the net price of the refrigerator, using each of the three methods just explained.

ANSWER $177.19

APPLICATION PROBLEMS

1. Find the trade discount and the net price for each of the following invoices. Prove each result by solving each problem by any two of the methods illustrated or by reworking the problem after changing the order in which the discounts are deducted.

a. An invoice of $560 subject to discounts of 25% and 20%
b. An invoice of $196 subject to discounts of 25%, 20%, and 10%
c. An invoice of $725 subject to discounts of 20% and $16\frac{2}{3}$%
d. An invoice of $342 subject to discounts of $33\frac{1}{3}$% and 20%
e. An invoice of $672 subject to discounts of 20% and $12\frac{1}{2}$%
f. An invoice of $234 subject to discounts of $16\frac{2}{3}$% and 10%
g. An invoice of $326 subject to discounts of 20%, 10%, and 5%
h. An invoice of $535 subject to discounts of 20%, $16\frac{2}{3}$%, and 10%

2. A new employee in the billing department of Hilton and Company misunderstood the company trade discount terms of 20% and 5% and allowed a customer a discount of 25% on an invoice of $816. How much did this error cost the company? (Find the net price of $816, less 20% and 5%, and the net price of $816, less 25%. The difference between the two net prices is the cost of the error to the company.)

3. A county purchasing agent asks for bids on desks for the offices of a new administration building. The Executive Office Equipment Company quotes its desks at $164.90, less trade discounts of 20% and 10%. The Utility Desk Company quotes a comparable desk at $150, less 10% and 5%. Which is the better offer? By how much?

4. A hardware dealer received a bill for $1,096.50 for merchandise purchases, subject to discounts of 20%, 10%, and 10%. An additional 5% discount was allowed for prompt payment. What was the lowest amount at which the dealer could settle the bill in full?

36 SINGLE-DISCOUNT EQUIVALENTS

In the previous unit you found the net price after deducting each discount in a series of discounts. Now you will find one discount that is equal to a series of discounts. Here are two methods of finding a single-discount equivalent.

Example   **PROBLEM**   Find the single-discount equivalent of 20%, 12½%, and 10%.

SOLUTION

100% = list price
−20% = 20%, or ⅕, of 100%
 80%
−10% = 12½%, or ⅛, of 80%
 70%
− 7% = 10%, or 1/10, of 70%
 63% = net price

100% − 63% = 37%, single-discount
                    equivalent

or

100% − 20% = 80% = ⅘
100% − 12½% = 87½% = ⅞
100% − 10% = 90% = 9/10

100% × ⅘ × ⅞ × 9/10 = 63%, net price

100% − 63% = 37%, single-discount equivalent

Practice   **1.** Find the single-discount equivalent of each of the following series
Drills   of discounts.
a. 25% and 20%   c. 30%, 20%, and 10%
b. 20%, 10%, and 10%   d. 25%, 20%, and 16⅔%

2. A television dealer is allowed a discount of 25% and 20% on all
television sets purchased from a local manufacturer. If he bought
television sets listed in the trade catalog at $182 each, what amount of
trade discount did he receive and what was the net price of each set?
(Change the discount series to its single-discount equivalent.)

ANSWERS   1a. 40%   1b. 35.2%   1c. 49.6%   1d. 50%
                2. trade discount, $72.80; net price, $109.20

APPLICATION PROBLEMS

1. Find the single-discount equivalent of each of the following series of discounts.

a. 40% and 20%   c. 20%, 10%, and 5%   e. 25%, 20%, and 10%
b. $33\frac{1}{3}$% and 25%   d. $33\frac{1}{3}$%, 10%, and 10%   f. 10%, 10%, and 10%

2. Find the trade discount and the net price for each of the following invoices. Prove each by finding the single-discount equivalent for each discount series.

a. An invoice of $465 subject to discounts of 20% and 10%
b. An invoice of $605 subject to discounts of 20% and $2\frac{1}{2}$%
c. An invoice of $712 subject to discounts of 25% and 5%
d. An invoice of $890 subject to discounts of 20%, 10%, and 5%
e. An invoice of $348 subject to discounts of 25%, 20%, and 10%
f. An invoice of $148 subject to discounts of $37\frac{1}{2}$% and 20%
g. An invoice of $226 subject to discounts of 20%, 10%, and 10%
h. An invoice of $89.90 subject to discounts of 30% and $14\frac{2}{7}$%

3. Find the amount paid for the following items. Prove by using the single-discount equivalent of each discount series. Find the total amount paid for all the items.
a. 4 dozen kitchen chairs @ $63, less 20% and 10%
b. 2 dozen mirrors @ $72.80, less $33\frac{1}{3}$% and 10%
c. 18 bolsters @ $15.60, less 25% and 20%
d. 12 coffee tables @ $42.50, less 30% and 5%
e. $1\frac{1}{2}$ dozen cabinets @ $84, less 15% and 10%

4. On a bill of goods amounting to $7,500, which is better: a discount of 30%, 20%, and 10% or a discount of 50% and 10%? What percent better? What amount better? Prove each by reducing the discount series to its single-discount equivalent.

37   USING A DISCOUNT TABLE

Discount tables similar to the following one are used by many firms to find the single-discount equivalent of a series of discounts quickly and accurately.

The first column in this discount table (headed "Rate Percent") contains discounts taken one, two, or three at a time; the row at the top contains only one discount. Therefore, it is possible to find one discount equal to two, three, or four discounts in certain cases.

DISCOUNT TABLE

Rate Percent	5	7½	10	15	20	25	30	33⅓	40	50
2	.931	.9065	.882	.833	.784	.735	.686	.6533	.588	.49
2½	.9263	.9019	.8775	.8288	.78	.7313	.6825	.65	.585	.4875
5	.9025	.8788	.855	.8075	.76	.7125	.665	.6333	.57	.475
5-2½	.8799	.8568	.8336	.7873	.741	.6947	.6484	.6175	.5558	.4631
7½	.8788	.8556	.8325	.7863	.74	.6938	.6475	.6166	.555	.4625
7½-5	.8348	.8128	.7909	.7469	.703	.6591	.6151	.5858	.5273	.4394
10	.855	.8325	.81	.765	.72	.675	.63	.60	.54	.45
10-2½	.8336	.8117	.7898	.7459	.702	.6581	.6143	.585	.5265	.4388
10-5	.8123	.7909	.7695	.7268	.684	.6413	.5985	.57	.513	.4275
10-5-2½	.7919	.7711	.7503	.7086	.6669	.6252	.5835	.5558	.5002	.4168
10-10	.7695	.7493	.729	.6885	.648	.6075	.567	.54	.486	.405
10-10-5	.7310	.7118	.6926	.6541	.6156	.5771	.5387	.513	.4617	.3848
20-5	.722	.703	.684	.646	.608	.57	.532	.5067	.456	.38
20-10	.684	.666	.648	.612	.576	.54	.504	.48	.432	.36
25	.7125	.6938	.675	.6375	.60	.5625	.5250	.50	.45	.375
25-5	.6769	.6591	.6413	.6056	.57	.5344	.4988	.475	.4275	.3563
25-10	.6413	.6244	.6075	.5738	.54	.5063	.4725	.45	.405	.3375
25-10-5	.6092	.5932	.5771	.5451	.513	.4809	.4489	.4275	.3748	.3206

Example

PROBLEM Find the amount due on an invoice amounting to $286 subject to discounts of 30%, 7½%, and 5%. (Assume that the table entries represent fractional parts of $1.)

SOLUTION In the column at the left, find the row marked 7½—5 and follow it to the column headed by 30. The entry is .6151, or 61.51% of $1. If 61.51¢ is the amount due on $1, .6151 × $286, or $175.92, is due on an invoice amounting to $286, less 30%, 7½%, and 5%.

Practice Drills

Using the discount table, find the amount due on each of the following invoices.

1. $800, less 25% and 5%
2. $350, less 25%, 10%, and 10%

3. $1,200, less 20%, 10%, and 5%
4. $68.80, less 10%, 5%, and 2½%

ANSWERS 1. $570   2. $212.63   3. $820.80   4. $57.35

APPLICATION PROBLEMS

Using the discount table above, find the single-discount equivalent for each discount series, the amount of trade discount, and the net price for each of the following.

1. An invoice of $325, less a discount series of 10% and 5%
2. An invoice of $184.50, less a discount series of 20%, 10%, and 5%
3. An invoice of $467.85, less a discount series of 15%, 10%, and 5%
4. An invoice of $811, less a discount series of $33\frac{1}{3}$%, 10%, and 10%
5. An invoice of $526.30, less a discount series of 25%, 20%, and 10%
6. An invoice of $294.65, less a discount series of 30%, 25%, and 5%
7. An invoice of $900.75, less a discount series of 10%, 5%, and $2\frac{1}{2}$%
8. An invoice of $185.30, less a discount series of 40%, 10%, and $2\frac{1}{2}$%
9. An invoice of $87.40, less a discount series of 25%, 25%, and 5%
10. An invoice of $91.32, less a discount series of 20%, 10%, and $2\frac{1}{2}$%

38 CASH DISCOUNT: ORDINARY DATING

Ordinary dating refers to a date span that is mentioned on an invoice and that has no special qualifications. For example, goods purchased on March 1 at terms of 2/10, n/30 must be paid for by March 11 if the 2% discount is to be allowed.

To compute a cash discount under ordinary dating, find the number of days from the date of the invoice to the date when payment is received. Then deduct the cash discount from the total amount of the bill to find the amount due. Obviously, taking advantage of discounts can result in substantial savings for a buyer, and a delay of only one day in paying an invoice can be very costly.

Example | **PROBLEM** An invoice dated March 21 in the amount of $165 was received by the purchaser on March 22. The merchandise was purchased on March 20 at terms of 5/10, 2/30, n/60. Find the amount due if the invoice is paid March 31.

SOLUTION From March 21 to March 31 is 10 days. According to the terms, a 5% discount is allowed if the bill is paid in 10 days or less.

$165, less 5% = $156.75, amount of payment

Note: In computing the number of days for cash discount purposes, always use the date of the invoice, not the date on which the invoice was received or the date of the purchase. In this case, the date to use is March 21.

Practice Drills | 1. The Homer School of Languages purchased desks and other equipment from the World-Wide Seating Company on August 8 for a total of $2,279.50. The terms were 7/10, 3/30, n/60. If the invoice is paid on August 16, how much will be paid to the World-Wide Seating Company? How much if the invoice was paid on August 25?

2. Alpha Transfer and Storage submitted its invoice amounting to $5,778 for moving the Laytham Manufacturing Company from its old plant to a new location. The terms of the invoice, dated February 13, were 3/10, n/30. Laytham Manufacturing sent a check for $5,604.66 to Alpha Transfer and Storage on February 24. Was this the correct amount?

ANSWERS   1. $2,119.93; $2,211.11   2. No. The invoice was paid after the discount period; thus, the full amount of $5,778 was due.

APPLICATION PROBLEMS

Find the cash discount and the net amount paid on each of the following purchases.

	Gross Amount	Terms	Date of Invoice	Date Paid	Cash Discount	Net Amt. Paid
1.	$1,466	2/10, n/30	June 30	July 10	$ 29.32	$ 1436.68
2.	2,091	5/10, 2/30, n/90	Mar. 21	Apr. 1	104.55	1986.45
3.	3,687	4/10, n/30	Feb. 26	Mar. 8	147.48	3539.52
4.	2,674	3/30, n/60	July 23	Aug. 3	80.22	2593.78
5.	5,003	5/10, n/30	Apr. 19	Apr. 28	250.15	4752.85
6.	2,378	2/10, n/90	Jan. 11	Jan. 16	47.56	2330.44
7.	4,269	5/10, 2/30, n/60	May 25	June 1	_____	_____
8.	6,875	3/10, 1/30, n/90	Dec. 11	Dec. 21	_____	_____
9.	1,184	2/10, 1/30, n/60	Apr. 18	Apr. 30	_____	_____
10.	5,207	6/10, 3/30, n/90	Oct. 19	Nov. 7	_____	_____

39 CASH DISCOUNT: END-OF-MONTH AND PROXIMO DATING

In *end-of-month* (*E.O.M.*) *dating*, the discount days are counted from the end of the month following the date of the invoice — not from the date of the invoice. *Proximo* (*prox.*) *dating* means essentially the same thing as E.O.M. dating; the word "proximo" means "in the next month." Proximo dating is shown on invoices as "2/10, prox." or "5/10, 2/30, n/60, prox."

If an invoice is dated on or after the 26th of the month, on E.O.M. or prox. terms, a month's extension of time is allowed. Thus an invoice dated September 27, terms 3/10, E.O.M. or prox., is usually granted a 3% cash discount if paid up to and including November 10. If paid after the discount period, invoices with E.O.M. or prox. dating have a 20-day net period following the expiration of the cash discount period in which to make payment at the net price. After this time the bill is considered overdue and subject to an interest charge.

Example

PROBLEM   The terms of payment of a $118 bill dated April 5 are 5/10, E.O.M. How much is due if the bill is paid on May 10?

SOLUTION   Payment was made within 10 days after the end of the month following the date of the invoice.

5% of $118 = $5.90, cash discount
$118 − $5.90 = $112.10, amount due

Practice Drill

The Linen Shop purchased $1,476 worth of merchandise. The terms of the invoice were 8/10, E.O.M. If the invoice was dated June 17 and paid July 8, how much was due?

ANSWER $1,357.92

APPLICATION PROBLEMS

1. Find the cash discount and the amount due on the following invoices.
a. Amount of invoice, $160.50; terms, 5/10, E.O.M.; date of invoice, June 28; date paid, August 10.
b. Amount of invoice, $556.63; terms, 3/10, prox.; date of invoice, September 10; date paid, October 3.
c. Amount of invoice, $719.38; terms, 3/10, E.O.M.; date of invoice, April 30; date paid, June 1.
d. Amount of invoice, $1,090.95; terms, 2/10, E.O.M.; date of invoice, December 27; date paid, February 10.

2. Merchandise amounting to $348.50 was purchased July 22, terms 6/10, E.O.M.
a. What is the last day on which the cash discount may be taken?
b. If payment is made on August 2, what amount will pay the bill in full?
c. If the invoice was dated July 28, what is the final date on which the discount may be taken?

40 CASH DISCOUNT: RECEIPT-OF-GOODS DATING

Receipt-of-goods (R.O.G.) dating means that the discount period is counted after receipt of the goods and not after the date of the invoice. This method of dating is used when the time required for the delivery of goods is indefinite because of distance or because the transportation time is greater than the discount period.

Example | **PROBLEM**   An invoice for merchandise amounting to $202 is dated July 1, terms 3/10, n/30, R.O.G. The goods were received on July 12 and a check sent in payment on July 20. What was the amount of the check?

SOLUTION   A discount of 3% may be taken any time to July 22, 10 days from the date the goods were received.

$$3\% \text{ of } \$202 = \$6.06, \text{ cash discount}$$
$$\$202 - \$6.06 = \$195.94, \text{ amount paid}$$

If the bill was dated July 30, terms 3/10, n/30, R.O.G., and the goods were received on August 28, the purchaser would be entitled to the 3% discount up to and including September 7. If the net period is not stated, a 20-day period after the 10-day cash discount period is usually allowed. After this time, as with E.O.M. dating, the bill is overdue and subject to an interest charge.

Practice Drill | Goods invoiced at $289.50 were purchased on February 23, terms 6/10, n/30, R.O.G. How much did the goods cost if they were received on March 4 and a check was sent in payment on March 13?

ANSWER $272.13

APPLICATION PROBLEMS

Find the cash discount and the amount due the seller on the following invoices.

1. Amount of invoice, $93.75; terms, 4/30, R.O.G.; receipt of goods, May 13; date of invoice, March 16; date paid, June 7.
2. Amount of invoice, $187.64; terms, 1/10, R.O.G.; receipt of goods, October 4; date of invoice, August 1; date paid, October 13.
3. Amount of invoice, $6,227.40; terms, 4/30, R.O.G.; receipt of goods, February 13; date of invoice, February 2; date paid, March 10.
4. Amount of invoice, $214.40; terms, 1/10, R.O.G.; receipt of goods, October 9; date of invoice, October 9; date paid, October 20.

41 CASH DISCOUNT: EXTRA DATING

Extra dating means that the discount is granted for a period of time in addition to the period first specified in the terms. Extra dating is often used in seasonal sales. To induce retailers to buy goods out of season, such as snow-removing equipment in July or air-conditioning equipment in January, wholesalers and manufacturers may offer extra dating. Extra dating is shown on invoices as "5/10-90x," "5/10-90 extra," or "5/10-90 ex."

Example

PROBLEM A bill for a heating unit costing $685 and installed on August 18 was dated August 15, terms 5/10-90x. What is the last payment date on which the 5% cash discount may be taken? What amount would pay the bill in full any time up to the last discount date?

SOLUTION The terms "5/10-90x" mean that a 5% cash discount may be taken if payment is made any time within 100 days (10 days plus 90 extra days) from the date of the invoice. The last payment date is 100 days from August 15. 100 days from August 15 is November 23.

$$5\% \text{ of } \$685 = \$34.25, \text{ cash discount}$$
$$\$685 - \$34.25 = \$650.75, \text{ amount due}$$

Practice Drill

Electric blankets costing a total of $827.75 were purchased on April 26 and received on May 12. The invoice, dated May 7, indicated 3/10–90x terms.
1. What is the last payment date on which the 3% discount may be taken?
2. What was the net cost of the blankets if the bill was paid before the last discount date?

ANSWERS 1. August 15   2. $802.92

APPLICATION PROBLEMS

Find the cash discount and the amount due the seller on each of the following invoices.

1. Amount of invoice, $787.50; terms, 3/30-90 extra; date of invoice, April 16; date paid, August 1.

2. Amount of invoice, $3,265; terms, 2/15-60x; date of invoice, July 19; date paid, October 1.

3. Amount of invoice, $375.28; terms, 1/10-30 ex.; date of invoice, August 1; date paid, September 1.

4. Amount of invoice, $700; terms, 6/10-90x; date of invoice, July 19; date paid, September 20.

42 COMMISSION SALES

The commission and other charges connected with the sale of merchandise by a commission merchant are always based on the gross proceeds. To find the net proceeds, follow these steps.
1. Find the gross proceeds by multiplying the number of articles sold by the retail price per article.

2. Find the total charges. Such charges as commission and guaranty are percentages of the gross proceeds. A guaranty charge is collected when a commission merchant guarantees payments in an account sale or agrees to reimburse the purchaser or seller for damaged merchandise.

3. Deduct the total charges from the gross proceeds to arrive at the net proceeds.

Example

PROBLEM Hilton & Sons, commission merchants of Chicago, Illinois, received a consignment of 275 crates of blueberries, 310 crates of strawberries, and 1,240 bags of potatoes from Harold Nanton of Fort Wayne, Indiana. They sold the blueberries at $4.80 per crate, the strawberries at $5.10 per crate, and the potatoes at $2.35 per bag. The charges were as follows: freight and cartage, $108.60; commission, $3\frac{1}{2}$%; and guaranty, 1%. Prepare an account sales as of June 27, 19—.

SOLUTION

ACCOUNT SALES

HILTON & SONS
Commission Merchants
Chicago, Ill.

Sold for Account of: June 27, 19—

Harold Nanton
31 Dover Pkwy., Fort Wayne, Ind.   46805

19—								
June	22	275 crates Blueberries	@ $4.80	$1,320	00			
	24	310 crates Strawberries	@ $5.10	1,581	00			
	25	1,240 bags Potatoes	@ $2.35	2,914	00			
			Gross Proceeds			$5,815	00	
		Charges:						
		Freight and cartage		$ 108	60			
		Commission, $3\frac{1}{2}$% of $5,815		203	53			
		Guaranty, 1% of $5,815		58	15	370	28	
			Net Proceeds			$5,444	72	

Practice Drill

Silver and Hodges, Inc., commission merchants of Chicago, Illinois, received a consignment of 5,600 bushels of corn from Ross Brothers of Monona, Iowa. They sold the corn at $1.86 a bushel. The charges were as follows: storage and handling, 7 cents a bushel; commission, $5\frac{1}{2}$%; and guaranty, $1\frac{3}{8}$%. Find the net proceeds.

ANSWER $9,307.90

APPLICATION PROBLEMS

Prepare an account sales for each problem, showing the details of each sale and the charges.

1. A fruit grower shipped 315 barrels of apples to an agent, to be sold on a commission of $4\frac{1}{2}$%. The apples were sold at an average price of $4.95 a barrel. A guaranty charge of $1\frac{1}{2}$% was made by the agent, and freight and drayage amounted to $59.90. Find the net proceeds.

2. A commission merchant received from a mill a consignment of 1,175 barrels of flour. Freight charges paid by him amounted to $416; cartage, 12¢ a barrel; and cooperage, $37.70. The following sales were made: 250 barrels at $11.90, 370 barrels at $10.10, 120 barrels at $13.05, and the remainder at $12 a barrel. The commission merchant's charges for service were $3\frac{1}{2}$% for selling, 1% for collection, and $1\frac{3}{4}$% for guaranty and insurance. Find the net proceeds.

3. A commission merchant received a shipment of 5,000 bushels of corn sent to him by a wholesale dealer. The charges were as follows: freight and cartage, $2\frac{3}{4}$¢ a bushel; storage and handling, $2\frac{1}{2}$¢ a bushel; commission, 4%; and guaranty, $1\frac{3}{4}$%. The corn was sold at $1.57 a bushel. Find the net proceeds.

4. A consignment of 84 tons of hay was received by a commission merchant. The following sales were made: 30 tons at $26.50 a ton, 45 tons at $23.65 a ton, and the remainder at $21.75 a ton. The freight and cartage charges were $335; storage, $73; insurance, $41.80; guaranty, $1\frac{1}{2}$%; and commission, $3\frac{1}{2}$%. Find the net proceeds.

5. A commission merchant sold for his principal 7,200 bushels of wheat at $1.56 a bushel, charging $3\frac{1}{2}$% commission. Other charges amounted to $711.50. With the net proceeds of the sale he purchased flour for his principal at $8.30 a barrel, charging $3\frac{1}{2}$% commission for buying.
a. Find the net proceeds of the sale.
b. How many barrels of flour were purchased?
c. What was the unexpended sum?

43 COMMISSION PURCHASES

The *gross cost* of goods bought through a commission merchant is equal to the prime cost of the merchandise purchased plus the commission and other charges incurred in connection with the transaction. The gross cost is calculated as follows.
1. Find the prime cost by multiplying the number of articles bought by the cost per article.
2. Find the total charges. The commission and the guaranty charges are percentages of the prime cost.
3. Add the total charges to the prime cost to arrive at the gross cost.

Example | **PROBLEM** Heller & Wagner, commission merchants of Dallas, Texas, bought on the order of Parke & Tull of Memphis, Tennessee, 625 pounds of coffee at 38 cents and 410 pounds of tea at 52 cents. The charges were as follows: cartage and storage, $41.60; commission, $4\frac{1}{2}$%; and guaranty, $\frac{3}{4}$%. Prepare an account purchase as of June 28, 19—.

SOLUTION

ACCOUNT PURCHASES

HELLER & WAGNER
Commission Merchants
Dallas, Texas

Bought for Account of: June 28, 19—

Parke & Tull

5 Pennsylvania Blvd., Memphis, Tenn.   38103

19—							
June	18	625 pounds Coffee	@ $.38	$	237	50	
		410 pounds Tea	@ $.52		213	20	
			Prime Cost				$ 450	70
		Charges:					
		Cartage and storage		$	41	60	
		Commission, $4\frac{1}{2}$% of $450.70			20	28	
		Guaranty, $\frac{3}{4}$% or $450.70			3	38	65	26
			Gross Cost				$ 515	96

Practice | A commission merchant is requested to purchase 75 barrels of sugar,
Drill | 250 pounds to a barrel, at 5.75 cents a pound. The commission charges are $4\frac{1}{4}$%, and the other charges are $148.65. Find the gross cost of the sugar.

ANSWER $1,272.60 $, 05.75$

APPLICATION PROBLEMS

Prepare an account purchases for each problem, showing the details of each purchase and the charges associated with it.

1. A commission merchant purchased for a customer 3,400 bushels of wheat at $1.56 a bushel. The freight and cartage charges were $562 and the commission charges, $4\frac{1}{2}$%. Find the gross cost of the wheat.

2. A principal requested his agent to buy for him 450 bales of cotton, 500 pounds in a bale, at 26¢ a pound. The charges were as follows: guaranty and insurance, $1\frac{1}{2}$%; freight and drayage, $21.80; and commission, $3\frac{1}{2}$%. Find the gross cost of the cotton.

3. A commission merchant was requested to purchase 120 barrels of sugar, 250 pounds to a barrel, at 12.05¢ a pound. The commission charges were $3\frac{1}{2}$%; and the other charges, $202.10. Find the gross cost of the sugar.

4. A principal received from his agent an account purchase showing a total of $1,771.65 due for a purchase of bales of cotton. The associated charges were as follows: commission, $3\frac{1}{2}$%; freight and cartage, $43.70; storage, $6.10; and other expenses, $14.10. If the cotton cost 26¢ a pound, and each bale contained 500 pounds, find the number of bales purchased.

5. A principal received from his agent an account purchase showing the following purchases: 245 crates of eggs, 30 dozen to a crate, at 48¢ a dozen; and 525 bushels of potatoes, 60 pounds to a bushel, at 2.49¢ a pound. The associated charges were as follows: cartage, $128.50; commission, $5\frac{1}{4}$%; other, $71.70. Find the total amount charged to the principal's account.

PROBLEMS FOR PART FOUR

Discounts & Commissions

34 Find the discount and net price of each of the following purchases, using any of the three methods described in this unit.

1. $745, less 25%
2. $660, less $12\frac{1}{2}$%
3. $1,110, less 20%
4. $360, less 30%
5. $1,740, less 25%
6. $800, less $16\frac{2}{3}$%

35 Find the trade discount and the net price in each of the following. Prove each result by using any two of the methods illustrated to solve the problem, or by reworking the problem after changing the order in which the discounts are deducted.

1. $1,740, less 20% and 10%
2. $2,350, less 25% and 5%
3. $875, less 20% and 20%
4. $260, less 10% and 10%
5. $1,420, less 10% and 5%
6. $935, less 20% and 5%
7. $750, less 25%, 20%, and 10%
8. $1,240, less $33\frac{1}{3}$%, 25%, and 10%

9. Bicycles are sold by a manufacturer for $28.60 each, less 18%. A cash discount of $1\frac{1}{2}$% is allowed if payment is made within 10 days from the date of the invoice. Find the net cash price of 15 bicycles purchased on February 27 and paid for on March 8.

36 Using the two methods given in this unit, find the single-discount equivalent for each of the following discount series.

1. 20% and 10%
2. 25% and 10%
3. 10% and 10%
4. 30% and 10%
5. 20%, 10%, and $12\frac{1}{2}$%

6. 25% and $6\frac{2}{3}$%
7. $16\frac{2}{3}$% and 10%
8. 20% and $16\frac{2}{3}$%
9. 30% and $14\frac{2}{7}$%
10. 20%, 10%, and $16\frac{2}{3}$%

37 Using the discount table on page 59, find the amount due on the following invoices.

1. An invoice of $728, less a discount series of 20% and 10%
2. An invoice of $384, less a discount series of 10%, 5%, and $2\frac{1}{2}$%
3. An invoice of $176, less a discount series of 30%, 10%, and 10%
4. An invoice of $280, less a discount series of 25%, 20%, and 5%
5. An invoice of $525, less a discount series of 40%, 10%, and 5%
6. An invoice of $86.75, less a discount series of 15%, 10%, and $2\frac{1}{2}$%
7. An invoice of $132, less a discount series of 10%, 10%, and $2\frac{1}{2}$%
8. An invoice of $640, less a discount series of 20%, 10%, and 5%
9. An invoice of $263.70, less a discount series of 25%, 10%, and $2\frac{1}{2}$%
10. An invoice of $411.90, less a discount series of 50%, 25%, and 5%
11. An invoice of $750, less a discount series of 10%, $7\frac{1}{2}$%, and 5%
12. An invoice of $393.40, less a discount series of 40%, 25%, and 10%

38 Find the cash discount and the net amount paid in each of the following.

	Gross Amount	Terms	Date of Invoice	Date Paid	Cash Discount	Net Amt. Paid
1.	$2,460	5/10, n/30	Sept. 29	Oct. 9	$_____	$_____
2.	1,685	2/10, n/30	Feb. 25	Mar. 7	_____	_____
3.	3,674	5/30, n/60	Aug. 21	Sept. 1	_____	_____
4.	1,008	4/10, n/30	Dec. 18	Dec. 27	_____	_____
5.	1,372	3/10, n/90	Jan. 7	Jan. 15	_____	_____
6.	6,093	5/10, 2/30, n/90	Oct. 20	Nov. 1	_____	_____
7.	3,186	3/10, 1/30, n/60	Apr. 12	Apr. 24	_____	_____
8.	4,208	8/10, 4/30, n/90	July 15	Aug. 3	_____	_____

39 Find the cash discount and the amount due on the following invoices.

1. Amount of invoice, $787.40; terms, 4/10, E.O.M.; date of invoice, April 28; date paid, June 10.
2. Amount of invoice, $436.77; terms, 5/10, prox.; date of invoice, November 10; date paid, December 3.
3. Amount of invoice, $1,220.40; terms, 6/10, E.O.M.; date of invoice, September 30; date paid, November 1.

40

Find the cash discount and the amount due the seller on the following invoices.

1. Amount of invoice, $820.20; terms, 5/30, R.O.G.; receipt of goods, July 13; date of invoice, May 16; date paid, August 7.
2. Amount of invoice, $99.65; terms, 1/10, R.O.G.; receipt of goods, February 4; date of invoice, December 1 (preceding year); date paid, February 13.

41

Find the cash discount and the amount due the seller on the following invoices.

1. Amount of invoice, $12,778; terms, 4/15-30x; date of invoice, September 9; date paid, November 1.
2. Amount of invoice, $550.50; terms, 3/10-90 extra; date of invoice, August 15; date paid, November 15.

42

Find the total charges and the net proceeds of each of the following commission sales. Find the totals for each column.

	Gross Proceeds	Freight and Cartage	Collection and Guaranty	Commission	Other Charges	Total Charges	Net Proceeds
1.	$360	$13.25	2% = $ 7.20	4% = $ 14.4	$ 9.24	$ 44.09	$ 315.91
2.	120	14.00	2½% = 3.00	2½% = 3.00	3.25	23.25	96.75
3.	320	10.98	1½% = 4.80	3% = 9.60	5.16	30.54	289.46
4.	190	5.40	3% = 5.70	3½% = 6.65	7.84	25.59	164.41
5.	463	21.75	1¼% = 5.79	4% = 18.52	12.59	58.65	404.35
6.	975	39.90	½% = 4.88	2½% = 24.38	64.87	133.13	841.87
	$___	$___	$___	$___	$___	$___	$___

43

Find the gross cost of each of the following commission purchases. Find the totals for each column.

	Prime Cost	Freight and Cartage	Guaranty	Commission	Other Charges	Total Charges	Gross Cost
1.	$785	$43.25	3% = $ 23.55	6% = $ 47.10	$35.30	$ 149.20	$ 934.20
2.	615	59.75	2½% = ___	4½% = ___	19.80	___	___
3.	588	12.16	1% = ___	3½% = ___	28.75	___	___
4.	900	8.95	2% = ___	5% = ___	38.92	___	___
5.	326	17.16	1½% = ___	4½% = ___	54.30	___	___
6.	403	23.84	2½% = ___	5% = ___	47.16	___	___
	$___	$___	$___	$___	$___	$___	$___

PART FIVE
Retail Store Computations

Operating a retail store successfully is one of the greatest challenges in the world of business. The retail store owner is the "complete" businessman in that he performs all the basic functions of an enterprise—buying, financing, pricing, selling, and servicing. The notion that just about anyone can operate a retail store successfully is a myth; the number of retail businesses that fail each year is proof that genuine managerial talent is needed to succeed in retailing. Among other things, the successful retailer must know what, when, and where to buy; how to price his merchandise for a profit; and how to estimate and analyze merchandise turnover.

Following are terms that are important in retail business computations.

List price   The price at which an item is listed for sale in a catalog. The retailer pays the price listed, less a trade discount.

Trade discount   The percent of the list price by which an item is reduced for sale to the retailer.

Gross cost   The sum of the amount on the invoice and any *buying expenses,* or additional expenses, associated with the purchase. Such expenses as insurance and transportation are often classified as buying expenses.

Net cost   The difference between the gross cost and any sales returns and allowances.

Cost price   The retailer's net cost per unit of merchandise.

Selling price   The amount charged to the retail customer for a unit of merchandise. The *net selling price* is the difference between the selling price and the sum of the operating expenses and the selling expenses, if any.

Markon   The difference between the cost of an item to the retailer, or the amount on the invoice plus the associated buying expenses, and the selling price.

Loss   The difference between the cost of an item and the selling price when the selling price is less than cost.

Operating expenses	The expenses incurred in conducting a business. These expenses, which are sometimes called *overhead,* can include salaries, supplies, rent, and utilities.
Selling expenses	The expenses incurred in the selling transaction. They can include the cost of advertising, display, and direct mail.
Markdown	The amount by which the retailer's regular selling price is reduced for a special sale.
Markup	The amount by which the regular selling price is increased.
Gross sales	The total dollar value of all units of merchandise sold, based on the selling price.
Sales returns and allowances	The amount of credit or discount allowed a customer for goods that are returned because of change of mind, damage, inferior quality, incorrect quantity, or some other reason.
Net sales	The difference between gross sales and sales returns and allowances.
Net return	The sum of the net cost and the amount of markon.
Inventory	The units of merchandise that a business keeps on hand for sale. Inventory is generally taken at certain specified intervals (for example, monthly, bimonthly, quarterly, or semiannually). Many businessmen speak of their periodic checks on the number of items on hand as *taking a physical inventory.*
Average inventory	The sum of the inventories taken over a specified period (generally a year) divided by the number of inventories included. An average inventory always includes at least a *beginning inventory* and an *ending inventory in its computation.*
Cost of goods available for sale	The sum of the cost of the beginning inventory, or of the merchandise that remained unsold from the previous period, and the cost of the merchandise purchased during the period.
Cost of goods sold	The difference between the cost of the goods available for sale during the period and the cost of the merchandise inventory at the end of the period.
Value of average inventory	The product of the number of units in the average inventory and the cost price of each unit. This value directly affects the amount of profit or loss reported for a time period.
Merchandise inventory rate	The cost of goods sold divided by the value of the average inventory. This rate is also called merchandise *turnover.* In general, the higher the turnover the better—as long as the orders of most customers can be speedily filled.

44 FINDING AMOUNT OF MARKON OR LOSS AND PERCENT OF MARKON OR LOSS

Markon is the difference between the cost of an item to a retailer and the amount for which he sells it. This difference is also called *margin* or *gross profit*. For example, a sporting goods store purchases tennis balls for 60 cents a can and sells them for $1 a can. The markon (or gross profit) is 40 cents (or $1.00 – $.60 = $.40). When the retailer sells a unit of merchandise for less than cost, he takes a loss.

Obviously, if he is to remain in business, the retailer must set his prices high enough to allow for both operating and other expenses and a profit on his investment. The amount of markon varies from store to store and from article to article in a particular store. Fashion goods and seasonal merchandise generally carry a higher markon than other types of merchandise. Articles on which there is relatively little competition may carry higher markons than highly competitive articles. Also, stores that offer customers credit, delivery, and other services usually have a higher markon than stores that sell on a strictly cash-and-carry basis, because of the cost of the services.

The percent of markon may be based on either the selling price or the cost price. Computation is easier when markon is based on the cost price, but it is sometimes more convenient for the retailer to base it on the selling price because the selling price is placed on price tags right on the sales items and can be easily checked when updating inventory and sales records. In contrast with the retail procedure for computing markon, which may vary from store to store, manufacturers and wholesalers usually base their markon on the cost price.

Amount of Markon or Loss

To find the *amount* of markon or loss, compute the difference between the cost price and the selling price.

Example | **PROBLEM** A tape recorder costs $30 and sells for $45. Find the amount of markon.

SOLUTION $45, selling price
                  –30, cost price
                  $15, amount of markon

If the tape recorder cost $45 and sold for $30, the *loss* would be $15 ($45 – $30 = $15), because the retailer would receive less than the item had cost him.

Percent of Markon or Loss

In some cases, the *percent* of markon or loss is based on the cost price; in others it is based on the selling price. In all situations calling for the computation of the percent of markon, the standard percentage formula can be used. You may then substitute the particular information you need to solve the problem at hand.

$$Rate \times Base = Percentage \; (or \; Amount)$$

$$Percent \; of \; Markon \times \begin{matrix} Cost \; Price \\ or \\ Selling \; Price \end{matrix} = \begin{matrix} Amount \; of \; Markon \\ or \; Loss \end{matrix}$$

Regardless of which price is used as a base for the markon or loss, the equation *Cost Price + Markon = Selling Price* can be used. By rewriting this equation, you can also compute either the cost price or the markon, as below.

$$Cost \; Price = Selling \; Price - Markon$$
$$Markon = Selling \; Price - Cost \; Price$$

MARKON OR LOSS BASED ON COST PRICE

When the markon or loss is based on the cost price, the percent of markon or loss is found by dividing the amount of markon or loss by the cost price. Carry out each division to three decimal places so that you can round off your answer to two places.

Example

PROBLEM A tape recorder costs $30 and sells for $45. Find the percent of markon based on the cost price.

SOLUTION $45 – $30 = $15, amount of markon
$15 ÷ $30 = .50, or 50%, percent of markon

Practice
Drills

1. An article costs $40 and sells for $50. Find the amount and percent of markon based on the cost price.
2. An electric heater costs $75 and sells for $90. Find the amount and percent of markon based on the cost price.

ANSWERS 1. $10, 25% 2. $15, 20%

MARKON OR LOSS BASED ON SELLING PRICE

When markon or loss is based on the selling price, the percent of markon or loss is found by dividing the amount of markon or loss by the selling price.

Example | **PROBLEM** A tape recorder costs $30 and sells for $45. Find the percent of markon based on the selling price.

SOLUTION $15 ÷ $45 = .33⅓, or 33⅓%, percent of markon

Practice Drills | 1. An article costs $45 and sells for $60. Find the amount and the percent of markon based on the selling price.
2. A bowling ball cost $20 and sells for $35. Find the amount and the percent of markon based on the selling price.

ANSWERS   1. $15, 25%   2. $15, 60%

APPLICATION PROBLEMS

1. Find the amount and percent of markon based on the cost price if an article costs $55 and sells for $62.

2. Find the amount and the percent of markon or loss based on the cost price in each of the following. Round each decimal fraction to two places before changing to a percent.

	Cost Price	Selling Price	Amount of Markon or Loss	Percent of Markon or Loss
a.	$33	$42	$	
b.	56	46		
c.	16	24		
d.	9	20		
e.	16	12		

3. Find the amount and percent of markon based on the selling price if an article costs $11 and sells for $18.

4. Find the amount and the percent of markon or loss based on the selling price in each of the following. Round each decimal fraction to two places before changing to a percent.

	Cost Price	Selling Price	Amount of Markon or Loss	Percent of Markon or Loss
a.	$18	$28	$	
b.	10	15		
c.	24	21		
d.	57	65		
e.	71	63		

45 FINDING COST PRICE

Percent of Markon Based on Selling Price

When the selling price and the percent of markon based on the selling price are given, the cost price can be computed as follows.
1. Using the standard percentage formula, find the amount of markon by multiplying the selling price by the percent of markon or loss.
2. Subtract the result of step 1 from the selling price to find the cost price. In the event of a loss instead of a markon, add the loss to the selling price to find the cost price.

Example

PROBLEM   A dinette chair that sold for $12.50 included a markon of 20% based on the selling price. Find the cost price.

SOLUTION   20% × $12.50 = $2.50, amount of markon
$12.50 − $2.50 = $10, cost price

Practice Drills

1. An article that sold for $18.45 included a markon of 33⅓% based on the selling price. Find the cost price.
2. Suppose that the article in problem 1 was sold at a loss of $6.15 based on the selling price. How much did the article cost?

ANSWERS   1. $12.30   2. $24.60

Percent of Markon Based on Cost Price

When the selling price and the percent of markon based on cost price are given, the cost price can be computed as follows.
1. Express the selling price as the sum of the percent equivalents of the cost price and the amount of markon.
2. Divide the selling price by the resultant percent. The result is the percent of the cost price the selling price represents.

Example

PROBLEM   A dinette chair that sold for $12.50 included a markon of 20% based on cost. Find the cost price.

SOLUTION
1. Cost price + markon = selling price
    100% of cost price + 20% of cost price = $12.50, selling price
    120% of cost price = $12.50, selling price
2. $12.50 ÷ 120% = $10.416, or approximately $10.42, cost price

Check: $12.50 − $10.42 = $2.08, amount of markon
           120% − 100% = 20%, percent of markon

Practice Drills

1. An electric can opener sells for $28, which includes a markon of 40% based on cost. Find the cost price.
2. A handbag sells for $13.20, which includes a markon of 20% based on cost. Find the cost.

ANSWERS   1. $20   2. $11

APPLICATION PROBLEMS

1. A 17-jewel gold watch that sells for $80 includes a markon of 25% of the selling price. Find the cost price.

2. Find the cost price in each of the following if the percent of markon or loss is based on the selling price.

	Selling Price	Percent of Markon	Percent of Loss	Markon	Loss	Cost Price
a.	$ 9.10	45%		$_____	$_____	$_____
b.	10.48	12½%		_____	_____	_____
c.	15.00		16⅔%	_____	_____	_____
d.	22.50	37½%		_____	_____	_____
e.	18.99		10⅓%	_____	_____	_____

3. Skis that sold for $125 included a markon of 15% based on the cost price. Find the cost price.

4. Find the cost price in each of the following if the percent of markon or loss is based on the cost price.

	Selling Price	Percent of Markon	Percent of Loss	Markon	Loss	Cost Price
a.	$50.00	25% +/ᵒ%		$_____	$_____	$_____
b.	33.15	10½%		_____	_____	_____
c.	17.85	/oo -	15%	_____	_____	_____
d.	7.70	40%		_____	_____	_____
e.	40.00		20%	_____	_____	_____

4δ FINDING SELLING PRICE

Percent of Markon or Loss Based on Cost Price

When the cost price and the percent of markon or loss based on cost are given, the selling price can be computed as follows.
1. Using the standard percentage formula, find the amount of markon by multiplying the cost price by the percent of markon.
2. Add the result of step 1 to the cost price to compute the selling price.

Example | **PROBLEM**   Tennis shoes cost $2.50. Find the selling price if the percent of markon is 40% of the cost price.

SOLUTION   1. 40% × $2.50 = $1.00, amount of markon
2. $2.50 + $1.00 = $3.50, selling price

Check: $3.50 – $2.50 = $1.00, amount of markon
140% – 100% = 40%, percent of markon

Practice Drills | 1. A jacket cost the retailer $38.40. Find the selling price if the percent of markon is 30% of cost.
2. A necktie cost the retailer $3.15. Find the selling price if the percent of markon is 15% of cost.

ANSWERS   1. $49.92   2. $3.62

Percent of Markon Based on Selling Price

When the cost price and the percent of markon based on the selling price are given, the selling price can be computed as follows.
1. Subtract the percent of markon from 100% to arrive at the percent of the selling price the cost price represents.
2. Using the standard percentage formula, compute the selling price.

Example | **PROBLEM**   Tennis shoes cost the retailer $2.50. Find the selling price if the percent of markon is 40% of the selling price.

SOLUTION
1. 100% – 40% = 60%, percent of selling price that the cost price represents
2. 60% × selling price = $2.50, cost price
$2.50 ÷ 60% = $4.166, or approximately $4.17, selling price

Check: $4.17 – $2.50 = $1.67, amount of markon
100% – 60% = 40%, percent of markon

Practice Drills | 1. A broiler that cost the retailer $17.32 was sold at a markon of 10% of the selling price. Find the selling price.
2. At what price was a set of golf clubs sold if the cost was $18.75 and a loss of 25% of the selling price was incurred?

ANSWERS   1. $19.25   2. $15

APPLICATION PROBLEMS

1. A book costs $3.60. Find the selling price if the percent of markon is $33\frac{1}{3}$% of the cost price.

2. Find the selling price in each of the following problems if the percent of markon or loss is based on the retailer's cost.

	Cost Price	Percent of Markon	Percent of Loss	Markon	Loss	Selling Price
a.	$ 3.75	25%		$____	$____	$____
b.	40.10	15%		____	____	____
c.	5.98		10%	____	____	____
d.	2.25		15%	____	____	____
e.	6.45	7%		____	____	____

3. If the percent of markon is $33\frac{1}{3}$% of the selling price for the article in problem 1, what is the selling price?

4. Find the selling price in each of the following if the percent of markon or loss is based on the selling price.

	Cost Price	Percent of Markon	Percent of Loss	Markon	Loss	Selling Price
a.	$ 9.45	50%		$____	$____	$____
b.	10.60		$12\frac{1}{2}$%	____	____	____
c.	6.49	10%		____	____	____
d.	4.06		20%	____	____	____
e.	6.90		15%	____	____	____

47 FINDING MARKDOWN AND MARKUP

Clearing shelves of shopworn, outmoded, or slow-moving merchandise is usually done by means of special sales—referred to as clearance, seasonal, and preinventory sales. The idea is that reduced, or "bargain," prices will encourage customers to buy. This reduction of a regular price to a new, lower price is called *markdown*.

When the wholesale price of merchandise is increased, the dealer must either accept a smaller markon or pass the increase along to the customer by raising the regular price. The amount by which the regular selling price is increased is called *markup*.

Amount of Markdown

To find the *amount* of markdown, subtract the reduced price from the regular selling price.

Example | **PROBLEM**   An executive desk that regularly sold for $147 was marked down to $115. What was the amount of markdown?

SOLUTION $147, regular selling price
                         −115, reduced selling price
                         $ 32, amount of markdown

Percent of Markdown

To find the *percent* of markdown, divide the regular selling price by the amount of markdown.

Example | **PROBLEM**   An executive desk that regularly sold for $147 was marked down to $115 for a special sale. What was the percent of markdown? (Use the amount of markdown computed above.)

SOLUTION
$32 ÷ $147 = .217, or approximately 22%, percent of markdown

When the price of merchandise is reduced, the "sale" price is usually announced as a discount or a percent off the regular selling price.

Example | **PROBLEM**   An executive desk was advertised at a 22% markdown on the regular selling price of $147.69. What was the reduced selling price?

SOLUTION   22% × $147.69 = $32.49, amount of markdown

                    $147.69, regular selling price
                    − 32.49, markdown
                    $115.20, reduced selling price

Practice Drills | 1. Suits marked to sell for $125 were marked down to $106.25 for a summer clearance sale. What was the amount of markdown and the percent of markdown?
2. A chair was advertised at a 40% markdown of the regular selling price of $63. What was the reduced selling price?

ANSWERS   1. $18.75, 15%   2. $37.80

Amount of Markup

To find the *amount* of markup, do the following.

1. Using the regular selling price and the percent of markon based on either the regular selling price or the regular cost price, determine the regular cost price.

2. Using the percent of cost increase given, compute the new cost price, the amount of markon, and the new selling price.

3. Subtract the regular selling price from the new selling price to compute the amount of markup.

Example | **PROBLEM** The Wilshire City Shop sold sweaters for $22.49 each, including a markon of 30% based on cost. If the cost to the retailer increases 10%, how much must the markup on the regular selling price be for the same percent of markon to be realized?

SOLUTION 1. Cost price + markon = selling price
Cost price + 30% cost price = selling price
130% cost price = $22.49, regular selling price
$22.49 ÷ 130% = $17.30, regular cost price

2. 10% × $17.30 = $1.73, increase in cost
$17.30 + $1.73 = $19.03, new cost price
30% × $19.03 = $5.71, amount of markon
$19.03 + $5.71 = $24.74, new selling price

3. $24.74 − $22.49 = $2.25, amount of markup

Percent of Markup

To find the *percent* of markup, divide the amount of markup by the regular selling price.

Example | **PROBLEM** The Wilshire City Shop is increasing the selling price of sweaters from $22.49 to $24.74. What is the percent of markup?

SOLUTION $24.74 − $22.49 = $2.25, amount of markup
$2.25 ÷ $22.49 = 10%, percent of markup

APPLICATION PROBLEMS

1. Skis were marked down 25% from the regular selling price of $172. What was the new selling price?

2. During a year-end sale, a jeweler marked a silver serving dish down 25%, making the new selling price $67.50. At this price, he still realized a 20% markon based on cost.
a. How much was the markdown?
b. What was the regular selling price?
c. Find the cost of the item to the retailer.

3. A calculator was purchased by a dealer for $184, less 20%. The selling price the dealer placed on the machine was 40% higher than cost. When he received a notice from the manufacturer that prices were being boosted 20%, the dealer increased his selling price so that he would continue to make the same 40% markon based on cost.
a. Find the regular selling price.
b. Find the new selling price.

48 FINDING GROSS COST AND SELLING PRICE

For some purchases, additional charges, called *buying expenses,* are computed and added to the amount of the invoice sent to the retailer. Such expenses, which are usually for insurance and transportation, are included in the retailer's cost. The result is called *gross cost.* The *net cost* is the difference between the gross cost and any sales and allowances. The *cost price* is the retailer's net cost per unit of merchandise. When there are no returns and allowances, the gross cost and net cost are the same.

Amount of Markon

When buying expenses are to be part of the gross cost of merchandise to the retailer, do the following.
1. Multiply the amount of the invoice by the percent of buying expenses to find the amount of buying expenses.
2. Add the buying expenses to the amount of the invoice to find the gross cost.
3. Subtract the gross cost from the selling price to find the markon.

Example | **PROBLEM** A retailer paid $360 for a freezer. The associated buying expenses were 12% of the cost of the freezer. Find the markon if the retailer sold the freezer for $470.40.

SOLUTION 1. 12% × $360 = $43.20, amount of buying expense
2. $3.60 + $43.20 = $403.20, gross cost
3. $470.40 − $403.20 = $67.20, amount of markon

Percent of Markon

To find the percent of markon based on cost, divide the markon by the gross cost. To find the percent of markon based on the selling price, divide the amount of markon by the selling price.

Example

PROBLEM Assuming the gross cost and selling price stated in the example solution on page 82, find the percent of markon based on the cost price and the selling price.

SOLUTION $67.20 ÷ $403.20 = 16⅔%, percent of markon based on
the cost price

$67.20 ÷ $470.40 = 14⅞%, percent of markon based on
the selling price

Practice
Drill

A tape recorder cost a retailer $172. The buying expenses were an additional 10%. The recorder was then sold for $236.50. Find the percent of markon based on net cost and selling price.

ANSWERS   25%, based on net cost; 20%, based on selling price

Selling Price

PERCENT OF MARKON BASED ON NET SELLING PRICE

The selling price is the amount the retail customer is charged. For accounting purposes, a retailer computes net selling price, which is the difference between the selling price and the sum of the operating and selling expenses, if any. When the amount of the invoice and the percent of markon based on the net selling price are known, the net selling price can be computed as follows.
1. Add the buying expenses to the amount of the invoice, less any returns and allowances, to find the net cost.
2. Add the percent of operating and, if applicable, selling expenses to the percent of markon. Subtract the result from 100% to find what percent of the selling price the net cost is.
3. Using the standard percentage formula, divide the net cost by the percent of net cost to find the selling price.

Example

PROBLEM A piano that costs $640, plus an additional 5% in buying expenses, is sold at a markon of 20% of the net selling price. Find the selling price if the operating expenses are 10%.

SOLUTION 1. 5% × $640 = $32, amount of buying expense
$640 + $32 = $672, net cost

2. 20% + 10% = 30%, the sum of the percent of markon and the percent of operating expenses
100% − 30% = 70%, percent of the selling price the net cost represents

3. 70% × selling price = $672
$672 ÷ 70% = $960, selling price

Practice Drill
The list price of a rocking chair was $48, less a 12½% trade discount. The buying expenses amounted to 10%, and the operating expenses amounted to 10%. Find the selling price if the markon of 25% was based on the net selling price.

ANSWER $71.08

PERCENT OF MARKON BASED ON NET COST

When the amount of the invoice and the percent of markon based on net cost are known, the selling price can be computed as follows.
1. Add the buying expenses to the amount of the invoice, less any returns and allowances, to compute the net cost. (Buying expenses are *always* based on the cost price.)
2. Multiply the percent of markon by the net cost to find the amount of markon.
3. Compute the amount of net return by finding the sum of the net cost and the amount of markon.
4. Subtract the percent of operating expenses from 100% to find the percent of net return. (Operating expenses, or the cost of doing business, are *always* based on the selling price.)
5. Divide the amount of net return by the percent of net return to find the selling price.

Example
PROBLEM A piano that costs $640, plus 5% buying expenses, is sold at a markon of 20% of the net cost. Find the selling price if the operating expenses are 10%.

SOLUTION 1. 5% × $640 = $32, amount of buying expenses
$640 + $32 = $672, net cost

2. 20% × $672 = $134.40, amount of markon

3. $672 + $134.40 = $806.40, amount of net return

4. 100% − 10% = 90%, percent of net return

5. $806.40 ÷ 90% = $896, selling price

Practice
Drill

An electric pressure cooker costs $120 list, less a 20% trade discount. Buying expenses were 5%, and operating expenses were 10%. Find the selling price if the markon of 30% was based on the net cost.

ANSWER $145.60

APPLICATION PROBLEMS

1. Find the selling price in each of the following problems if the percent of markon is based on the net selling price.

	Amount on Invoice	Percent of Buying Expenses	Net Cost	Percent of Markon	Percent of Operating Expenses	Selling Price
a.	$150	10%	$_____	25%	5%	$_____
b.	325	20%	_____	33⅓%	16⅔%	_____
c.	212	25%	_____	20%	10%	_____
d.	480	15%	_____	16⅔%	8⅓%	_____
e.	144	12½%	_____	30%	5%	_____

2. Find the selling price in each of the following problems if the percent of markon is based on the net cost.

	Amount on Invoice	Percent of Buying Expenses	Net Cost	Percent of Markon	Net Return	Percent of Operating Expenses	Selling Price
a.	$160	10%	$_____	15%	$_____	16⅔%	$_____
b.	360	8⅓%	_____	12½%	_____	10%	_____
c.	480	5%	_____	20%	_____	12½%	_____
d.	500	15%	_____	25%	_____	16⅔%	_____
e.	240	12½%	_____	15%	_____	14⅖%	_____

49 FINDING VALUE OF AVERAGE INVENTORY AND MERCHANDISE INVENTORY RATE

To determine the rate at which merchandise is sold, the owner must find the value of the average inventory, or the product of the number of units of merchandise usually on hand and either the estimated cost price or selling price per unit. Most businesses take inventory several times a year—some monthly, some bimonthly, others quarterly, and still others semiannually. The average inventory is the average of the total number of units on hand during a given period, usually a year. The intervals selected for this determination vary with the business.

The success of almost every business depends in large measure on the number of times it converts its average inventory into sales during a year. This conversion of merchandise is called *merchandise inventory rate,* or *turnover,* and is generally computed by dividing the cost of goods sold by the value of the average inventory.

Value of Average Inventory

When the inventory is taken annually, at the end of the year, the average inventory is found by taking the sum of the beginning inventory and the ending inventory and dividing by 2. This is called an *annual inventory.* When the inventory is taken semiannually, the average inventory is computed by taking the sum of the beginning inventory, the half-year inventory, and the ending inventory and dividing by 3. This is called a *semiannual inventory.* Average inventories computed on the basis of other regular intervals follow the same pattern.

The first example below illustrates the annual inventory, and the second illustrates the semiannual inventory.

Examples

1. *Annual Inventory—*if value is based on cost price

January 1 $16,745.10, value of beginning inventory based on cost price

December 31   + 22,991.60, value of ending inventory based on cost price

$39,736.70, total

$39,736.70 ÷ 2 = $19,868.35, value of average inventory based on cost price

2. *Semiannual Inventory—*if value is based on selling price

January 1 $ 87,465.86, value of beginning inventory based on selling price

June 30   74,333.10, value of half-year inventory based on selling price

December 31   + 92,961.43, value of ending inventory based on selling price

$254,760.39, total

$254,760.39 ÷ 3 = $84,920.13, value of average inventory based on selling price

Merchandise Inventory Rate

The merchandise inventory rate is generally computed by dividing the cost of goods sold during the overall period by the value of the average inventory based on cost.

In estimating the value of an inventory, some businesses use the selling price of the units of merchandise as the base; others use the net cost. Either approach can be used so long as it is used consistently. For example, a retailer who computes the value of the average inventory at selling price must either convert the value of the average inventory to cost price or substitute the gross sales for the cost of goods sold.

Example

PROBLEM The Tidy-Home Hardware Store takes inventory every three months, computing its value at selling prices that include a markon of 30% based on cost. The inventories last year were as follows.

January 1	$ 76,593.84,	value of beginning inventory
March 31	55,087.68,	value of first-quarter inventory
June 30	63,438.25,	value of half-year inventory
September 30	99,019.59,	value of third-quarter inventory
December 31	+ 41,674.73,	value of ending inventory
	$335,814.09,	total

Find the merchandise inventory rate if the cost of goods sold for the year was $294,780.55.

SOLUTIONS

METHOD 1

By this method, the merchandise inventory rate is computed on the basis of cost price.

$335,814.09 ÷ 5 = $67,162.82, value of average
inventory based on selling price

Cost price + 30% cost price = $67,162.82

130% cost price = $67,162.82, value of average inventory based on selling price

$67,162.82 ÷ 130% = $51,663.71, value of average inventory based on cost price

$294,780.55 ÷ $51,663.71 = 5.7057, or approximately 5.71, merchandise inventory rate

METHOD 2

By this method, the merchandise inventory rate is computed on the basis of selling price.

$335,814.09 ÷ 5 = $67,162.82, value of average inventory based on selling price

$294,780.55 + 30% of $294,780.55 = $383,214.71, gross sales

$383,214.71 ÷ $67,162.82 = 5.7057, or approximately 5.71, merchandise inventory rate

1. At the beginning of the year, a retail merchant had an inventory valued at $8,764. The inventory at the end of the year was valued at $10,095. If the cost of goods sold during the year was $51,098, what was the merchandise inventory rate for the year?

2. A firm computes the value of its inventory at selling prices. Its inventory on January 1 was valued at $36,715 and on December 31 was valued at $24,920. If the markon averages $33\frac{1}{3}$% of the selling price and the cost of goods sold during the year was $138,317, find the merchandise inventory rate.

ANSWERS 1. 5.42   2. 6.73

APPLICATION PROBLEMS

1. The following information was taken from the books of a local business: inventory at the beginning of the year, $35,000; inventory at the end of the year, $28,000; cost of goods sold during the year, $124,000. Find the average inventory and the merchandise inventory rate. Carry the division out to three decimal places, and round off to two places.

2. The value of the average inventory of a business was $9,375, computed at selling prices.
a. If the net sales for the year were $72,640, find the merchandise inventory rate.
b. The average markon is 32% of the selling price. If the cost of goods sold during the year amounted to $49,395, find the merchandise inventory rate.

3. A retail business had an average inventory, computed at selling prices, valued at $26,810. The markon for each unit of merchandise was 35% of the selling price. Find the merchandise inventory rate if the cost of goods sold during the year was $117,628.88.

PROBLEMS FOR PART FIVE

Retail Store Computations

44

1. A pair of sandals cost $2.52 and sold for $3.50.
a. Find the amount and percent of markon based on the cost price.
b. Find the amount and percent of markon based on the selling price.

2. A transistor radio cost $30.08 and sold for $33.84.
a. Find the amount and percent of markon based on the cost price.
b. Find the amount and percent of markon based on the selling price.

45

1. A camera that sold for $41.66 included a markon of 27%.
a. Find the cost if the markon is based on the selling price.
b. Find the cost if the markon is based on the cost price.

2. An electronic calculator that sold for $300 included a markon of 35%.
a. Find the cost if the markon is based on the selling price.
b. Find the cost if the markon is based on the cost price.

46

1. Units of merchandise cost a retailer $98.40.
a. Find the selling price if the percent of markon is 20% of the cost price.
b. Find the selling price if the percent of markon is 20% of the selling price.

2. Felt-tipped pens cost a jobber $25.20 a gross (12 dozen).
a. Find the selling price if the percent of markon is $66\frac{2}{3}$% of the cost price.
b. Find the selling price if the percent of markon is 40% of the selling price.

47

1. A color television set marked to sell for $408 was marked down to $358 for an anniversary sale. What were the amount and percent of markdown?

2. A clothes dryer was advertised at a 15% markdown of the regular selling price of $278.05. What was the reduced selling price?

3. A playground set sold for $59.14, representing a markon of 14.27% based on cost and of 12.49% based on the selling price. If the cost price is increased 15%, what new selling price must be charged in order to realize the same percent of markon?

48

1. A dress cost a retailer $13.50 and sold for $27.
a. What was the percent of markon based on the cost price?
b. What was the percent of markon based on the selling price?

2. A sofa cost $280, less 20%, plus 5% buying expenses and 10% operating expenses.
a. Find the selling price if a markon of 30% is based on the net selling price.
b. Find the selling price if a markon of 30% is based on the net cost.

49

1. A department store takes inventory every three months, computing goods at selling prices. The inventories taken last year were as follows.

Date	Value	Date	Value
January 1	$49,310	September 30	$101,860
March 31	73,300	December 31	68,090
June 30	68,540		

Find the average inventory and the merchandise inventory rate if the gross sales for the year were $315,575.

2. Determine the merchandise inventory rate from the following statement.

```
Sales ..................................................................................$235,000
Beginning inventory ................$ 42,000
Purchases ...................................  176,000
     Total.......................................................................$218,000
Ending inventory ...........................................   59,000
Cost of goods sold ...................................................  159,000
     Gross profit ...................................................$  76,000
```

3. At the beginning of the year, an automobile supply store had an inventory valued at $84,200, based on the selling price. Six months later, the inventory was valued at $69,800. At the end of the year, the inventory was valued at $53,600. The markon, on the average, was 28% of the selling price. The gross sales for the year were $487,000, and the cost of goods sold was $350,340.
a. What was the estimated value of the average inventory, based on the cost price?
b. What was the merchandise inventory rate (1) if the average inventory valued at the selling price was used and (2) if the average inventory valued at the cost was used?

PART SIX

Simple-Interest Computations

The subject of interest arises in many business computations. *Interest* is "rent" for the use of money. When a businessman or consumer borrows money, he pays the lender a fee for its use. On the other hand, when he invests money in a bank, savings and loan association, or other financial institution, he allows that institution the use of his money; in return, he receives "rent," or interest, on that money for the full time of its use.

Interest is a major source of income for banks. Two factors determine how much interest is charged for a loan: the amount of the loan, known as the *principal*, and the length of time given the borrower to repay the loan.

The interest rate is expressed as a percent. A rate of 6%, for example, means that the borrower must pay $6 for each $100 that he borrows for a period of one year. If the loan is made for a period of time less than a year, a proportionately smaller amount is charged. The borrower usually pays the interest after using the money, although in some cases the interest is deducted before the money is given to him.

Following are the terms used in computing interest.

Simple-interest method
The simple-interest method of computing interest requires payment at the end of the time period. It is computed by means of the formula $I = P \times R \times T$.

Banker's method
The banker's method of computing interest is based on a 360-day year, assuming that each of the 12 months has 30 days.

6%, 60-day method
The 6%, 60-day method of computing interest is also known as the "banker's" method, since it is also based on a 360-day year. This method is merely a shortcut for computing interest, based on 6% interest for a period of 60 days.

Accounting method
The accounting method of computing interest is a variation of the 6%, 60-day method. One finds the interest for 6 days at 6%, then the interest for 1 day at 6%, and finally the interest for the desired number of days at 6%.

Accurate-interest method
Accurate interest is based on a 365-day year. Often called "exact interest," this method of computing interest is used by the U.S. Government.

50 360-DAY BANKER'S METHOD

Banks and other commercial firms have long computed interest charges on the basis of a 360-day year. This method is simple to use since it assumes that each of the 12 months has 30 days; and although the method favors the lender, the practice is legally accepted. The 360-day method is often used in computing interest on long-term loans that are paid on an installment basis such as those for real estate, automobiles, and furniture. It is commonly referred to as the banker's method.

To find the amount of interest by the banker's method, study the following examples.

Examples

PROBLEM 1 Arthur Melton borrowed $1,200 on February 1 from the Moline National Bank and promised to pay back the money in 90 days at 6% interest. What amount will Mr. Melton have to pay the bank when the loan is due?

SOLUTION A $1,200 x 6% = $72, interest for 1 year
90 days = $\frac{1}{4}$ of a year
$\frac{1}{4}$ of $72 = $18, interest for 90 days
interest ($18) + principal ($1,200) = $1,218, amount to be repaid

SOLUTION B Most people use a formula, such as that given below, for organizing their work. Then they use cancellation to simplify the arithmetic.

$$Interest = Principal \times Rate \times Time$$

or

$$I = P \times \frac{R}{100} \times \frac{T}{360}$$

or

$$I = P \times R \times T$$

where P = $1,200, R = 6%, and T = 90 days

$$Interest = \$1,200 \times \frac{6}{100} \times \frac{90}{360} = \$18$$

Amount to be repaid = $1,200 + $18 = $1,218

PROBLEM 2 A $720 loan was to be repaid in 5 months with interest at $4\frac{1}{2}$%. Find the interest cost of the loan.

SOLUTION $I = P \times R \times T$

where $P = \$720$, $R = 4\frac{1}{2}$%, and $T = 5$ months

$$\text{Interest} = \$\overset{\overset{\overset{3}{\cancel{60}}}{\cancel{720}}}{} \times \frac{\overset{9}{\cancel{200}}}{\underset{10}{\underset{2}{}}} \times \frac{\overset{5}{\cancel{5}}}{\cancel{12}} = \frac{\$27}{2} = \$13.50$$

Note: When the banker's year (360 days) is used and the time is given in days, divide the number of days by 360 to find out for what fraction of a year the money has been borrowed. If the time is given in months, divide the number of months by 12.

Practice Drills

Use the formula just presented to find the interest on the following loans.

1. $724 at 6% for 90 days
2. $356 at 5% for 39 days
3. $518 at 3% for 110 days
4. $996 at $4\frac{1}{2}$% for 48 days

ANSWERS   1. $10.86   2. $1.93   3. $4.75   4. $5.98

APPLICATION PROBLEMS

Find the interest using the formula $I = P \times R \times T$.

	Amount of Loan	Rate of Interest	Time of Loan	Interest
1.	$ 820	6%	90 days	$_____
2.	4,012	$4\frac{1}{2}$%	52 days	_____
3.	912	6%	75 days	_____
4.	268	5%	108 days	_____
5.	574	7%	60 days	_____
6.	1,926	4%	42 days	_____
7.	335	8%	84 days	_____
8.	614	3%	112 days	_____

51   BANKER'S 6%, 60-DAY METHOD

The method most used in business for computing simple interest is the 6%, 60-day method. It is based on a 360-day year and on the following principle: The interest on $1 for 1 year at 6% is 6¢. If $1 will earn 6¢ in 1 year, it will earn $\frac{1}{6}$ of 6¢, or 1¢, in $\frac{1}{6}$ of a year. One-sixth of 1 year (360 days) is equal to 60 days. Therefore, the interest on $1 at 6% for 60 days is 1¢. Thus, to find the interest on any amount for 60 days at 6% interest rate, move the decimal point in the principal two places to the left.

Examples | **PROBLEM 1**   Find the interest on a 60-day loan of $1,000 at 6% interest.

SOLUTION $1,000 ÷ 100 = $1,0.00. = $10, interest

PROBLEM 2   Find the interest on a 60-day loan of $8,975 at 6% interest.

SOLUTION $8,975 ÷ 100 = $8,9.75. = $89.75, interest

Using the 6%, 60-Day Method for Periods Other Than 60 Days

The 6%, 60-day method may also be used to compute interest for periods of time other than 60 days. In such cases, follow these steps.
1. Find the interest at 6% for 60 days.
2. Divide the time in days into aliquot parts of 60. (Only fractions with a numerator of 1 should be used in computing time.)
3. Compute interest for each time period by taking the same part of the interest as of the time.
4. Add these partial sums to determine the total interest.

Examples | **PROBLEM 1**   Find the simple interest on $264 at 6% for 86 days by the 6%, 60-day method.

SOLUTION   Move the decimal point in the principal two places to the left to find the interest for 60 days at 6%. To find the remaining 26 days' interest, divide the time into fractions of 60 days, with numerators of 1.

$2.64   = 60 days' interest at 6% on $264
 .88   = 20 days' interest ($\frac{1}{3}$ of 60 days)
 .264 = 6 days' interest ($\frac{1}{10}$ of 60 days)
―――――――――
$3.784⎫
  or ⎬= 86 days' interest at 6% on $264
$3.78 ⎭

PROBLEM 2   Find the simple interest on $193 at 6% for 38 days by the 6%, 60-day method.

SOLUTION $1.93   = 60 days' interest at 6% on $193
_____

.965   = 30 days' interest ($\frac{1}{2}$ of 60 days)
.193   = 6 days' interest ($\frac{1}{10}$ of 60 days)
.0643 = 2 days' interest ($\frac{1}{30}$ of 60 days)
_____

$1.2223
or   }= 38 days' interest at 6% on $193
$1.22

When the interest for 60 days is not used directly in finding the final interest, always write it down *first,* for this value is used to find all the other interest values in the solution. If the 60-day interest is not to be added to the others, draw a line beneath it to keep it separate.

When division yields a remainder, interest computations must be carried to the fourth decimal place for accuracy in the cents column. If the third place after the decimal point in the answer is 5 or more, add 1¢ to the interest charge. If it is less than 5, drop all numbers after the second place.

Practice Drills

Find the simple interest at 6% by the banker's 60-day method.

1. $311 for 99 days   3. $872 for 111 days
2. $209 for 66 days   4. $358 for 19 days

ANSWERS   1. $5.13   2. $2.30   3. $16.13   4. $1.13

Using the 6%, 60-Day Method for Rates Other Than 6%

When you know how to apply the 6%, 60-day method to periods of time other than 60 days, you will find it easy to use where the rate is other than 6%. There are two methods.

METHOD 1

To find interest at a rate other than 6%, compute the interest on a 6% basis and then adjust to the desired rate.

Example

PROBLEM   Find the interest on $480 at 5% for 99 days.

SOLUTION   First compute interest at 6% using the 60-day method.

$4.80 = 60 days' interest at 6% on $480
2.40 = 30 days' interest at 6% ($\frac{1}{2}$ of 60 days)
.48 = 6 days' interest at 6% ($\frac{1}{10}$ of 60 days)
.24 = 3 days' interest at 6% ($\frac{1}{20}$ of 60 days)
_____
$7.92 = 99 days' interest at 6% on $480

Then convert to the desired rate by using the appropriate fraction to increase or decrease the 6% base. For example, 5% is $\frac{5}{6}$ of 6%, or 6% minus $\frac{1}{6}$.

$7.92 = 99 days' interest at 6% on $480
1.32 = 99 days' interest at 1% on $480 ($\frac{1}{6}$ of 6%)
$6.60 = 99 days' interest at 5% on $480 ($\frac{5}{6}$ of 6%)

METHOD 2

Use the decimal-point-placement approach of the 6%, 60-day method in computations at other interest rates.

To find the interest on any principal, at any rate percent, for as many days as that rate percent is contained in the banker's year of 360 days, move the decimal point in the principal two places to the left. For example, point off two places to the left in the principal to obtain the following: 3% for 120 days, 4% for 90 days, $4\frac{1}{2}$% for 80 days, 5% for 72 days, $7\frac{1}{2}$% for 48 days, 8% for 45 days, and 9% for 40 days.

Example | **PROBLEM** Find the interest on $480 at 5% for 99 days.

SOLUTION $4.80 = 72 days' interest at 5% on $480
1.20 = 18 days' interest ($\frac{1}{4}$ of 72 days)
.60 = 9 days' interest ($\frac{1}{8}$ of 72 days or $\frac{1}{2}$ of 18 days)
$6.60 = 99 days' interest at 5% on $480

Practice Drills | Find the interest on each of the following loans by the two methods just explained.

1. $250 at 4% for 80 days
2. $375 at 5% for 36 days
3. $329 at $7\frac{1}{2}$ % for 146 days
4. $550 at $6\frac{1}{2}$% for 286 days

ANSWERS 1. $2.22   2. $1.88   3. $10.01   4. $28.41

APPLICATION PROBLEMS

Find the interest at 6% by the banker's 60-day method.

1. $582 for 84 days
2. $292 for 56 days
3. $415 for 49 days
4. $672 for 70 days

5. $432 for 54 days
6. $864 for 29 days
7. $684 for 53 days
8. $712 for 42 days

Find the interest on each of the following loans by the two methods just explained. The result of one method will act as a check on the accuracy of the other.

9. $502 at 5% for 93 days

10. $2,500 at $4\frac{1}{2}$% for 105 days

11. $653 at 6% for 29 days

12. $468 at 3% for 42 days

13. $234 at $4\frac{1}{2}$% for 281 days

14. $435 at $3\frac{1}{2}$% for 119 days

15. $580 at 2% for 94 days

16. $686 at $7\frac{1}{2}$% for 134 days

52 ACCOUNTING METHOD

In the accounting method of computing interest, use the following steps.

1. Point off three places to the left of the decimal point in the principal. The result is the interest for 6 days at 6%.

2. Divide by 6. The quotient is the interest for 1 day.

3. Multiply by the stated number of days. The product is the interest for the required number of days at 6%.

Examples

PROBLEM 1   Find the interest on $1,080 for 72 days at 6%.

SOLUTION
$$
\begin{array}{ll}
6)\$1.080 & = \text{6 days' interest at 6\%} \\
\$ \ .180 & = \text{1 day's interest at 6\%} \\
\times \ \ 72 & \\
\hline
\$12.96 & = \text{72 days' interest at 6\%}
\end{array}
$$

PROBLEM 2   Find the interest on an $840 loan if made for 48 days at an interest rate of 8%.

SOLUTION
$$
\begin{array}{ll}
6)\$ \ .840 & = \text{6 days' interest at 6\%} \\
\$ \ .140 & = \text{1 day's interest at 6\%} \\
\times \ \ 48 & \\
3)\$6.720 & = \text{48 days' interest at 6\%} \\
2.24 & = \text{48 days' interest at 2\% } (\tfrac{1}{3} \text{ of 6\%}) \\
\hline
\$8.96 & = \text{48 days' interest at 8\%}
\end{array}
$$

Practice Drill

A businessman borrowed $1,800 for 78 days. If he paid $7\frac{1}{2}$% on the loan, what was his interest cost?

ANSWER $29.25

APPLICATION PROBLEMS

Find the interest on the following loans by the accounting method.

	Amount of Loan	Rate of Interest	Time of Loan	Interest
1.	$ 840.00	6%	96 days	$_____
2.	450.50	6¾%	59 days	$_____
3.	1,200.00	7½%	22 days	$_____
4.	320.00	8%	84 days	$_____
5.	2,670.00	7%	110 days	$_____

53 ACCURATE-INTEREST METHOD

Accurate interest is based on a 365-day year. It is often called *exact interest* because the exact number of days of a loan is calculated.

Finding the Exact Number of Days

The exact number of days must be found when computing the interest on United States Government securities, accrued interest on bonds, and bank loans. Interest is found by counting the actual number of days from the first day to the last, excluding the first day and including the last. (In most states the interest is computed from noon on the first day to noon on the last day. To simplify the counting of days, the first day is excluded and all of the last day is counted.) If, however, the first day were counted and the last day not counted, the total number of days between the dates would still be the same.

Example | **PROBLEM**   Find the exact number of days from October 19, 1973, to January 5, 1974.

SOLUTION

12 days left in October
30 days in November
31 days in December
+ 5 days in January
78 days, exact time

Practice Drills | Find the exact number of days in each of the following time periods.
1. April 10 to July 20
2. February 12 to October 15
3. November 8, 1973, to May 31, 1974

ANSWERS 1. 101   2. 245   3. 204

The method of computing accurate interest, using the exact number of days, differs only slightly from the method used for a 360-day year. Follow these steps.

1. Compute the exact number of days for which interest is to be found.

2. Place this number over 365. The result is the exact time and its fractional part of a year.

3. Compute the interest by using the formula $I = P \times R \times \dfrac{T}{365}$.

Example

PROBLEM   Leo Corsini borrowed $750 at $7\frac{1}{2}$% from June 27, 1973, to December 24, 1973. Find the accurate interest.

SOLUTION   There are 180 days from June 27 to December 24.
To make $7\frac{1}{2}$% easy to use in the cancellation process, change the rate to a simple fraction.

$$7\frac{1}{2}\% = \frac{7\frac{1}{2}}{100} = \frac{15}{200}$$

$$\overset{3}{\underset{4}{\cancel{\underset{150}{\$750}}}} \times \frac{\cancel{15}}{\cancel{200}} \times \frac{\overset{45}{\cancel{180}}}{\underset{73}{\cancel{365}}} = \frac{2025}{73} = \$27.74, \text{ accurate interest}$$

Practice Drill

Find the interest due on 50 U. S. Government bonds bought August 30 and sold December 31 of the same year; par value, $100; interest rate, 5%.

ANSWER $84.24 (123 days)

APPLICATION PROBLEMS

1. Find the exact number of days.

a. March 16 to October 9
b. January 23 to April 7
c. October 15 to October 29
d. August 27 to December 31
e. May 1 to September 18

2. Using the accurate-interest method, find the interest on these loans.

a. $650 at 6% from August 23, 1973, to March 18, 1974
b. $384 at 5% from March 2, 1973, to October 17, 1973
c. $472 at 4% from February 11, 1973, to August 16, 1974

     d. $228 at $7\frac{1}{2}$% from April 27, 1973, to February 14, 1974
     e. $915 at 7% from June 29, 1973, to September 26, 1973
     f. $746 at 9% from July 30, 1973, to December 23, 1973
     g. $533 at 3% from May 26, 1973, to March 12, 1974
     h. $829 at $4\frac{1}{2}$% from August 8, 1973, to July 5, 1974

3. A homeowner borrowed $3,250 from his bank to renovate his house. The charge for the loan was $5\frac{1}{2}$% ordinary simple interest computed for exact time. If the loan was made on March 11, 1973, and repaid on February 1, 1974, how much was the interest charge?

54 USING TIME AND INTEREST TABLES

Bankers and other lenders who must frequently determine the exact number of days between two dates and find simple interest use tables. Tables obviously save a great deal of time since they eliminate the necessity of making computations.

Using a Time Table

The time table illustrated on page 101 shows the exact number of days from any day of any month to the corresponding day of any other month. In addition, the time table gives the exact day of the year represented by each date of the year.

    Assume that you wish to compute the exact number of days from May 18 to November 14. The time table is used as follows.
1. Read down the May column until you reach the same line as 18 in the Day of Month column. The number is 138.
2. Read down the November column until you reach the same line as 14 in the Day of Month column. The number is 318.
3. Subtract 138 from 318. The answer is 180, the number of days from May 18 to November 14.

Example | **PROBLEM** Find the number of days from August 12, 1973, through March 3, 1974, using the time table.

SOLUTION   August 12 is the 224th day of the year. Since there are 365 days in a year, the number of days from August 12 until the end of the year is 141 (365 − 224). March 3 is the 62nd day of the following year. Add these 62 days to the 141 days for a total of 203 days.

TIME TABLE

Day of Month	Jan.	Feb.	Mar.	April	May	June	July	Aug.	Sept.	Oct.	Nov.	Dec.
1	1	32	60	91	121	152	182	213	244	274	305	335
2	2	33	61	92	122	153	183	214	245	275	306	336
3	3	34	62	93	123	154	184	215	246	276	307	337
4	4	35	63	94	124	155	185	216	247	277	308	338
5	5	36	64	95	125	156	186	217	248	278	309	339
6	6	37	65	96	126	157	187	218	249	279	310	340
7	7	38	66	97	127	158	188	219	250	280	311	341
8	8	39	67	98	128	159	189	220	251	281	312	342
9	9	40	68	99	129	160	190	221	252	282	313	343
10	10	41	69	100	130	161	191	222	253	283	314	344
11	11	42	70	101	131	162	192	223	254	284	315	345
12	12	43	71	102	132	163	193	224	255	285	316	346
13	13	44	72	103	133	164	194	225	256	286	317	347
14	14	45	73	104	134	165	195	226	257	287	318	348
15	15	46	74	105	135	166	196	227	258	288	319	349
16	16	47	75	106	136	167	197	228	259	289	320	350
17	17	48	76	107	137	168	198	229	260	290	321	351
18	18	49	77	108	138	169	199	230	261	291	322	352
19	19	50	78	109	139	170	200	231	262	292	323	353
20	20	51	79	110	140	171	201	232	263	293	324	354
21	21	52	80	111	141	172	202	233	264	294	325	355
22	22	53	81	112	142	173	203	234	265	295	326	356
23	23	54	82	113	143	174	204	235	266	296	327	357
24	24	55	83	114	144	175	205	236	267	297	328	358
25	25	56	84	115	145	176	206	237	268	298	329	359
26	26	57	85	116	146	177	207	238	269	299	330	360
27	27	58	86	117	147	178	208	239	270	300	331	361
28	28	59	87	118	148	179	209	240	271	301	332	362
29	29	....	88	119	149	180	210	241	272	302	333	363
30	30	....	89	120	150	181	211	242	273	303	334	364
31	31	....	90	......	151	......	212	243	......	304	......	365

Note: For a leap year, add 1 day to each number of days after February 28.

Practice Drills

Using the time table above, find the number of days in the following.

1. From April 23 to September 9
2. From June 10, 1973, through January 31, 1974

ANSWERS   1. 139 days   2. 235 days

Using a Simple-Interest Table

After the time in days has been determined, the banker's interest (360-day basis) can be computed by using an interest table like the one on page 103. Follow these steps to find the simple interest.

1. In the horizontal section at the top of the table, find the specified rate of interest.

2. Use the Time column to find the row for the number of days.

3. Assume that you wish to find the interest at $5\frac{1}{2}$% on a loan of $500 for a period of 16 days. Find the row for 16 days, moving your finger until you reach the column for $5\frac{1}{2}$%. This amount represents the interest on $100.

4. Divide the interest so determined by 100 (move the decimal point two places to the left) to find the interest on $1.

5. Multiply the interest on $1 by the given principal. The result is the required interest. In the example mentioned above in step 3, this would be .002444 × $500, or $1.22.

Examples

PROBLEM 1   Find the interest on $750 at $3\frac{1}{2}$% for 25 days.

SOLUTION   The amount at the intersecting point of the column headed by 3½% and the row for 25 days is .2431. Divide .2431 by 100 by moving the decimal point two places to the left. The quotient is $.002431, the interest on $1 for 25 days at 3½%. Multiply .002431 by $750. The product is the required interest, $1.82.

PROBLEM 2   Find the interest on $227.30 for 96 days at 6%.

SOLUTION   The number of days, 96, is not listed in the simple-interest table. Therefore, it is necessary to find the interest for 3 months, or 90 days, and then for 6 days, to reach a total of 96 days.

interest on $100 for 90 days at 6% = $1.5
interest on $100 for   6 days at 6% =   .100
interest on $100 for 96 days at 6% = $1.600

$1.60 ÷ 100 = $.016, interest on $1 for 96 days at 6%
.016 x $227.30 = $3.6368, or $3.64, interest required

Practice Drill

An $850 bank loan was made on August 18 and repaid December 7 at $5\frac{1}{2}$% interest. Using the simple-interest table on page 103, compute the amount of interest due.

ANSWER $14.42

SIMPLE-INTEREST TABLE

($100 on a 360-Day-Year Basis)

Time	2½%	3%	3½%	4%	4½%	5%	5½%	6%	6½%	7%
1 day	.0069	.0083	.0097	.0111	.0125	.0139	.0153	.0167	.0181	.0194
2 days	.0139	.0167	.0194	.0222	.0250	.0278	.0306	.0333	.0361	.0389
3 days	.0208	.0250	.0292	.0333	.0375	.0417	.0458	.0500	.0542	.0583
4 days	.0278	.0333	.0389	.0444	.0500	.0556	.0611	.0667	.0722	.0778
5 days	.0347	.0417	.0486	.0556	.0625	.0694	.0764	.0833	.0903	.0972
6 days	.0417	.0500	.0583	.0667	.0750	.0833	.0917	.1000	.1083	.1167
7 days	.0486	.0583	.0681	.0778	.0875	.0972	.1069	.1167	.1264	.1361
8 days	.0556	.0667	.0778	.0889	.1000	.1111	.1222	.1333	.1444	.1556
9 days	.0625	.0750	.0875	.1000	.1125	.1250	.1375	.1500	.1625	.1750
10 days	.0694	.0833	.0972	.1111	.1250	.1389	.1528	.1667	.1806	.1944
11 days	.0764	.0917	.1069	.1222	.1375	.1528	.1681	.1833	.1986	.2139
12 days	.0833	.1000	.1167	.1333	.1500	.1667	.1833	.2000	.2167	.2333
13 days	.0903	.1083	.1264	.1444	.1625	.1806	.1986	.2167	.2347	.2528
14 days	.0972	.1167	.1361	.1556	.1750	.1944	.2139	.2333	.2528	.2722
15 days	.1042	.1250	.1458	.1667	.1875	.2083	.2292	.2500	.2708	.2917
16 days	.1111	.1333	.1556	.1778	.2000	.2222	.2444	.2667	.2889	.3111
17 days	.1181	.1417	.1653	.1889	.2125	.2361	.2597	.2833	.3069	.3306
18 days	.1250	.1500	.1750	.2000	.2250	.2500	.2750	.3000	.3250	.3500
19 days	.1319	.1583	.1847	.2111	.2375	.2639	.2903	.3167	.3431	.3694
20 days	.1389	.1667	.1944	.2222	.2500	.2778	.3056	.3333	.3611	.3889
21 days	.1458	.1750	.2042	.2333	.2625	.2917	.3208	.3500	.3792	.4083
22 days	.1528	.1833	.2139	.2444	.2750	.3056	.3361	.3667	.3972	.4278
23 days	.1597	.1917	.2236	.2556	.2875	.3194	.3514	.3833	.4153	.4472
24 days	.1667	.2000	.2333	.2667	.3000	.3333	.3667	.4000	.4333	.4667
25 days	.1736	.2083	.2431	.2778	.3125	.3472	.3819	.4167	.4514	.4861
26 days	.1806	.2167	.2528	.2889	.3250	.3611	.3972	.4333	.4694	.5056
27 days	.1875	.2250	.2625	.3000	.3375	.3750	.4125	.4500	.4875	.5250
28 days	.1944	.2333	.2722	.3111	.3500	.3889	.4278	.4667	.5056	.5444
29 days	.2014	.2417	.2819	.3222	.3625	.4028	.4431	.4833	.5236	.5639
1 month	.2083	.2500	.2917	.3333	.3750	.4167	.4583	.5000	.5417	.5833
2 months	.4167	.5000	.5833	.6667	.7500	.8333	.9167	1.0000	1.0833	1.1667
3 months	.6230	.7500	.8750	1.0000	1.1250	1.2500	1.3750	1.5000	1.6250	1.7500
4 months	.8333	1.0000	1.1667	1.3333	1.5000	1.6667	1.8333	2.0000	2.1667	2.3333
5 months	1.0417	1.2500	1.4583	1.6667	1.8750	2.0833	2.2917	2.5000	2.7083	2.9160
6 months	1.2500	1.5000	1.7500	2.0000	2.2500	2.5000	2.7500	3.0000	3.2500	3.5070

APPLICATION PROBLEMS

1. Find the exact time in days in the following problems, using the time table for the exact number of days on page 101.

    a. May 28, 1973, to February 16, 1974
    b. October 19, 1973, to July 1, 1974
    c. July 7, 1973, to January 18, 1974

d. November 11, 1973, to May 9, 1975
e. April 21, 1973, to September 13, 1973
f. December 30, 1973, to January 20, 1974
g. February 27, 1973, to July 1, 1974

2. Using the simple-interest table on page 103, find the amount due on the following loans.

a. $720 at 6% for 3 months
b. $720 at 4% from May 19, 1973, to October 19, 1973
c. $246 at 6% for 120 days
d. $550 at 4% for 25 days
e. $900 at 5% for 150 days
f. $562.50 at 7% for 80 days
g. $109.39 at 6% from November 30, 1972, to March 1, 1974
h. $843.17 at 3% from February 17, 1973, to April 16, 1973
i. $468.13 at $4\frac{1}{2}$% from December 15, 1973, to August 5, 1974

55 FINDING FACTORS TO PRODUCE A GIVEN YIELD

How much principal will be required to produce a given amount of interest income, or *yield,* when the time and the interest rate are known? In how much time will a given yield be produced when the principal and interest rate are given? At what rate will a given yield be realized when the principal, interest, and time are given? Lenders frequently ask such questions as these.

Finding Principal

There are two methods used to determine the principal necessary to produce a given yield when the time and the interest rate are given.

Example | **PROBLEM** Find the principal necessary to yield $135 in 6 months at 6%.

SOLUTION A First find the interest charge on $1 for the time and the interest rate given; then divide the yield on $1 into the total yield desired to find the principal.

The interest on $1 at 6% for 6 months or 180 days is $.03.

$$\$135 \div .03 = \$4,500, \text{ principal}$$

SOLUTION B Apply the formula *Yield* ÷ *Rate* ÷ $\dfrac{Time}{360}$ = *Principal.*

$$\$135 \div \frac{6}{100} \div \frac{180}{360} = \$\overset{45}{\cancel{135}} \times \frac{100}{\cancel{6}} \times \frac{\overset{60}{\cancel{360}}}{\underset{3}{\cancel{180}}} = \$4,500,\ \text{principal}$$

Practice Drills

1. $500 income is desired in 60 days on a 5% investment. Find the principal by the method shown in Solution A.
2. $240 income is desired in 3 months on a 4% investment. Find the principal by the method shown in Solution B.

ANSWERS 1. $60,000   2. $24,000

Finding Time

The following method is used to find the time necessary to produce a given yield when the principal and the interest rate are given.
1. Find the interest charge for 1 year on the principal at the rate given.
2. Use the formula $\dfrac{Yield\ desired}{Interest\ for\ 1\ year}$ *of 360 days* = *Time required*

Example

PROBLEM Find the time necessary to yield $540 on $36,000 at 5%.

SOLUTION The interest on $36,000 at 5% for 1 year is $1,800.

$$\frac{\overset{3}{\cancel{\$540}}}{\underset{10}{\cancel{\$1,800}}} \text{ of } \overset{36}{\cancel{360}} = 108 \text{ days, time}$$

Practice Drills

1. Find the time necessary to yield $90 on $7,500 at 6%.
2. In how much time will $2,400 produce $64 income if invested at 4%?

ANSWERS 1. 72 days   2. 240 days

Finding Rate

Two methods are used to determine the rate necessary to produce a given yield when the principal, interest, and time are given.

Example

PROBLEM When $384 was invested for 150 days, $6.40 interest was earned. Find the rate percent necessary to produce this yield.

SOLUTION A   Find the interest on the principal for the given time at 1%.

$3.84 = 60 days' interest at 6% on $384
  3.84 = 60 days' interest at 6% on $384
  1.92 = 30 days' interest ($\frac{1}{2}$ of 60 days' interest)
_____
$9.60 = 150 days' interest at 6% on $384
$1.60 = 150 days' interest at 1% ($\frac{1}{6}$ of 6%) on $384

Divide the interest at 1% into the given interest to find the rate.

$6.40 ÷ $1.60 = 4%, interest rate

SOLUTION B   The formula *Interest = Principal × Rate × $\frac{Time}{360}$*

can also be expressed as *Interest ÷ Principal ÷ $\frac{Time}{360}$ = Rate.*

$$\$6.40 \div \$384 \div \frac{150}{360} = \overset{.04}{\underset{}{\$6.40}} \times \frac{1}{\underset{32}{\cancel{\$384}}} \times \frac{\overset{12}{\cancel{360}}}{\underset{5}{\cancel{150}}} = .04,\ \text{or}\ 4\%,\ \text{rate}$$

Practice Drills

1. $600 invested for 6 months earned $18 interest. At what rate was the money invested?

2. Find the rate necessary to produce $125 if $6,000 is invested for 150 days.

  6,40 ÷ 384 × 360 ÷ 150

ANSWERS   1. 6%   2. 5%

APPLICATION PROBLEMS

Find the principal necessary to produce the yield given in each of the following problems.

1. Yield, $810; time, 90 days; interest rate, 6%
2. Yield, $225; time, 9 months; interest rate, 5%
3. Yield, $375; time, 120 days; interest rate, $4\frac{1}{2}$%

Find the time necessary to produce the yield given in each of the following problems.

4. Principal, $7,200; interest rate, 5%; yield, $99
5. Principal, $18,000; interest rate, 6%; yield, $67.50
6. Principal, $8,600; interest rate, $3\frac{1}{2}$%; yield, $301

Find the interest rate necessary to produce the yield given in each of the following problems.

7. Principal, $322.50; time, 128 days; yield, $17.20
8. Principal, $1,400; time, 144 days; yield, $22.40
9. Principal, $1,150; time, 96 days; yield, $13.80

PROBLEMS FOR PART SIX

Simple-Interest Computations

50 Find the interest using the formula $I = P \times R \times T$.

1. $428 at 6% for 90 days
2. $584 at 5% for 76 days
3. $724 at 4% for 82 days
4. $468 at 6% for 46 days
5. $236 at 7% for 30 days
6. $860 at 3% for 68 days

7. $662 at 6% for 75 days
8. $196 at 9% for 60 days
9. $388 at $5\frac{1}{2}$% for 82 days
10. $570 at 6% for 96 days
11. $326 at $7\frac{1}{2}$% for 45 days
12. $645 at 8% for 66 days

51 Find the interest at 6% by the banker's 60-day method.

1. $250 for 90 days
2. $440 for 136 days
3. $1,200 for 120 days
4. $209 for 96 days
5. $136 for 147 days
6. $8,000 for 240 days

Find the interest by either of the two methods given in this unit.

7. $715 at 8% for 54 days
8. $338 at 4% for 82 days

9. $292 at 7% for 36 days
10. $840 at 3% for 72 days

52 Find the interest charge on each of the following loans by the accounting method.

	Amount of Loan	Rate of Interest	Time of Loan	Interest
1.	$ 948	5%	73 days	$_____
2.	1,260	$7\frac{1}{2}$%	90 days	_____
3.	200	8%	182 days	_____
4.	8,440	4%	80 days	_____
5.	750	6%	44 days	_____

53 Using the accurate-interest method, find the interest on these loans.

1. $375 for 75 days at 6%
2. $946 for 125 days at 4%
3. $720 for 84 days at 6%
4. $480 for 93 days at 6%
5. $950 for 54 days at 6%
6. $325 for 73 days at 6%

7. $520 for 200 days at 5%
8. $180 for 112 days at $4\frac{1}{2}$%
9. $240 for the period March 18, 1973, to Dec. 5, 1973 at 6%
10. $570 for the period August 30, 1973, to Jan. 12, 1974 at $7\frac{1}{2}$%

54 Find the exact number of days, using the time table on page 101.

1. October 24, 1973, to April 15, 1974
2. July 11, 1973, to September 9, 1973
3. May 31, 1973, to January 2, 1974
4. February 28, 1973, to September 30, 1973
5. June 14, 1973, to December 11, 1974

Find the exact time, the accurate interest, and the amount due on each of the following loans, using the time table on page 101.

6. $396 at $4\frac{1}{2}$% from May 24, 1973, to October 19, 1973
7. $432 at 6% from August 14, 1973, to December 9, 1973
8. $640 at 6% from March 28, 1973, to November 10, 1973
9. $168 at 5% from December 9, 1973, to February 2, 1974
10. $824 at 8% from November 21, 1973, to June 6, 1974
11. $505 at $7\frac{1}{2}$% from April 27, 1973, to February 18, 1974

$Y \div R \div T/360 = P$

55 Find the principal necessary to produce the yield given in each of the following problems.

1. Yield, $360; time, 180 days; interest rate, $7\frac{1}{2}$%
2. Yield, $378; time, 144 days; interest rate, $3\frac{1}{2}$%
3. Yield, $4,740; time, 250 days; interest rate, 6%

Find the time necessary to produce the yield given in each of the following problems.

4. Principal, $16,350; interest rate, 4%; yield, $228.90
5. Principal, $32,520; interest rate, $4\frac{1}{2}$%; yield, $1,000
6. Principal, $40,500; interest rate, 5%; yield, $810

Find the interest rate necessary to produce the yield given in each of the following problems.

7. Principal, $1,860; time, 72 days; yield, $9.30
8. Principal, $1,692; time, 50 days; yield, $16.45
9. Principal, $4,800; time, 90 days; yield, $51

$Y \div P \div T/360 = Y \div P \div 360 = \%$

10. $94.79 interest was earned on $3,250 invested for 5 months. Find the rate percent of interest received.

11. $84.60 income was earned in 6 months on a 6% investment. How much was invested?

PART SEVEN

Notes & Drafts

Sometimes a customer who purchases merchandise from a wholesaler or manufacturer and cannot pay cash or does not have a line of credit is required to sign a promissory note for the amount of the purchase. A *promissory note* is a written promise to pay a certain amount at a definite time in the future. Often a note will be *interest-bearing,* and the amount of interest expressed as a percent on the note. Some notes do not carry interest and are thus referred to as *noninterest-bearing.*

Occasionally a business firm needs cash and sells some of the notes it holds to a local bank. Selling a note to a bank is referred to as *discounting a note.* At the time the note is discounted (sold) the bank takes a deduction from the amount that is due on the note at maturity. This charge is called a *bank discount,* which is simply an interest charge that is collected at the beginning of the discount period instead of at the end of the period.

Like a note, a draft can be sold, or discounted, to a bank. A *draft,* sometimes called a *bill of exchange,* is a written order from one person to another to pay a certain amount at a definite time.

Payments on a written financial obligation in advance of the maturity date are called *partial payments.* Assume that Joe Bender, owner, manager, and chief mechanic of the Pineville Auto Body Shop, started his business a year ago. Before he opened his shop, Joe borrowed $7,500 from the Pineville State Bank. He signed a two-year promissory note at 7% interest and gave it to the bank for the loan. As Joe's business flourished he wanted to reduce the amount of his obligation. He knew he couldn't pay it all, but he could make a sizable payment from time to time. After seven months, Joe went to the Pineville State Bank and told the vice president that he would like to begin making payments on his note; he had some ready cash he didn't actually need for the business, and besides, he wanted to save as much interest as possible. The situation that Joe Bender was in—that of making periodic payments on his note at the bank—is very common in business. Sometimes it is just the reverse: the borrower can't pay the note in full when it is due but makes a partial payment at that time and asks for an extension. In other cases, arrangements are made for periodic payments at the time the note is signed.

56 DATE OF MATURITY AND TERM OF DISCOUNT

Following is an illustration of a note. Before making any computations, it is necessary to understand what is on the face of the note.

On this note $3,000 is the *face value*. A to Z Construction Co. (Lloyd T. Blackstone) is the *maker* (the one who owes the money), and Pacific Northwest Wholesale Lumber Co. is the *payee* (the one who receives the money). The *maturity date*, or the due date, of the note is October 14, 1973.

Finding Date of Maturity on Notes

In order to determine the amount of bank discount on a note, it is necessary to find the *date of maturity* and the *term of discount*. The date of maturity is found by counting from the date of the note the exact number of days, months, or years indicated on the face of the note. When the term of a note is given in months, the day of the month in which the note becomes due is the same as the date of the note. An exception would be a 3-month note dated November 30, because February has fewer than 30 days. The note would become due on the last day in February.

Examples | **PROBLEM 1** Find the date of maturity of a 3-month note dated November 30.

SOLUTION   Nov. 30 to Dec. 30 = 1st month
Dec. 30 to Jan. 30 = 2d month
Jan. 30 to Feb. 28 = 3d month

3 months from Nov. 30 = Feb. 28, date of maturity

PROBLEM 2   Find the date of maturity on a 60-day note that was dated December 31.

SOLUTION   Jan. = 31 days (60 − 31 = 29, days left)
Feb. = 28 days (29 − 28 = 1, days left)
Mar. = <u>1</u> day
60 days

60 days from Dec. 31 = Mar. 1, date of maturity

Practice Drill

Find the date of maturity.

1. 90-day note dated July 12
2. 3-month note dated July 12
3. 60-day note dated January 31
4. 4-month note dated October 31

ANSWERS   1. October 10   2. October 12   3. April 1   4. February 28

Finding Term of Discount on Notes

To find the term of discount—that is, the number of days from the day the bank discounts the note to the day the note becomes due—find the date of maturity and the exact number of days from the discount date to the date of maturity. If a note is discounted on the day on which it is made, the term of discount is the same as the time the note has to run.

In finding the term of discount, do not count the discount date (first day), but do count the date of maturity (last day).*

Example

PROBLEM   Find the term of discount of a 60-day note dated November 28 and discounted December 7.

SOLUTION   The date of maturity is January 27 (60 days from November 28). The term of discount is the number of days from December 7 to January 27.

Dec. 7 to Dec. 31 = 24 days (excluding Dec. 7)
Jan. 1 to Jan. 27 = <u>27</u> days (including Jan. 27)

51 days, term of discount

The amount of the bank discount is based on the maturity value of the note. If the note is noninterest-bearing, the maturity value will be the same as the face value. If the note is interest-bearing, the maturity value will be equal to the face value plus the interest due on the note. The method of determining the amount of the bank discount is the same as that used in finding interest.

*In some states the discount date, as well as the maturity date, is included in the term of discount.

Practice Drills

Find the term of discount.

1. 60-day note dated May 19, discounted June 3
2. 6-month note dated July 30, discounted October 31
3. 75-day note dated December 11, discounted February 2

ANSWERS 1. 45 days (due July 18)   2. 91 days (due January 30)
3. 22 days (due February 24)

APPLICATION PROBLEMS

1. A 60-day note dated May 11 was discounted June 1. What were the date of maturity and the term of discount?

2. What is the due date of a 4-month note dated March 30? If the note is discounted May 31, what is the term of discount?

3. A note dated October 19 had 90 days to run. If it was discounted November 1, what were the maturity date and the term of discount?

4. Find the date of maturity and the term of discount of each of the following notes.

Date of Note	Time to Run	Discount Date	Date of Maturity	Term of Discount
a. Oct. 17	3 months	Dec. 1	_____	_____
b. Jan. 18	75 days	Feb. 11	_____	_____
c. Aug. 12	120 days	Oct. 19	_____	_____
d. June 16	5 months	Sept. 3	_____	_____

57 PROCEEDS OF DISCOUNTED NOTES

Noninterest-Bearing Notes

To determine the proceeds of a discounted note that bears no interest, find the date of maturity and the term of discount. Then find the bank discount computing the interest on the face value of the note for the term of discount at the discount rate.

Besides a discount charge, banks often charge a fee for collecting the amount due on a note or other commercial paper. This additional charge, called a *collection fee*, is based on the face of the paper. For example, if the face value of a note is $1,200, and the collection fee is $\frac{1}{4}$ of 1%, the bank will ask for $3 as a charge for collecting the note. After the bank has deducted the discount and the collection fee, the remaining value of the note is called the *proceeds*. The proceeds are found by subtracting the discount and the collection fee from the face value of the note.

Example | **PROBLEM** Find the proceeds of the following note if it is discounted August 11 at 5% and a charge of $\frac{1}{4}$% is made for collection.

$ 1,500.00	Erie, Pennsylvania	July 18, 19--

Sixty days _____ after date I promise to pay

to the order of

Harold Smith

Fifteen hundred and 00/100------------------------------------- Dollars

Payable at _____ Provident Trust Company

Value received

No ___74___ Due Sept. 16, 19--   Samuel Fletcher

SOLUTION

Face value of note	$1,500.00
Date of maturity (60 days from July 18)	Sept. 16
Term of discount	36 days
(August 11 to September 16)	
Bank discount	$7.50
(interest on $1,500 for 36 days at 5%)	
Collection fee	+ 3.75

($\frac{1}{4}$% is $\frac{1}{4}$ of 1%. Take 1% of $1,500, which equals $15; $\frac{1}{4}$ of 1% equals $\frac{1}{4}$ of $15.)

Total charges (add bank discount and collection fee)	− 11.25
Proceeds	$1,488.75

(subtract total charges made by bank from value of note at maturity)

Practice Drill | On April 17, Hull received a 3-month note from Clark for $612. He discounted the note on May 29 at 6%. Find the proceeds.

ANSWER $607

Interest-Bearing Notes

Most business firms consider promissory notes as loans to the makers and thus charge interest on them. When such notes are discounted at the bank, the procedure for finding the proceeds is similar to that for noninterest-bearing notes. The only difference is that the maturity value on which the discount is based includes the interest on the note.

Example | **PROBLEM** Find the proceeds of the following interest-bearing note if it is discounted February 18 at 6%, and a charge of $\frac{1}{10}$% is made for collection.

$ ____1,750.00____   ____Waco, Texas____   December 18, _19__

____Three months____ _after date_ _I_ _promise to pay_

to the order of ____Henry Booth____

Seventeen hundred fifty and 00/100------------------------------------_Dollars_

Payable at ____Peoples National Bank____

Value received with interest at 5%

_No_ ___619___ _Due_ March 18, 19--   _Allen Lawrence_

SOLUTION

Face value of note	$1,750.00

Interest on note:

$17.50 = interest at 5% for 72 days on $1,750

 4.375 = interest at 5% for 18 days ($\frac{1}{4}$ of 72 days)

$21.875 = interest at 5% for 90 days on $1,750	+	21.88
Value at maturity...		$1,771.88

Date of maturity ....March 18

   (3 months from December 18)

Term of discount:

   (Number of days from February 18, date of
   discount, to March 18, date of maturity)

Feb. 18 to Feb. 28	10 days
Mar. 1 to Mar. 18	+ 18 days
Total	28 days

Bank discount:

$17.7188 = interest at 6% for 60 days on $1,771.88

 5.9062 = interest at 6% for 20 days ($\frac{1}{3}$ of 60 days)

 1.7718 = interest at 6% for 6 days ($\frac{1}{10}$ of 60 days)

  .5906 = interest at 6% for 2 days ($\frac{1}{30}$ of 60 days or
                        $\frac{1}{3}$ of 6 days)

$ 8.2686 = interest at 6% for 28 days on $1,771.88 = $8.27

Collection fee:

$\frac{1}{10}$ of 1% of $1,771.88

1% of $1,771.88 = $17.7188

$\frac{1}{10}$ of 1% = $\frac{1}{10}$ of $17.7188 = $1.77188, or		+ 1.77
Total charges		− 10.04
Proceeds		$1,761.84

Practice Drill

Barton received from Owen a 90-day, 4% interest-bearing note for $480, dated February 11. If he discounted the note on April 1 at 6%, what was the amount he received from the bank?

ANSWER $481.49

Do   **APPLICATION PROBLEMS**   *Mays*

1. Smith discounted his own 3-month, $2,400 note at the bank on May 19. The bank discount rate was 5%. How much did Smith receive?

2. On July 14, Burke discounted at 6% a $900, 3-month note that he had received from Fields on June 3. The bank made a $\frac{1}{4}$% charge for collection. How much did Burke receive from the bank?

3. Find the proceeds of each of the following notes.

	Note A	Note B	Note C	Note D
Face value of note	$4,200.00	$5,350.00	$2,475.00	$1,580.00
Time to run	3 months	2 months	60 days	90 days
Rate of interest	6%	6%	6%	6%
Interest on note	$_____	$_____	$_____	$_____
Value at maturity	$_____	$_____	$_____	$_____
Date of note	Aug. 3	June 15	Jan. 31	Feb. 15
Discount date	Aug. 14	July 3	Feb. 2	Mar. 18
Rate of discount	6%	5%	7%	8%
Rate of collection	$\frac{1}{8}$%	$\frac{1}{10}$%	$\frac{1}{4}$%	$\frac{1}{8}$%
Date of maturity	_____	_____	_____	_____
Term of discount	_____	_____	_____	_____
Bank discount	$_____	$_____	$_____	$_____
Collection fee	_____	_____	_____	_____
Total charges	$_____	$_____	$_____	$_____
Proceeds	$_____	$_____	$_____	$_____

58 PARTIAL PAYMENTS: UNITED STATES RULE

Two methods are used to determine the amount of interest and principal due the lender at any point in the time span of the note or at its maturity date. These are the *United States Rule* and the *Merchant's Rule*.

The United States Rule was determined by a Supreme Court decision; and although it originally had specific application to financial activities involving the federal government, it has been accepted by most states as the official legal method of determining partial payments. The rule is applied (1) when the partial payment is more than the interest, and (2) when the partial payment is less than the interest.

Partial Payment More Than Interest

By the United States Rule, when the partial payment is more than the interest due at the time of payment, the amount in excess of the interest goes toward discharging the principal. Each subsequent interest charge is computed on the balance of the principal. Each payment must first be applied to the paying of interest that has accrued to the date of payment. This method is usually used on long-term notes—those having more than 1 year to run. (A fundamental principle of the United States Rule is that interest cannot be charged on interest.) Use the following steps to determine the amount due at maturity.

1. Find the number of full years, if any, and the exact time for the period less than a year between the date of the note and the date of the first payment.
2. To the face of the note, add the banker's interest for the time found in step 1.
3. From this total, deduct the first partial payment.
4. To the new balance, add the interest for the time between the first and second partial payments.
5. From this total, deduct the second partial payment.
6. Repeat these steps until the amount due at maturity is determined.

Example

PROBLEM   A note for $1,240, dated August 1, 1972, due in 2 years, with interest at 6%, had the following payments endorsed upon it: February 11, 1973, $250; November 19, 1973, $375; and April 1, 1974, $200. Find the amount due at maturity.

SOLUTION

Amount Due	Time to Date of Payment	Interest to Date of Payment	Total Amount	Payment	Balance Due
$1,240.00	194 days	$40.09	$1,280.09	$250.00	$1,030.09
1,030.09	281 days	48.24	1,078.33	375.00	703.33
703.33	133 days	15.59	718.92	200.00	518.92
518.92	122 days	10.55	529.47	. . .	529.47*

* Due at maturity.

1. The exact number of days from the date of the note to the date of the first payment (August 1, 1973, to February 11, 1974) is 194 days.
2. The banker's interest on the amount due ($1,240) at 6% for 194 days is $40.09.
3. Since the amount of the first payment is more than the interest, add the interest to the amount due; from this total amount deduct the first payment to find the balance due.

$1,240 + $40.09 = $1,280.09, amount due Feb. 11, 1973
$1,280.09 − $250 = $1,030.09, balance due

The balance due becomes the amount due on which the interest to the date of the next payment is computed.

4. Find the time from the date of the first payment to the date of the second payment (February 11, 1973, to November 19, 1973). To arrive at the balance due, compute the interest for this time at 6% on the amount due after the first payment was made ($1,030.09). Add this interest to the amount due to arrive at the total amount due.

5. Subtract the second payment from this total amount due.

6. Repeat these steps for each payment made. After the last payment has been deducted, find the time and interest on the last amount due from the date of the last payment to the date of maturity. The sum of this interest plus the balance due after the last payment was made is the amount due at maturity.

Practice Drill

A note for $3,500, dated July 15, 1972, due in $2\frac{1}{2}$ years, with interest at 6%, had the following payments endorsed upon it: December 30, 1972, $1,000; November 17, 1973, $500; and January 2, 1974, $250. Find the amount due at maturity.

ANSWER $2,129.19

Partial Payment Less Than Interest

If the amount of one or more payments is less than the interest due for the period of the payment, the balance due after the payment is made would still be higher than the total amount due (which includes the interest) before the payment is made, because more interest is being computed on the amount due than is being covered in the payment. Thus, the amount due remains the same, regardless of payments, until the sum of the payments exceeds the sum of the interest due to date. To determine whether the sum of the payments is less than the sum of the interest, follow these steps.

1. Find the interest to the date of the next payment.

2. Add the two payments together.

3. If the sum of the payments is less than the sum of the interest, add subsequent payments until you reach a sum that will equal or exceed the total interest to the date of the last payment added. (Remember that the United States Rule does not permit compound interest.)

Example | **PROBLEM** A note for $1,300 dated August 8, 1971, due in 3 years, with interest at 6%, had the following payments endorsed upon it: September 8, 1972, $125; August 8, 1973, $25; and January 12, 1974, $250. Find the amount due at maturity.

SOLUTION

Amount Due	Time to Date of Payment	Interest to Date of Payment	Total Amount	Payment	Balance Due
$1,300.00	1 year, 31 days	$84.72	$1,384.72	$125.00	$1,259.72
1,259.72	334 days	70.12 ⎫	None	25.00 ⎫	1,259.72
1,259.72	157 days	32.96 ⎭		250.00 ⎭	
		($103.08)	1,362.80	($275.00)	1,087.80
1,087.80	208 days	37.71	1,125.51	. . .	1,125.51*

* Due at maturity.

In this particular problem, the second payment ($25.00) is less than the interest from the date of the first payment to the date of the second payment ($84.72). If the interest were added to the amount due and the payment deducted, the balance due would be greater than the amount due at the time of the payment. It would then be necessary to find the interest for the next payment on a balance larger than the amount on which the interest for the preceding payment was computed. This excess would be due to the excess of the interest over the first payment and would result in the compounding of interest.

1. Since compounding interest is contrary to the United States Rule, it is necessary to find the interest from the second payment to the third payment on the amount due ($1,259.72) at the time of the second payment. If the sum of the two payments ($25 + $250) is greater than the sum of the two interest amounts ($70.12 + $32.96), add the total interest to the amount due at the time of the second payment ($1,259.72 + $103.08 = $1,362.80). From this total amount due, subtract the sum of the payments to obtain the new balance due ($1,362.80 − $275.00 = $1,087.80).

2. Determine the time and the interest from the third payment to the date of maturity. Add the interest to the amount due to find the total amount due at maturity.

If the sum of the last payments came to less than the sum of the two interest amounts, you would find the interest from the last payment to the date of maturity on $1,259.72. To this amount you would add the total interest. Finally, from this total amount you would subtract the sum of the payments to arrive at the balance due at maturity.

Practice
Drills

1. A note for $5,200, dated August 8, 1972, due in 3 years, with in-
terest at 6%, had the following payments endorsed upon it: September
8, 1973, $500; August 8, 1974, $100; and January 12, 1975, $1,000.
Find the amount due at maturity.
2. A note for $4,270, dated July 1, 1973, due in 2 years, with interest
at 7%, had the following payments endorsed upon it: October 19, 1974,
$100; and January 2, 1975, $2,500. Find the amount due at maturity.

ANSWERS   1. $4,502.06   2. $2,196.79

APPLICATION PROBLEMS

Solve the following problems, using the United States Rule.

1. The following payments were made on a 3-year, 5% mortgage
amounting to $3,750 and dated September 18, 1972: March 18, 1973,
$750; December 18, 1973, $750; and January 18, 1974, $1,000. Find
the balance due on the mortgage at maturity.

2. Payments were endorsed as follows on a 2-year note dated March
17, 1973, amounting to $1,700, with interest at 5%: October 19, 1973,
$400; and July 18, 1974, $475. Find the balance due on the note at
maturity.

3. A note for $1,800, dated July 15, 1972, due in 3 years, with interest
at 6%, had the following payments endorsed upon it: December 30,
1972, $500; November 17, 1973, $250; and January 2, 1974, $125.
Find the amount due at maturity.

59 PARTIAL PAYMENTS: MERCHANT'S RULE

The Merchant's Rule of computing partial payments has evolved out
of the experiences of businessmen dealing with one another. It is
simpler to apply than the United States Rule and, therefore, is much
more popular in the transaction of business between commercial firms
and institutions. It must be emphasized, however, that when one firm
brings suit against another for payment of a debt, the amount of the
obligation is computed according to the United States Rule, since this
is the method that is recognized in the courts.

To find the amount due at maturity by the Merchant's Rule, follow these steps.

1. Add the interest to date of maturity to the face value of the note to find the maturity value.

2. Find the interest on each payment from the date of the payment to the date of maturity. (Use the banker's 60-day interest method and exact time.)

3. From the maturity value of the note subtract the sum of the payments plus the interest on the payments. The difference is the amount due at maturity.

Example

PROBLEM   Kaufman purchased $300 worth of merchandise on July 25, 1973, giving in payment his 6-month note at 6% interest. He paid $125 on September 1 and $125 on October 15. How much did he still owe on the note at maturity?

SOLUTION

Face value of note	$300.00	
Interest to date of maturity (6 months)	+ 9.00	
Value of note at maturity		$309.00
Deduct:		
Interest on payments:		
6% on $125 from Sept. 1, 1973 to		
Jan. 25, 1974 (146 days)	$ 3.04	
6% on $125 from Oct. 15, 1973 to		
Jan. 25, 1974 (102 days)	2.13	
Payments ($125 + $125)	+ 250.00	−255.17
Amount due at maturity		$ 53.83

To find the value of the note at maturity in this problem, the interest at 6% for 6 months on $300 was determined first. In transactions of this kind, interest on a 6-month note is equal to $\frac{1}{2}$ of 1 year's interest. 6% of $300 for 1 year equals $18. The interest for $\frac{1}{2}$ year or 6 months equals $\frac{1}{2}$ of $18, or $9. The interest plus the face of the note equals the value of the note at maturity.

The interest was then computed on each payment from the date of the payment to the date of maturity. The sum of the interest on the two payments plus the payments subtracted from the value of the note at maturity is equal to the amount due on the note at maturity.

$309 − $255.17 = $53.83, amount due at maturity

Practice Drill

A note for $1,500, dated October 17, 1973, due in 9 months, with interest at 6%, had the following payments endorsed upon it: January 2, 1974, $50; May 15, 1974, $100; and June 1, 1974, $500. Find the amount due at maturity.

ANSWER $910.90

APPLICATION PROBLEMS

1. Find the amount due at maturity on an 8-month, 6% note for $700, dated April 18, 1973, if payments were endorsed upon it as follows: July 1, $150; August 8, $100; and September 1, $100.

2. A note for $750, dated October 17, 1973, due in 9 months, with interest at 6%, had the following payments endorsed upon it: January 2, 1974, $25; May 15, 1974, $50; and June 1, 1974, $250. Find the amount due at maturity.

3. A $400 note, dated March 20, 1973, with interest at 6%, and due in $2\frac{1}{2}$ years, was endorsed for payments as follows: January 3, 1974, $50; October 5, 1974, $50; and April 4, 1975, $50. Find the balance due at maturity.

60 PROCEEDS OF DISCOUNTED DRAFTS

Notice how the following illustration of a draft differs from that of a note.

In a draft, the *drawer* (the one who writes, or draws, the draft) is authorizing the *drawee* (the one who owes the money) to pay the *payee* (the one who receives the money). In some instances the drawer may be the payee. A *bank draft* is a bill of exchange, the drawer and drawee of which are banks. A *sight draft* is one payable on presentation. Our work on drafts is based on *time drafts*—that is, drafts payable at a given time after demand or sight or date.

Finding Maturity Date & Term of Discount on Drafts

A draft that is payable at a certain number of days *sight* or *after sight* must first be accepted by the drawee because the date of maturity is determined from the *date of the acceptance.*

A draft payable a certain number of days *after date* does not have to be accepted in order to compute the date of maturity and the term of discount. The date of maturity of such a draft is computed from the date of the draft regardless of the date of acceptance.

The term of discount on date drafts is the exact number of days from the discount date to the maturity date. The term of discount on sight drafts is the exact number of days from the date of acceptance to the date of maturity. Each is found the same way as for notes.

Examples | **PROBLEM 1** Find the maturity date and the term of discount of the following draft if discounted March 1.

$750.00   Jersey City, New Jersey   January 31, 19 --

Three months after sight   *Pay to*

the order of   Henry Keller

Seven hundred fifty and 00/100 - *Dollars*

Value received and charge the same to account of

To William Ellsworth
4 Rue Street, Newton, New Jersey   *Fred West*

Accepted: February 28, 19--

SOLUTION This draft is payable 3 months after sight. The phrase "after sight" means "after the date of acceptance," regardless of the date of the draft. To find the date of maturity of such a draft, count ahead from the date of acceptance the number of months given. The maturity date would be 3 months after February 28, or May 28. If it were payable "90 days after sight," the date of maturity would be 90 days after February 28, or May 29.

The term of discount is the number of days from the discount date, March 1 (the day after the acceptance date), to May 28, the date of maturity. The term of discount is 88 days.

PROBLEM 2 Find the maturity date of the same draft if payable "Three months after date" or "90 days after date."

SOLUTION Find the date of maturity by counting the number of months given from the date of the draft. (The date of acceptance is ignored because on date drafts there is no date of acceptance.) The date of maturity would be 3 months after January 31, or April 30.

If the draft were payable "90 days after date," the date of maturity would be 90 days after January 31, or May 1.

Practice Drill

A bill of exchange dated March 20 was payable 3 months after sight. If the bill was accepted April 21 and discounted April 25, what were the maturity date and the term of discount?

ANSWERS July 21, maturity date; 87 days, term of discount

Finding Proceeds on Discounted Drafts

The proceeds are found in the same way as for notes. Subtract the discount and collection fee from the face of the draft.

Examples

PROBLEM 1 Find the proceeds of the following draft accepted April 24 and discounted May 8 at 6%.

$2,185.00	Chelsea, Massachusetts	February 25, 19--
Two months after sight		Pay to
the order of	Norman Walker	
Twenty-one hundred eighty-five and 00/100--------------------------------- Dollars

Value received and charge the same to account of
To Harold Fried
8 Lee Avenue, Boston, Massachusetts
Raymond Gregg

SOLUTION

Face value of draft	$2,185.00
Date of maturity (2 months after April 24)	June 24
Term of discount (May 8 to June 24)	47 days
Bank discount (interest on $2,185 at 6% for 47 days)	$17.12
Collection fee ($\frac{1}{10}$% of $2,185)	+ 2.19
Total charges	− 19.31
Proceeds	$2,165.69

PROBLEM 2   Find the proceeds if the draft that Raymond Gregg gave to Norman Walker was due "2 months after date" instead of "2 months after sight," and was discounted March 3 instead of May 8, all other conditions remaining the same.

SOLUTION   Find the date of maturity by counting ahead 2 months from February 25, the date of the draft, instead of 2 months from April 24, the date on which Harold Fried accepted the draft.

Face value of draft	$2,185.00
Date of maturity (2 months after Feb. 25)	April 25
Term of discount (March 3 to April 25)	53 days
Bank discount (interest on $2,185 at 6% for 53 days)	$19.30
Collection fee ($\frac{1}{10}$% of $2,185)	+2.19
Total charges	− 21.49
Proceeds	$2,163.51

Practice Drill

A $312.50 draft, dated September 1 and due 90 days after date, is accepted September 3. The draft was discounted September 8 at 5%; collection fee, $\frac{1}{10}$%. Find the proceeds of the discounted draft.

ANSWER $308.59

APPLICATION PROBLEMS

1. Find the date of maturity and the term of discount of each of the following drafts.

Date of Draft	When Payable	Acceptance Date	Date of Maturity	Discount Date	Term of Discount
a. July 17	60 days after sight	Aug. 2	_____	Aug. 14	_____
b. Nov. 1	3 months after date	Nov. 7	_____	Nov. 17	_____
c. Sept. 5	4 months after sight	Nov. 4	_____	Nov. 12	_____
d. Feb. 6	80 days after date	Mar. 2	_____	Apr. 3	_____
e. Apr. 16	75 days after sight	Apr. 26	_____	May 6	_____
f. June 7	120 days after date	July 17	_____	Aug. 27	_____

2. Find the proceeds of each of the following drafts on which a collection fee is charged.

	Draft A	Draft B	Draft C	Draft D
Face value of draft	$7,658.00	$4,315.00	$9,375.00	$4,380.00
Date of draft	June 12	Feb. 18	June 21	Sept. 25
When due	90 days after sight	4 months after date	60 days after date	75 days after sight
Acceptance date	June 18	Mar. 19	July 22	Oct. 1
Discount date	July 21	May 20	July 29	Nov. 3
Rate of discount	5%	4%	7%	$4\frac{1}{2}\%$
Date of maturity	Sept 12th	————	————	————
Term of discount	————	————	————	————
Bank discount	$————	$————	$————	$————
Collection fee	————$(\frac{1}{8}\%)$	————$(\frac{1}{10}\%)$	————$(\frac{1}{4}\%)$	————$(\frac{1}{5}\%)$
Total charges	$————	$————	$————	$————
Proceeds	$————	$————	$————	$————

PROBLEMS FOR PART SEVEN
Notes & Drafts

56 Find the date of maturity and the term of discount on each of the following notes.

	Date of Note	Time	Discount Date	Date of Maturity	Term of Discount
1.	May 20	3 months	June 8	————	————
2.	July 28	60 days	August 10	————	————
3.	September 14	6 months	December 24	————	————
4.	November 30	90 days	December 26	————	————
5.	January 9	4 months	April 1	————	————
6.	March 17	45 days	March 29	————	————
7.	May 23	30 days	June 2	————	————
8.	July 6	5 months	September 13	————	————
9.	February 15	80 days	March 12	————	————
10.	April 7	75 days	May 14	————	————

57

1. Find the proceeds on the following discounted notes.

	Note A	Note B	Note C	Note D
Face value of note	$375.00	$8,535.00	$875.00	$1,640.00
Time to run	6 months	75 days	2 months	4 months
Date of note	Jan. 12	Apr. 14	May 7	July 15
Discount date	Mar. 3	May 2	June 6	Aug. 2
Rate of discount	7%	$4\frac{1}{2}$%	$7\frac{1}{2}$%	5%
Rate of collection	$\frac{1}{6}$%	$\frac{1}{8}$%	$\frac{1}{2}$%	$\frac{1}{10}$%
Date of maturity	_____	_____	_____	_____
Term of discount	_____	_____	_____	_____
Bank discount	$_____	$_____	$_____	$_____
Collection fee	_____	_____	_____	_____
Total charges	$_____	$_____	$_____	$_____
Proceeds	$_____	$_____	$_____	$_____

2. Find the bank discount at 5% and the proceeds of a 90-day, 6% interest-bearing note for $724 that Diehl received from King on August 8 and discounted on August 12.

3. On August 11, Edison received a 75-day, $4\frac{1}{2}$% interest-bearing note for $1,200 from Ford. He discounted the note on September 1 at 6%. How much did Edison receive from the bank?

4. On June 9, Loomis discounted an 80-day, 5% interest-bearing note for $1,350, which he received from Martin on May 14. If the bank charged 6% discount and $\frac{1}{10}$% collection fee, how much did Loomis receive?

58

Solve the following problems, using the United States Rule.

1. A note for $900, dated July 17, 1972, with interest at 6%, was reduced by the following payments: October 8, 1973, $50; December 17, 1974, $50; and January 2, 1975, $50. Find the amount due on the note on July 17, 1975.

2. A note for $827, dated July 1, 1972, due in 2 years, with interest at 7%, had the following payments endorsed upon it: October 19, 1973, $20; and January 2, 1974, $500. Find the amount due at maturity.

3. The payments endorsed on the back of the following note were May 27, 1973, $200; August 15, 1973, $150; and September 30, 1973, $1,000. Find the amount due at maturity.

```
$ __2,500.00__          Jersey City, New Jersey          October 19, 1972

        Fifteen months                   after date  I   promise to pay

to the order of                        Fred H. Rose

Twenty-five hundred and 00/100------------------------------------------ Dollars

Payable at                       The Bergen Trust Company

Value received  with interest at 6%

No. __984__   Due January 19, 1973          Raymond Stimson
```

59 | Solve the following problems by the Merchant's Rule.

1. Find the amount due at maturity on a 5-month, 6% note for $800, dated May 3, 1973, if payments were endorsed upon it as follows: July 1, $200; August 5, $100; September 1, $100.

2. A $550 note, dated March 15, 1973, with interest at 6%, and due in $2\frac{1}{2}$ years, was endorsed for payments as follows: January 3, 1974, $50; October 5, 1974, $50; April 4, 1975, $50. Find the balance due at maturity.

3. Zimbalist received from Arleigh a 6-month, 6% note for $840, dated February 1, 1973, upon which the following payments were endorsed: March 1, 1973, $100; April 15, 1973, $50; May 30, 1973, $250. How much did Arleigh still owe on the note at maturity?

60 | **1.** Find the proceeds of the draft shown below, assuming that it was accepted on November 5 of the same year in which it was drawn for the following.
a. Discounted November 12, 19—, at 6%; collection fee, $\frac{1}{8}$%
b. Discounted November 27, 19—, at 5%; collection fee, $\frac{1}{10}$%
c. Discounted December 18, 19—, at $7\frac{1}{2}$%; collection fee, $\frac{1}{4}$%

```
$7,500.00               Troy, New York          October 17, 19--
               Ninety days after sight                   Pay to

the order of                    William O'Neil

Seventy-five hundred and 00/100-------------------------------- Dollars

Value received and charge the same to account of
To Nicholas Brennan
    334 Lord Avenue, Schenectady, New York   }   Francis Burke

                                        Accepted: November 5, 19--
```

2. You draw a 4-months' sight draft amounting to $500 on Kester and Ronald, which they accept on June 3. If you discount the draft at your bank on July 1 at 6%, how much do you receive?

3. How much will a bank pay on a draft amounting to $840, dated March 6, due 75 days after date, accepted April 7, and discounted May 2 at 6%?

4. Find the proceeds of a 75-day sight draft amounting to $225, accepted December 18, and discounted December 24 at 5% with a collection fee of $\frac{1}{8}$%.

5. Find the amount that the bank will pay on a $1,500 draft dated October 19, due 4 months after date, accepted November 1, and discounted November 7 at 6% with a collection fee of $\frac{1}{4}$%.

PART EIGHT

Compound Interest, Present Worth & Installment Interest

The simplest definition of *compound interest* is that it is interest earned on interest; that is, it is simple interest computed on the sum of the principal and the interest that has been earned during a previous period. When interest is periodically added to the principal so that the new sum can be used as the principal for the following time period and this procedure is repeated for a certain number of time periods, the final sum is called the *compound amount*. The difference between the compound amount and the original principal is the *compound interest,* which is computed most often in connection with savings accounts, where the depositor's savings earn interest; at specified times (annually, semiannually, or quarterly), the interest is added to the original deposit and thus results in a larger amount on which interest is applied.

The *present worth* (or present value) of a debt is the sum that will equal the amount of the debt at maturity if invested at a given rate of interest for a given length of time.

The *installment plan* of buying is enormously popular with consumers, particularly for purchasing expensive items "on time." Every consumer needs to understand the cost of install- ment buying. At the time he buys merchandise on the installment plan, the buyer makes a down payment. He pays the remainder of the purchase price in equal payments (usually monthly) that include a carrying charge for the convenience of using the installment plan.

Although there are many sources from which an individual or a business may borrow money, many people prefer the services of finance companies and other so-called small-loan agencies, even though the interest rates charged by these agencies are generally higher than those of banks. Congress passed the so-called "Truth-In-Lending Law" on July 1, 1969, for the protection of borrowers. The law makes it mandatory for any institution or organization that lends money or sells products or services on an installment plan to reveal to the customer the annual rate of interest he is paying and to disclose any charges in connection with credit transactions.

61 COMPOUND INTEREST

Interest may be compounded annually, semiannually, quarterly, monthly, and even daily.

Computing Interest Compounded Annually

When interest is compounded only once a year, the following procedure for computing the interest is used.

1. Find the simple interest for 1 year at the given rate on the principal.

2. Add the interest to the principal to arrive at the amount that is to be used as the principal at the beginning of the second year.

3. Find the simple interest for 1 year on the new principal. The sum of this interest plus the principal used to find this interest will be the principal to be used the third year.

4. Repeat these steps as many times as the number of years for which the compound interest is to be computed. The final result of these computations is called the compound amount. The difference between the result and the principal is called the compound interest.

Compound interest is not computed on amounts less than $1 by most banks and should not be so computed in the problems in this unit.

Example

PROBLEM   R. F. Kranz deposited $1,500 in the Impeccable Mutual Savings Association. If the earnings of the association warranted a 5% annual dividend (interest), and if the dividends were compounded annually, how much compound interest did Kranz receive at the end of 3 years if he permitted the earnings to accumulate?

SOLUTION

Principal	Interest	Compound Amount	At End Of
$1,500.00	$75.00	$1,575.00	First year
1,575.00	78.75	1,653.75	Second year
1,653.75	82.69	1,736.44	Third year

Compound amount = $1,736.44
Principal   =   1,500.00
Compound interest = $ 236.44

Practice Drill

An investment firm pays 6% interest, compounded annually, on all deposits. How much compound interest would an investor receive at the end of 4 years on a $2,500 deposit?

ANSWER $656.16

Computing Interest Compounded Semiannually, Quarterly, Etc.

When interest is compounded semiannually, the interest must, of course, be computed twice a year; quarterly, four times a year; and so on. To find the rate of interest when interest is compounded at shorter than annual intervals, divide the annual rate by the appropriate fraction of a year; i.e., semiannually, by 2; quarterly, by 4; and so on.

Example

PROBLEM   Harvey Jackson deposited $4,500 in the Fortune Savings and Loan Association. The association paid $6\frac{1}{2}$% interest compounded semiannually. What was the compound amount of Jackson's deposit after 2 years?

SOLUTION   Compound amount = $5,114.12

Principal	Interest $3\frac{1}{4}$%*	Compound Amount	At End Of
$4,500.00	$146.25	$4,646.25	$\frac{1}{2}$ year
4,646.25	151.00	4,797.25	1 year
4,797.25	155.90	4,953.15	$1\frac{1}{2}$ years
4,953.15	160.97	5,114.12	2 years

*$3\frac{1}{4}$% semiannual rate is the same as $6\frac{1}{2}$% annual rate.

Practice Drill

$1,720 was deposited in a bank and left undisturbed for 3 years. At the end of this time, how much did the depositor have on deposit in the bank if 6% interest had been credited to his account and the interest was compounded annually and semiannually?

ANSWERS   annually, $2,048.50; semiannually, $2,053.66

Using a Compound-Interest Table

Banks and other financial houses use tables to find compound interest. One such table is shown on page 132. The amounts in this table are rounded off to 4 places. If $1 were the only amount involved, 2 places would be enough. When large sums of money are involved, 6-, 8-, and even 10-place tables are used to ensure accuracy and exactness. The difference in the amount of interest on large original balances can be substantial.

The table is used in the following manner.

1. In the left column find the number of years or periods for which the interest is to be computed.

2. Follow horizontally to the column headed by the interest rate used to find the result of compounding $1 annually for the period specified.

COMPOUND INTEREST: AMOUNT OF $1 COMPOUNDED ANNUALLY

Year	$1\frac{1}{2}$%	2%	$2\frac{1}{2}$%	3%	$3\frac{1}{2}$%	4%	5%	6%
1	1.0150	1.0200	1.0250	1.0300	1.0350	1.0400	1.0500	1.0600
2	1.0302	1.0404	1.0506	1.0609	1.0712	1.0816	1.1025	1.1236
3	1.0457	1.0612	1.0769	1.0927	1.1087	1.1249	1.1576	1.1910
4	1.0614	1.0824	1.1038	1.1255	1.1475	1.1699	1.2155	1.2625
5	1.0773	1.1041	1.1314	1.1593	1.1877	1.2167	1.2763	1.3382
6	1.0934	1.1262	1.1597	1.1941	1.2293	1.2653	1.3401	1.4185
7	1.1098	1.1487	1.1887	1.2299	1.2723	1.3159	1.4071	1.5036
8	1.1265	1.1717	1.2184	1.2668	1.3168	1.3686	1.4775	1.5938
9	1.1434	1.1951	1.2489	1.3048	1.3629	1.4233	1.5513	1.6895
10	1.1605	1.2190	1.2801	1.3439	1.4106	1.4802	1.6289	1.7908
11	1.1779	1.2434	1.3121	1.3842	1.4600	1.5395	1.7103	1.8983
12	1.1956	1.2682	1.3449	1.4258	1.5111	1.6010	1.7959	2.0122
13	1.2136	1.2936	1.3785	1.4685	1.5640	1.6651	1.8856	2.1329
14	1.2318	1.3195	1.4130	1.5126	1.6187	1.7317	1.9799	2.2609
15	1.2502	1.3459	1.4483	1.5580	1.6753	1.8009	2.0789	2.3966
16	1.2690	1.3728	1.4845	1.6047	1.7340	1.8730	2.1829	2.5404
17	1.2880	1.4002	1.5216	1.6528	1.7947	1.9479	2.2920	2.6928
18	1.3063	1.4282	1.5597	1.7024	1.8575	2.0258	2.4066	2.8543
19	1.3270	1.4568	1.5987	1.7535	1.9225	2.1068	2.5270	3.0256
20	1.3469	1.4859	1.6387	1.8061	1.9898	2.1911	2.6533	3.2071
21	1.3671	1.5157	1.6796	1.8603	2.0594	2.2788	2.7860	3.3996
22	1.3876	1.5460	1.7216	1.9161	2.1315	2.3699	2.9253	3.6035
23	1.4084	1.5769	1.7646	1.9736	2.2061	2.4647	3.0715	3.8197
24	1.4295	1.6084	1.8087	2.0328	2.2833	2.5633	3.2251	4.0489
25	1.4509	1.6406	1.8539	2.0938	2.3632	2.6658	3.3864	4.2919

3. Multiply this result by the principal to find the compound amount.
4. Find the difference between the principal and the compound amount to find the compound interest.

Examples

PROBLEM 1 Using the compound-interest table, find the compound amount and the compound interest on $625 at 5%, compounded annually, for 8 years.

SOLUTION Find 8 years in the left column and follow horizontally to the column headed 5% to find that $1 at compound interest amounts to $1.4775. A principal of $625 would result in a compound amount of 625 × $1.4775, or $923.44.

$923.44	–	$625	=	$298.44
(compound amount)		(principal)		(compound interest)

PROBLEM 2 Using the compound-interest table, find the compound amount and the compound interest on $387 at 6%, compounded semiannually, for 11 years.

SOLUTION To find interest compounded semiannually, take one-half the given rate and double the time. The interest for 11 years at 6% compounded semiannually is the same as for 22 years at 3% compounded annually. The table shows that the result of taking $1 for 22 years at 3% is $1.9161. To take $387 for the same period and rate of interest, multiply $1.9161 by 387.. The compound amount is $741.53.

$741.53	–	$387	=	$354.53
(compound amount)		(principal)		(compound interest)

To find the interest compounded quarterly, take one-fourth the given rate and 4 times the time.

Practice Drills

Using the compound-interest table, find the compound amount and the compound interest on each of the following.

1. $4,215 at $3\frac{1}{2}$%, compounded annually, for 6 years
2. $820 at 3%, compounded semiannually, for 10 years
3. $1,264 at 6%, compounded quarterly, for 5 years

ANSWERS   1. compound amount, $5,181.50; compound interest, $966.50
2. compound amount, $1,104.46; compound interest, $284.46
3. compound amount, $1,702.48; compound interest, $438.48

$\wp$ o APPLICATION PROBLEMS

1. Find the compound interest and the compound amount for each of the following.

	Principal	Interest Rate	Time to Run	Compounded	Compound Interest	Compound Amount
a.	$ 860	6%	4 years	Annually	$_____	$_____
b.	750	$4\frac{1}{2}$%	3 years	Annually	_____	_____
c.	4,000	3%	2 years	Annually	_____	_____
d.	3,500	2%	2 years	Annually	_____	_____
e.	2,000	$2\frac{1}{2}$%	2 years	Annually	_____	_____
f.	4,500	$3\frac{1}{2}$%	3 years	Annually	_____	_____

2. Find the compound interest and the compound amount for each of the following.

	Principal	Interest Rate	Time to Run	Compounded	Compound Interest	Compound Amount
a.	$640	5%	2 years	Semiannually	$_____	$_____
b.	925	4%	1 year	Quarterly	_____	_____
c.	340	6%	$1\frac{1}{2}$ years	Quarterly	_____	_____
d.	575	5%	2 years	Semiannually	_____	_____
e.	660	4%	$2\frac{1}{2}$ years	Semiannually	_____	_____
f.	835	6%	6 months	Monthly	_____	_____

3. Using the compound-interest table on page 132, find the compound amount and the compound interest for each of the following.

	Principal	Interest Rate	Time to Run	Compounded	Compound Interest	Compound Amount
a.	$860	5%	6 years	Annually	$_____	$_____
b.	426	5%	3 years	Semiannually	_____	_____
c.	350	$3\frac{1}{2}$%	9 years	Annually	_____	_____
d.	230	5%	15 years	Annually	_____	_____
e.	450	$3\frac{1}{2}$%	12 years	Annually	_____	_____
f.	593	4%	6 years	Semiannually	_____	_____
g.	608	3%	5 years	Semiannually	_____	_____
h.	784	6%	4 years	Quarterly	_____	_____
i.	965	6%	2 years	Quarterly	_____	_____
j.	722	8%	3 years	Quarterly	_____	_____

4. A local merchant borrows $5,000 for 1 year from a business associate. Interest is to be computed at the rate of 6% a year, compounded quarterly. How much will the merchant have to pay at the end of the year when he repays the loan? If simple interest were to be paid on the loan instead of compound interest, how much less would the loan cost the merchant?

5. On July 1, 19X6, Jim Alcott deposited $5,000 in a savings account at his bank. The bank paid 4% yearly interest, compounded quarterly. The next July 1, Alcott deposited an additional $5,000 in his account. How much did he have in the bank on July 1, 19X8, if he made no additional deposits or withdrawals?

62 PRESENT WORTH

The difference between the present worth and the value at maturity is called the *true discount*. It is really the interest on the present worth of the debt for the time it has yet to run before maturity. True discount differs from bank discount in that true discount is equivalent to simple interest paid on the principal at maturity; whereas bank discount is equivalent to simple interest paid in advance on the principal (plus interest, if any).

Present Worth at Simple Interest

To determine the present worth of a debt where simple interest is involved, proceed as follows.

1. Find the interest on $1 for the time and rate given and add it to $1.
2. Divide the debt to be paid by the compound amount. The quotient is the *present worth.*

Example | **PROBLEM** Monroe owes Sanders $250, due in 6 months. Sanders is willing to accept a sum today that at 5% interest will amount to the value of the debt at maturity. Find the amount that Monroe will have to pay Sanders. Find how much less than $250 Sanders will receive.

SOLUTION

Interest on $1 for 6 months at 5% = $.025
$1 + $.025 = $1.025, compound amount of $1 at 5% for 6 months
$250 ÷ 1.025 = $243.90, present worth of $250 debt
$250 − $243.90 = $6.10, true discount

If $1 invested today at 5% amounts to $1.025 in 6 months, it follows that to have $250 in 6 months from today it is necessary to see how many times as much $250 is of $1.025. The ratio of these two amounts is 243.90. Therefore, $243.90 invested today at 5% will amount to $250 in 6 months.

To check the accuracy of these computations, find the interest on the present worth for the time and rate given; then add the interest to the present worth. The sum of the present worth plus the interest must be equal to the maturity value of the debt.

Check:

Interest on $243.90 for 6 months at 5% = $6.10
$243.90 + $6.10 = $250, debt at maturity

Practice | 1. A debt has value at maturity of $890. Find the present worth if the
Drills | interest is 6%.

2. What sum invested at $4\frac{1}{2}$% interest will amount to $5,000 in 1 year?

ANSWERS 1. $855.77   2. $4,784.69

Using a Present-Worth Table

Just as most banks and loan agencies use tables to find compound interest, they also use tables to find the present worth of an amount. The table on page 136 shows present worth.

PRESENT WORTH OF $1 AT COMPOUND INTEREST

Year	$\frac{1}{2}$%	1%	2%	3%	4%	5%	6%
1	0.9950	0.9901	0.9804	0.9709	0.9615	0.9524	0.9434
2	0.9901	0.9803	0.9612	0.9426	0.9246	0.9070	0.8900
3	0.9851	0.9706	0.9423	0.9151	0.8890	0.8638	0.8396
4	0.9802	0.9610	0.9238	0.8885	0.8548	0.8227	0.7921
5	0.9754	0.9515	0.9057	0.8626	0.8219	0.7835	0.7473
6	0.9705	0.9420	0.8880	0.8375	0.7903	0.7462	0.7050
7	0.9657	0.9327	0.8706	0.8131	0.7599	0.7107	0.6651
8	0.9609	0.9235	0.8535	0.7894	0.7307	0.6768	0.6274
9	0.9561	0.9143	0.8368	0.7664	0.7026	0.6446	0.5919
10	0.9513	0.9053	0.8203	0.7441	0.6756	0.6139	0.5584
11	0.9466	0.8963	0.8043	0.7224	0.6496	0.5847	0.5268
12	0.9419	0.8874	0.7885	0.7014	0.6246	0.5568	0.4970
13	0.9372	0.8787	0.7730	0.6810	0.6006	0.5303	0.4688
14	0.9326	0.8700	0.7579	0.6611	0.5775	0.5051	0.4423
15	0.9279	0.8613	0.7430	0.6419	0.5553	0.4810	0.4173
16	0.9233	0.8528	0.7284	0.6232	0.5339	0.4581	0.3936
17	0.9187	0.8444	0.7142	0.6050	0.5134	0.4363	0.3714
18	0.9141	0.8360	0.7002	0.5874	0.4936	0.4155	0.3503
19	0.9096	0.8277	0.6864	0.5703	0.4746	0.3957	0.3305
20	0.9051	0.8195	0.6730	0.5537	0.4564	0.3769	0.3118
21	0.9006	0.8114	0.6598	0.5375	0.4388	0.3589	0.2942
22	0.8961	0.8034	0.6468	0.5219	0.4220	0.3418	0.2775
23	0.8916	0.7954	0.6342	0.5067	0.4057	0.3256	0.2618
24	0.8872	0.7876	0.6217	0.4919	0.3901	0.3101	0.2470
25	0.8828	0.7798	0.6095	0.4776	0.3751	0.2953	0.2330
26	0.8784	0.7720	0.5976	0.4637	0.3607	0.2198	0.2812
27	0.8740	0.7644	0.5859	0.4502	0.3468	0.2074	0.2678
28	0.8697	0.7568	0.5744	0.4371	0.3335	0.1956	0.2551
29	0.8653	0.7493	0.5631	0.4243	0.3207	0.1846	0.2429
30	0.8610	0.7419	0.5521	0.4120	0.3083	0.1741	0.2314
40	0.8191	0.6717	0.4529	0.3066	0.2083	0.1420	0.0972
50	0.7793	0.6080	0.3715	0.2281	0.1407	0.0872	0.0543
60	0.7414	0.5504	0.3048	0.1697	0.0951	0.0535	0.0303
70	0.7053	0.4983	0.2500	0.1263	0.0642	0.0329	0.0169
80	0.6710	0.4511	0.2051	0.0940	0.0434	0.0202	0.0095
90	0.6383	0.4084	0.1683	0.0699	0.0293	0.0124	0.0053
100	0.6073	0.3697	0.1380	0.0520	0.0198	0.0076	0.0029

Present Worth at Compound Interest

The present worth that will amount to a given maturity value at a definite time in the future and at a specific rate of compound interest can be computed in two ways.

METHOD 1

Using the compound-interest table on page 132, do the following.
1. Find the amount of $1 compounded annually at the specified rate of interest for the number of years to the maturity date.
2. Divide the given maturity value by the amount of $1 to find the present worth, or principal.

Example

PROBLEM   Find the present worth that will amount to $1,947.50 in 15 years at 3% interest, compounded annually.

SOLUTION   The amount of $1 compounded annually at 3% interest for 15 years shown in the interest table is 1.5580.

$1,947.50 ÷ 1.5580 = $1,250, present worth

Practice Drills

1. What sum invested today at 5% interest, compounded annually, will amount to $2,500 in 10 years?

2. Find the present worth of a $1,000 debt due in 7 years if interest is compounded semiannually at 3%.

ANSWERS   1. $1,534.78   2. $8,118.20

METHOD 2

Using the present-worth-of-$1 table on page 136, do the following.
1. Find the present worth of $1 at the specified rate of compound interest for the number of years to the maturity date.
2. Multiply the given maturity value by the present worth of $1 to find the principal.

Examples

PROBLEM 1   Rita Doberman owes $2,500, which is due in 6 years. How much must she invest today at 5% interest, compounded annually, to accumulate the sum she needs to pay the debt at maturity?

SOLUTION   The present worth of $1 at 5% compound interest for 6 years is shown in the present-worth-of-$1 table to be .7462.

2,500 x $.7462 = $1,865.50, present worth

PROBLEM 2 $826.40 was invested at 6% interest, compounded semiannually. In how many years will this investment amount to $1,250?

SOLUTION   Use the compound-interest table* on page 132.

1,250 ÷ $826.40 = $1.5126

---

* A slight discrepancy in amounts shown in the compound-interest table and the present-worth-of-$1 table between 14 years at 3% and 7 years at 6% is due to the compound interest earned on the additional interest in the 14-year period. This discrepancy is insignificant and can be ignored in all computations.

$1.5126 = the amount of $1 compounded annually for 14 years at 3%. $1 compounded annually for 14 years at 3% = $1 compounded semi-annually for 7 years at 6%.

or

Use the present-worth-of-$1 table on page 136.

$$\$826.40 \div \$1,250 = .6611$$

$.6611 = the present worth of $1 invested for 14 years at 3% (if interest is compounded annually) or for 7 years at 6% (if interest is compounded semiannually).

Practice Drills

1. An investment account showed a balance of $2,174.25. How long will it take for this sum to grow to $2,500 if 2% interest, compounded quarterly, is earned?

2. A debt of $3,750 is due in 6 years. If interest is computed at 4%, compounded annually, what is the present worth of the debt?

ANSWERS 1. 7 years   2. $2,963.63

$\mathcal{D}$ o   **APPLICATION PROBLEMS**

1. Find the present worth and the true discount on each of the following debts.

	Amount of Debt	When Due	Value of Money	Present Worth	True Discount
a.	$1,200.00	60 days	6%	$	$
b.	890.00	4 months	6%		
c.	750.80	6 months	6%		
d.	3,095.00	90 days	4%		
e.	470.50	3 months	5%		
f.	650.90	6 months	3%		
g.	5,000.00	1 year	4%		
h.	960.00	9 months	3%		

2. If money is worth 5%, to how much will an investment of $3,725 amount in 135 days?

3. A fur coat can be purchased for $450 cash or for $525 on 9-month credit terms. If money is worth 5%, how much does the buyer gain by paying cash?

4. Find the present worth in each of the following. (Use the table on page 136 to find the present worth.)

	Amount of Debt	Due In	Rate of Interest	Compounded	Present Worth
a.	$ 680	10 years 2ᵖ	6% 3	Semiannually	$_____
b.	2,000	4 years	5%	Annually	_____
c.	500	6 years	4%	Annually	_____
d.	5,000	10 years	6%	Annually	_____
e.	7,500	15 years	4%	Annually	_____
f.	3,500	12 years 2⁴	4% 2	Semiannually	_____
g.	8,000	9 years 1⁹	6% 3	Semiannually	_____
h.	12,500	7 years /⁴	4% 2	Semiannually	_____

63 COMPUTING CARRYING CHARGES AND INTEREST RATES

The seller includes a carrying charge on the installment price to provide himself a return on the use of his money, to pay for the extra expense of collection and bookkeeping, and to provide for losses on payments.

Computing Carrying Charges

To compute the carrying charge on an installment sale, do the following.
1. Find the installment price by adding the sum of the installment payments to the down payment.
2. Subtract the cash price from the installment price.

Example

PROBLEM A television set may be purchased for $330 cash or on the installment plan for $72 down and $60 a month for 5 months. Find the amount by which the installment price exceeds the cash price.

SOLUTION Installment price:

Down payment	$ 72
Monthly payments (5 × $60)	+ 300
	$372
Cash price	− 330
Carrying charge	$ 42

Practice Drill

Jackson bought a motorcycle for $420 cash. He could have purchased it on the installment plan for $60 down and 24 monthly payments of $17.80 each. If he had purchased the motorcycle on the installment plan, what would the carrying charge be?

ANSWER $67.20

Computing Interest Rate

The amount by which the installment price exceeds the cash price may be considered as interest which the buyer is charged for the privilege of using the merchandise while he is paying for it. In effect, the buyer is borrowing money from the seller, and the difference between the cash price and the down payment represents the amount of the loan.

To compute the interest rate on an installment purchase, do the following.
1. Find the interest charge.
2. Apply the formula *Interest = Principal × Rate × Time* (in years).

Example

PROBLEM An oil burner is offered for $1,400 cash or on the installment plan for $320 down and 9 monthly payments of $140 each. Find the rate of interest paid by the buyer if he chooses the latter.

SOLUTION
Installment price:

Down payment	$ 320
Monthly payments (9 x $140)	+ 1,260
	$1,580
Cash price	– 1,400
Carrying charge	$ 180

It should be noted that the original price of the oil burner was $1,400. The buyer paid $320 down, owing a balance of $1,080. This amount that he has yet to pay ($1,080, original debt) is the principal of the debt. Since the debt must be paid off in 9 months, $120 ($1,080 ÷ 9) must be paid each month. Since $140 is actually paid each month, the remaining $20 of each monthly payment must be considered partial payment of the interest charge. On each of the nine $140 monthly payments, $120 is applied to the principal and $20 to the interest.

For computation purposes, the interest for 1 month, plus interest for 2 months, plus interest for 3 months, and so on, until 9 months, is the same as the interest for 45 months (1 + 2 + 3 + 4 + 5 + 6 + 7 + 8 + 9). Therefore, the interest amounting to $180 paid on $120 monthly payments for 9 months is equivalent to interest paid on $120 for a period of 45 months.

Computing the period during which interest was paid can be simplified by multiplying the last number (9) by the next consecutive number (10) and dividing the product (90) by 2. The quotient (45) is the same as the sum just found. This method of finding the total number of months, or interest period, can be applied in every situation.

Apply the interest formula.

Interest = Principal x *Rate* × *Time* (in years)

$$\$180 \ = \ \$120 \ \times \ R \ \times \ \frac{45^*}{12}$$

$$\$180 \ = \ \left(\$\overset{10}{\cancel{120}} \times \frac{45}{\cancel{12}} \right) \times \ R$$

$$\$180 \ = \ \$450 \times R$$

$$\$180 \ \div \ \$450 = R$$

.40, or 40% = *R* (rate of interest)

The interest formula may also be shown as follows.

$$Rate = \frac{Interest}{Principal \ x \ Time} \quad \text{or} \quad R = \frac{I}{P \ x \ T}$$

$$Rate = \frac{\$180}{\underset{\$\cancel{120} \ x \ \frac{45}{\cancel{12}}}{10}} = \frac{\$180}{\$450} = \frac{2}{5} = .40 = 40\%$$

Remember, the $140 monthly payment is not the monthly principal of the debt, since $140 includes partial payment of the debt plus the interest due for that month. The monthly principal is the quotient found by dividing the original debt by the number of monthly payments. The original debt is the amount the buyer still owes after he makes the down payment. *(Original debt = cash price — down payment.)*

The method just explained for finding the rate of interest is easy but time consuming. A speedier method of computing the interest rate is to apply the following formula.

$$Rate = \frac{24 \ x \ C}{P \ x \ (n + 1)}$$

C = installment charge
P = principal of original debt
n = number of installments

In this problem, *C* = $180, *P* = $1,080, and *n* = 9.

$$R = \frac{\overset{2}{\cancel{24}} \times \$\cancel{180}}{\$\underset{6}{\cancel{1,080}} \times \underset{5}{\cancel{10}^{**}}} = \frac{2}{5} = .40 = 40\%$$

This formula can be applied only if the installments are always the same amount and the installment payments are made at regular intervals. The constant in this formula (24, or 12 × 2, for monthly intervals) can be replaced with 104 (or 52 × 2) for weekly intervals and 8 (or 4 × 2) for quarterly intervals.

---

* 45 months must be changed to $\frac{45}{12}$ of a year.

** This is the number of installments plus 1.

Practice Drill | A homeowner can buy a rug for $180 cash or "on time" for $18 down and $15 a month for 12 months. What rate of interest is charged on the installment purchase?

ANSWER 20.5+%

APPLICATION PROBLEMS

1. Find the carrying charge on each of the following installment purchases.

Article	Down Payment	No. of Pay-ments	Amount of Each Payment	Installment Price	Cash Price	Carrying Charge
a. Transistor radio	$16.00	6	$ 8.00	$_____	$ 60.00	$_____
b. Record player	15.00	7	12.00	_____	94.00	_____
c. Vacuum cleaner	32.50	8	9.25	_____	96.50	_____
d. Tape recorder	29.50	15	8.50	_____	149.50	_____
e. Typewriter	27.00	10	12.42	_____	135.00	_____
f. Television set	36.00	12	13.80	_____	180.00	_____
g. Refrigerator	72.00	18	10.15	_____	215.00	_____

2. Harold Miller bought a dining-room suite for $349.50 cash. The suite could also be purchased on the installment plan for $34.95 down and 30 monthly payments of $11.65 each. What would the carrying charge be if the suite were purchased on the installment plan?

3. A sound movie projector can be purchased for $675 cash or $135 down and 18 monthly payments of $35 each. If the projector is purchased on the deferred-payment plan, what carrying charge will the buyer pay?

4. An electric mixer can be purchased for $32 cash or on the installment plan for $6 a month for 6 months with no down payment. Find the rate of interest paid by an installment buyer. Check your answer by using the formula

$$\frac{24 \times C}{P \times (n + 1)}$$

5. Find the rate of interest that a buyer will have to pay on each of the following installment purchases. Compute the rate of interest to the nearest tenth of a percent.

Article	Down Pay-ment	No. of Pay-ments	Monthly Pay-ment	Install-ment Price	Cash Price	Interest (Carrying Charge)	Total Period (in Months)	Rate of Interest (%)
a. Fur coat	$150	14	$60	$_____	$930	$_____	_____	_____
b. Drier	15	18	15	_____	225	_____	_____	_____
c. Chest	90	8	45	_____	390	_____	_____	_____
d. Desk	90	7	45	_____	360	_____	_____	_____
e. Piano	150	12	75	_____	900	_____	_____	_____
f. Radio	20	16	8	_____	132	_____	_____	_____
g. Washer	40	4	80	_____	314	_____	_____	_____
h. Ring	42	12	24	_____	300	_____	_____	_____
i. Clock	10	8	8	_____	66	_____	_____	_____
j. Camera	21	12	12	_____	150	_____	_____	_____

64 COMPUTING PAYMENTS BASED ON A FIXED RATE OF INTEREST

When a car is sold on credit, a down payment is usually required and a fixed rate of interest is charged on the balance. Thus, if a $2,400 car is sold for $\frac{1}{3}$ down and the balance payable in equal monthly installments over a period of 18 months with interest at 6%, the monthly payments are determined as follows.

Examples

Cost of car	$2,400
Down payment	− 800
Balance due	$1,600
Interest on $1,600 at 6% for 18 months	+ 144
Amount due	$1,744

$1,744 ÷ 18 = $96.89, monthly payment for 18 months

On the basis of these computations, is it correct to say that the rate of interest charged is 6%? The answer is "No" for the following reason: The $144 represents the interest on $1,600 for the entire period of 18 months. However, after the first monthly payment is made, only $1,503.11 ($1,600 − $96.89) is owed. After the second payment is made, only $1,406.22 ($1,503.11 − $96.89) is owed. Each month the balance is reduced by $96.89, but the interest payment is still based on the original $1,600. At no time after the first month was $1,600 the true principal. What, then, is the actual rate of interest that is being charged? To determine the actual rate either one of the formulas on the following page may be used.

$$Rate = \frac{Interest}{Principal \times Time}$$

$$Rate = \frac{144}{\left(\begin{array}{cc} 200 \\ \cancel{400} & 19 \\ \cancel{1,600} \times \cancel{171} \\ \cancel{18} & \cancel{12} \\ \cancel{9} & 3 \end{array}\right)} = \frac{144}{\dfrac{3,800}{3}}$$

$$Rate = \frac{144}{1} \times \frac{3}{3,800} = \frac{432}{3,800} = .1136, \text{ or } 11.4\%$$

or

$$R = \frac{24 \times C}{P \times (n + 1)}$$

$$R = \frac{24 \times \$144}{\$1,600 \times 19} = \frac{3,456}{30,400} = .1136, \text{ or } 11.4\%$$

Thus, 11.4%, not 6%, is the rate of interest actually charged. Leaving the actual monthly principal in its traditional form as shown often makes it easier to compute the interest rate.

PROBLEM   A college student bought a used car for $680 on the following terms: $80 down and the balance, $600, to be paid over a 12-month period at 5% interest. Find the amount of his monthly payments and the rate of interest.

SOLUTION

5% of $600 = $30, interest
$600 + $30 = $630, total debt
$630 ÷ 12 = $52.50, monthly payment

$600 ÷ 12 = $50.00, monthly principal
Period for which monthly principal was borrowed:
$$1 + 2 + 3 \ldots + 12 = 78 \text{ months}$$

or

$$\frac{12 \times 13}{2} = \frac{156}{2} = 78 \text{ months}$$

$$R = \frac{I}{P \times T} = \frac{\$30}{\dfrac{\cancel{25}}{\cancel{\$50}} \times \dfrac{\cancel{13}}{\cancel{78}}} = \frac{\$30}{\$325} = .092, \text{ or } 9.2\%,$$

rate of interest

or

$$I = P \times R \times T$$
$$\$30 = \$50 \quad \times R \times \frac{78}{12}$$
$$\$30 = \$325 \times R$$
$$\$30 \div \$325 = R$$
$$.092, \text{ or } 9.2\% = R, \text{ rate of interest}$$

or

$$\frac{24 \times C}{P \times (n + 1)} = \frac{24 \times \$30}{\cancel{\$600} \times 13} = \frac{6}{65} = .092, \text{ or } 9.2\%, \text{ rate of interest}$$

with $\frac{\cancel{24}}{\cancel{\$600}}\,^{6}_{20}\,^{}_{5}$ reductions shown.

Practice Drills

A new car was financed by an auto loan company by means of a $2,400 loan, payable in equal monthly installments over a 30-month period at $7\frac{1}{2}\%$.

1. What was the amount of each monthly payment?
2. What was the actual rate of interest paid?

ANSWERS 1. $95   2. 14.5%

APPLICATION PROBLEMS

1. Find the amount of the monthly payment and the rate of interest on each of the following automobile loans. Compute the rate of interest to the nearest tenth of a percent.

	Cost	Down Pay-ment	No. of Pay-ments	Interest Rate Quoted	Interest Carrying Charge	Monthly Payment	Monthly Principal	Time (in Mos.)	Rate of Interest (%)
a.	$3,000	$600	12	6%	$_____	$_____	$_____	_____	_____
b.	1,500	500	18	4%	_____	_____	_____	_____	_____
c.	3,200	800	30	5%	_____	_____	_____	_____	_____
d.	3,600	600	18	6%	_____	_____	_____	_____	_____
e.	1,325	325	24	5%	_____	_____	_____	_____	_____
f.	2,500	500	20	5%	_____	_____	_____	_____	_____

2. An auto loan company offers to finance the purchase of a car by granting a $2,100 loan payable monthly over a 2-year period at a $7\frac{1}{2}\%$ interest rate. A bank offers to arrange a similar loan for the same period at the same rate of interest, payable on the decreasing balance. Which is the better loan for the borrower? How much better?

3. Hilton received from his bank an $1,800 automobile loan at $6\frac{1}{2}\%$ interest. The debt was to be paid in equal monthly installments over a 15-month period. What rate of interest was Hilton actually paying?

65 INTEREST ON UNPAID MONTHLY BALANCES AND PAST-DUE ACCOUNTS

When merchandise is sold on the deferred-payment plan, payable in monthly installments, it is a common practice for the seller to collect interest on the unpaid balance when each installment is collected.

Interest on Unpaid Monthly Balances

Interest on unpaid monthly balances is computed by the banker's 60-day method; the time is based on a 30-day month and a 360-day year.

PROBLEM   On October 1, a tape recorder was purchased for $280. The terms were $40 in cash and the balance in monthly payments of $60 each, with interest at 6%. The interest was to be paid on the balance due at the time each installment was made. Find the amount of each monthly installment, including interest.

SOLUTION $280 (purchase price) − $40 (cash payment) = $240, balance due in 4 monthly installments of $60 each, plus interest on the unpaid monthly balances

Date of Installment Payments	Unpaid Balance	Interest for Month	Amount Due	Installment Paid	Balance Due
Nov. 1	$240	$1.20	$241.20	$61.20	$180
Dec. 1	180	.90	180.90	60.90	120
Jan. 1	120	.60	120.60	60.60	60
Feb. 1	60	.30	60.30	60.30	. . .

Practice Drill

On September 1, Hargrove bought an electric typewriter for $585 on the following terms: $75 in cash, and the balance in monthly installments of $85 each, with interest at 5% on the unpaid balance. Each installment, plus the interest, was paid on the first day of each month. Find the amounts of the first and the sixth payments, including interest.

ANSWERS   first payment, $85 + $2.13 (interest) = $87.13;
sixth payment, $85 + $.35 (interest) = $85.35

Interest on Past-Due Accounts

When a customer owes an overdue balance for merchandise or services he has obtained, he may be charged interest on the unpaid balance. It is customary to add to the sum of the "on account" sales the interest on all past-due amounts from the due date to the date on which the entire account is paid. From this total is deducted the interest on each cash payment received on account from the date of such payment to the date of settlement to find the amount necessary to pay the account in full.

The interest is computed by the banker's 60-day method, and the time by the exact-time method.

A record of the transactions with each customer is kept in the ledger in a form similar to that shown in the following example.

Example

PROBLEM The account of Fred M. Roberts appears as follows in the records of Smithtown, Inc. Roberts wants to pay his account in full on August 8. Find the balance due on that date if interest at 6% is computed on the past-due invoices and is added to the account, and interest on the payments made on account is deducted from the amount due.

Name *Fred M. Roberts*
Address *8614 Memorial Drive, Fort Lee, New Jersey*

DATE	EXPLANATION	POST. REF.	DEBIT	CREDIT	BALANCE
19 Mar. 28	*Inv. 36B7102; terms, 60 days*	*S1*	901 40		901 40
Jun. 1	*Cash*	*CR1*		200 00	701 40
5	*Inv. 78K3610; terms, 30 days*	*S2*	350 00		1 051 40
15	*Cash*	*CR1*		300 00	751 40

SOLUTION Payment for the March 28 sale is due in 60 days, or May 27. The exact time from May 27 to August 8, date of settlement, is 73 days. The banker's interest on $901.40 for 73 days at 6% is $10.97. The interest on $350 for 34 days (July 5 to August 8) at 6% is $1.98.

The interest on the $200 payment from June 1 to August 8, 68 days, at 6% is $2.27. The interest on the $300 payment for 54 days at 6% is $2.70.

$$\$901.40 + \$350 + \$10.97 + \$1.98 = \$1{,}264.35$$
$$\$200.00 + \$300 + \$\ 2.27 + \$2.70 = \underline{504.97}$$
$$\text{Balance due on August 8} = \$\ \ \ 759.38$$

Practice Drill

The account of Irving Pasteur appeared as follows on the ledger of Rialto Furnishers, Inc. On July 5, Pasteur closed out his account by paying the balance due. How much did he owe on this date if interest at 5% was charged on past-due invoices and credited on payments made on account?

Name *Irving Pasteur*					
Address *73 Main Street, Egerton, Pennsylvania*					

DATE	EXPLANATION	POST. REF.	DEBIT	CREDIT	BALANCE
Feb. 27	*Invoice 136041; terms, 30 days*	*S2*	480 00		480 00
Mar. 8	*Invoice 201862; terms, 60 days*	*S2*	720 00		1200 00
12	*Cash*	*CR1*		250 00	950 00
Apr. 16	*Invoice 416207; terms, 60 days*	*S3*	690 00		1640 00
May 31	*Cash*	*CR2*		500 00	1140 00

ANSWER $1,147.93

APPLICATION PROBLEMS

1. Find the total amount paid on each of the following installment purchases, including interest at 6% on the unpaid balance.

	Date of Purchase	Purchase Price	Cash Down Payment	Monthly Payments	No. of Payments	Total Interest Paid	Payments Plus Interest
a.	June 1	$750	$150	$150	_____	$_____	$_____
b.	Mar. 1	550	150	100	_____	_____	_____
c.	Nov. 1	360	60	60	_____	_____	_____
d.	Apr. 1	270	45	75	_____	_____	_____
e.	Aug. 1	750	150	120	_____	_____	_____

2. The Liberty Sporting Goods Shop sold an outboard motor on August 1 for $375 on the following terms: $75 in cash, and the balance in monthly installments of $60 each, with interest at 6%. The interest was payable on the balance due at the time each installment was made. What was the amount of each installment? Submit your solution on a form similar to the one on page 146.

3. Find the amount due on the settlement of Michael Allan's account if interest is charged on past-due invoices and credited on payments made on account. The date of settlement is November 1; the interest rate, 6%.

		Accts. Rec/Michael Allan					Account No. *111*	
DATE	EXPLANATION	POST. REF.	DEBIT	DATE	EXPLANATION	POST. REF.	CREDIT	
Aug. 5	*60 days*	*S3*	570 00	*Aug. 20*	*Cash*	*CR2*	150 00	
Sept. 8	*30 days*	*S4*	700 00	*Sept. 1*	*Cash*	*CR3*	400 00	

INTEREST ON SMALL LOANS

Many small-loan agencies are in the business of lending small amounts of money to individuals and small businesses on little or no security at the rate of interest fixed by law. Loans up to $1,500 are considered small loans in many areas.

These small-loan agencies make it easy to obtain a loan (often they are the only sources a high-risk individual can turn to for needed cash). Thus, they take great risks and, accordingly, charge high interest rates on money lent. The rate of interest these agencies are permitted to charge and the regulations by which they must operate are governed by law in most states.

Small-loan agencies are subject to much public criticism because of their high interest rates; yet they obviously perform a vital service or they would not stay in business. As a consumer and future business employee, you should be aware of the way in which interest is computed on small loans.

Example | **PROBLEM** The Finance Corporation offers loans at the rates below.

Amount of Loan	Monthly Payments		
	15 Months	18 Months	20 Months
$100	$ 8.08	$ 6.97	$ 6.41
$200	16.15	13.93	12.83
$300	24.23	20.90	19.24
$500	39.26	33.69	30.92

A $100 loan is to be repaid in 15 monthly payments. Find the interest cost of the loan and the rate of interest on the decreasing balance.

SOLUTION According to the loan-rate table given, the monthly payments for the $100 loan over the 15-month period will be $8.08 each.

15 × $8.08 = $121.20, amount returned to loan company over entire period

$121.20 — $100 (amount borrowed) = $21.20, interest, or cost of loan

Monthly principal = original debt ÷ number of payments

$$= \$100 \div 15, \text{ or } \frac{\$100}{15}$$

Total period for which the monthly principal was borrowed =

$$1 + 2 + 3 \ldots + 14 + 15$$

or

$$\frac{15 \times 16}{2} \text{ (short method)} = \frac{240}{2} = 120 \text{ months}$$

$$I = P \times R \times T$$

$$\$21.20 = \frac{100}{\cancel{15}_{3}} \times R \times \frac{\cancel{120}^{\cancel{10}^{2}}}{\cancel{12}}$$

$$\$21.20 = \frac{200}{3} \times R$$

$$\$21.20 \div \frac{200}{3} = R$$

$$.318, \text{ or } 31.8\% = R \text{ (rate of interest)}$$

or

$$R = \frac{24 \times C}{P \times (n + 1)}$$

$$C = \$21.20 \qquad P = \$100 \qquad n = 15$$

$$R = \frac{\overset{3}{\cancel{24}} \times \overset{1.06}{\cancel{\$21.20}}}{\underset{5}{\cancel{\$100}} \times \underset{2}{\cancel{16}}} = \frac{3.18}{10} = .318 = 31.8\%$$

Practice Drills

Find the amount of interest and the actual yearly rate of interest charged on the decreasing balance on each of the following loans. (Use the loan-rate table given in the problem on page 149.)

1. $500 loan, to be repaid in 20 months
2. $200 loan, to be repaid in 18 months
3. $300 loan, to be repaid in 15 months

ANSWERS 1. interest, $118.40; interest rate, 27.04%   2. interest, $50.74; interest rate, 32+%   3. interest, $63.45; interest rate, 31.7+%

APPLICATION PROBLEMS

Using the loan-rate table given in the problem on page 149, find the amount of interest and the actual yearly rate of interest charged on the decreasing balance of each of the following loans. Compute the rate of interest to the nearest tenth of a percent.

1. $300 loan, to be repaid in 20 months
2. $100 loan, to be repaid in 20 months
3. $200 loan, to be repaid in 18 months
4. $500 loan, to be repaid in 20 months
5. $200 loan, to be repaid in 15 months

PROBLEMS FOR PART EIGHT

Compound Interest, Present Worth & Installment Interest

1. Milton Murdock deposited $2,400 in a mutual savings company. If the earnings of the company warranted a 6% annual dividend, and if the dividends were compounded annually, how much compound interest did Murdock receive at the end of 4 years if he permitted the earnings to accumulate?

2. The sum of $25,000 was invested for a period of 10 years at 4% interest, compounded annually. To how much did the investment amount at the end of this time? How much more was earned in the 10-year period with compound interest than would have been earned with simple interest?

3. The employment contract of Millicent Askanazi, managing editor of a women's magazine, provided for a beginning yearly salary of $17,500, with annual increases of 5%. What was Millicent's salary the third year?

4. The sales of Can Do Corporation increased on an average of $4\frac{1}{2}$% a year over a 4-year period. If the sales the first year totaled $286,000, what were the total sales the fifth year?

5. Farrington deposited $2,850 in the Suburbia Savings Bank. The bank pays 4% interest, compounded semiannually. If no other deposits or withdrawals are made, what will be the compound interest and compound amount in Farrington's account after 10 years?

6. Using the compound-interest table on page 132, find the compound amount and the compound interest in each of the following.

	Principal	Interest Rate	Time	Compounded	Compound Interest	Compound Amount
a.	$608	3%	5 years	Semiannually	$_____	$_____
b.	784	6%	4 years	Quarterly	_____	_____
c.	965	6%	2 years	Quarterly	_____	_____
d.	722	8%	3 years	Quarterly	_____	_____

1. What sum of money invested at 6% interest will amount to $4,000 in 6 months?

2. What is the difference between the simple interest and the true discount on $3,600 for 1 year at 4%?

3. S. C. Marlin owes Barksdale Wholesalers $7,200, which must be paid in 90 days. How much invested today at 6% interest will amount to a sum sufficient to pay Marlin's debt when due?

4. An invoice amounting to $1,089.75 was due in 90 days. In payment, the purchaser gave his 90-day, 6% note for an amount that at maturity will equal the amount of the invoice. Find the face value of the note.

5. March Sales, Inc. owes Brainerd Corporation $840, which is due in 4 months. Brainerd Corporation offers a 10% discount if payment is made immediately. In order to obtain the money with which to take advantage of this discount, March Sales discounts its note at 6% at the bank. Find the face value of the note. How much does March Sales gain as a result of this transaction?

1. The Avis Company can purchase an electric typewriter for $520 cash or $104 down and 12 equal monthly installments of $39.25 each. By what percent will the installment price exceed the cash price? Compute the answer to the nearest tenth of a percent.

2. The Country Shop of Swan Lake air-conditioned its store. The cost was $2,460 cash or 15% down, with the balance to be paid off in 24 equal monthly installments. The store was charged 6% interest on the balance due plus an additional carrying charge of $48. How large were the monthly payments?

3. A washer-dryer combination can be purchased for $345 cash or on the installment plan for an additional 12%. A purchaser made a down payment of $75 and agreed to pay $15.57 each month. For how many months will he have to pay for this purchase?

4. You can buy a power lawn mower at the advertised price of $72.60 cash, or on the installment plan for $15 down and $10.81 a month for 6 months. If you buy the mower on the installment plan, what rate of interest will you be paying?

5. The cash price of a tape recorder is $192, less 15%. It can be bought on the partial payment plan at $16 a month for 12 months. What is the rate of interest on the installment plan?

1. Fred Rose bought an outboard motor for $310, paying $60 down and agreeing to pay the balance with interest at 6% in 10 equal monthly payments. Find the interest charge and the amount of each monthly payment.

2. A used car is advertised for $900. A $100 down payment is required. The balance is due in 20 equal payments with a 5% carrying charge. Find the actual rate of interest that the buyer would have to pay.

3. Stengel traded in his car for a current model listed at $3,875. The dealer accepted the trade-in as a down payment, allowing Stengel $1,500 for the used car. The monthly payments were spread over a 2-year period at $4\frac{1}{2}\%$ interest. How large were the monthly payments? What rate of interest was Stengel paying?

1. Find the total interest paid on each of the following installment purchases, including interest at 6% on the unpaid balance.

Date of Purchase	Purchase Price	Cash Down Payment	Monthly Payment	No. of Payments	Total Interest Paid	Payments Plus Interest
a. Feb. 1	$875	$ 75	$50			
b. Dec. 1	90	15	25			
c. Aug. 1	435	75	60			
d. July 1	500	100	80			
e. March 1	420	70	70			
f. April 1	375	75	50			

2. On December 1, Roger Donovan purchased an electric billing machine for $1,305. He paid $405 in cash and the balance in 4 equal monthly installments of $225 each, with interest at 6% on the unpaid balance. Compute the interest due with each payment. Submit your solution on a form similar to the one on page 146.

3. Find the amount due on the settlement of Eric Joel's account if interest is charged on past-due invoices and credited on payments made on account. The date of settlement is April 12; the interest rate, 5%.

\multicolumn{8}{c}{*Accts. Rec./ Eric Joel*   Account No. *114*}
DATE	EXPLANATION	POST. REF.	DEBIT	DATE	EXPLANATION	POST. REF.	CREDIT
19— Nov. 15	60 days	S5	381 00	19— Feb. 28	Cash	CR6	420 00
19— Jan. 20	30 days	S7	425 50	Mar. 10	Cash	CR6	340 00
Feb. 11	60 days	S7	741 60				

Using the loan-rate table in the problem on page 149, find the amount of interest and the actual yearly rate of interest charged on the decreasing balance of each of the following loans. Compute the rate of interest to the nearest tenth of a percent.

1. $500 loan, to be repaid in 15 months
2. $100 loan, to be repaid in 18 months
3. $300 loan, to be repaid in 15 months
4. $200 loan, to be repaid in 20 months
5. $500 loan, to be repaid in 18 months

PART NINE
Wage & Salary Administration

No mathematical computations performed in business are more important than those involving the wages and salaries of employees. Those who work with payrolls must not only be skillful in working with numbers, they must also know the various federal, state, and local laws governing minimum wages, overtime rates, and deductions for income tax and FICA (social security). In addition, they must know the firm's policies concerning employee benefits (such as insurance) for which deductions may be made from earnings. Most large firms have automated their payroll system, using computers for computations and issuing checks and payroll information. Thousands of small organizations, however, continue to use the "hand" method in payroll computations.

The compensation plans in use today include the following.

Straight-salary plan   Under the straight-salary plan, workers are paid a fixed amount each pay period. The salary is usually stated as a weekly, monthly, or annual amount, although most people are paid twice a month.

Hourly-rate plan   Millions of employees come under an hourly-rate plan, where they are paid an agreed amount per hour for a definite number of hours. Most factory workers are paid on such a plan.

Piece-rate plan   Under the piece-rate plan, the employee is paid a given amount for each "piece" that he produces. The piece-rate plan is a form of incentive compensation; an employee can greatly increase his earnings by producing more. There are several variations of this plan.

Bonus and premium-wage plan   This plan of compensation guarantees a minimum wage to the employee plus incentive pay based on the number of units produced over the quota set for him. Another form of this plan guarantees the employee a minimum wage plus a share of any time he saves.

Commission plan   Another incentive compensation plan is the commission plan, which applies primarily to sales personnel. A commission is usually computed as a percentage of the total value of the goods sold. Some salesmen are on commission entirely; others are paid a salary plus commission.

Profit-sharing plan   Many employees, particularly executives, are paid a regular salary plus a portion of the profits earned by the company. This method of compensation is becoming more and more popular as a way of rewarding employees for outstanding performance.

67 PAYROLL DEDUCTIONS

Regardless of the type of compensation plan, certain deductions are required to be taken by the employer from each employee's total (*gross*) earnings. These deductions include federal income tax, FICA (social security) tax, and, in some cases, city and state income taxes and unemployment tax. Other deductions may be made for hospitalization and life insurance, retirement, union dues, stock purchases, and so on.

Federal Income Tax

The income tax withheld from each employee's earnings is paid by the employer to the federal government. The amount withheld depends upon how much the employee earns and upon the number of exemptions he claims. In general, an employee is allowed 1 exemption for himself, 1 for his wife (unless she is employed and claims herself as an exemption), and 1 for each dependent (children, dependent relatives, *et al.*).

The federal income tax to be withheld from the earnings of an employee is found by using withholding tables provided by the Internal Revenue Service. Because the salaries of employees cover weekly, biweekly, semimonthly, and monthly periods of time, the government has prepared tables to cover each method of payment. Parts of the weekly federal income tax tables are shown on pages 159 and 160.

Example | **PROBLEM** Using the weekly federal income tax tables, find how much income tax is deducted from Jay King's weekly salary of $115.80 if he is single and claims himself as his only exemption.

SOLUTION Use the table for single persons. Follow down the columns headed by the words ''At least'' and ''But less than'' until you find two numbers, one less than $115.80 and one more. These will be 115 and 120. Follow across this row until you reach the column headed by the number 1. The amount, $15.70, is the federal income tax to be withheld.

Practice | Using the weekly federal income tax tables, find the tax to be deducted
Drills | weekly from the earnings of the following employees.

Employee	Status	Earnings	Exemptions	Tax
1. J. Stein	Single	$165.80	1	_____
2. H. Turin	Married	$143.95	3	_____
3. B. Wold	Single	$181.10	2	_____
4. A. Young	Married	$126.63	4	_____

ANSWERS 1. $24.70   2. $13.50   3. $26.30   4. $9.10

Social Security

Most employees, as well as employers, must contribute through a separate tax to the federal social security fund established by the Federal Insurance Contributions Act (FICA). The FICA (social security) tax on the employee's salary is computed on his gross earnings for the pay period and is deducted from his pay. The tax is levied on a maximum taxable income in any one year. As soon as an employee has earned the maximum (for example, $10,800) his employer stops making deductions from his salary for this tax.

As the federal government increases social security benefits, it also increases the rate at which deductions are computed and the maximum taxable income on which these deductions may be computed. The federal government provides employers with a table for determining the social security taxes to be withheld. A portion of such a table is shown on pages 158-159.

Example

PROBLEM   Find the tax on a weekly salary of $157.75, using the social security tax table.

SOLUTION   Follow down the Wages columns headed by the words "At least" and "But less than" until you come to $157.60 and $157.79. $157.75 falls between $157.60 and $157.79, so move right to the Tax to be Withheld column. The social security tax to be withheld is $8.20.

Practice Drills

Using the social security tax table, find the tax on the following salaries.

1. $170.30	3. $158.15	5. $195.70	7. $185
2. $162.40	4. $171.50	6. $199.60	8. $187.44

ANSWERS   1. $8.76   2. $8.44   3. $8.22   4. $8.92   5. $10.18
          6. $10.38   7. $9.62   8. $9.75

APPLICATION PROBLEMS

1. Using the weekly federal income tax tables on pages 159-160, find the tax to be deducted from the weekly earnings of these employees.

Employee	Status	Earnings	Exemptions	Tax
a. Aline Hosbach	Single	$212.50	1	_____
b. Ray Preston	Married	$300.25	3	_____
c. Richard Goodwin	Single	$197.60	2	_____
d. Helen Brown	Single	$218.50	1	_____

2. Using the social security tax table on pages 158-159, find the tax on the following salaries.

a. $160.60	c. $183.00	e. $172.80
b. $195.90	d. $150.00	f. $188.75

Social Security Employee Tax Table

5.2 percent employee tax deductions

Wages		Tax to be withheld	Wages		Tax to be withheld	Wages		Tax to be withheld	Wages		Tax to be withheld
At least	But less than		At least	But less than		At least	But less than		At least	But less than	
$149.91	$150.10	$7.80	$162.41	$162.60	$8.45	$174.91	$175.10	$9.10	$187.41	$187.60	$9.75
150.10	150.29	7.81	162.60	162.79	8.46	175.10	175.29	9.11	187.60	187.79	9.76
150.29	150.49	7.82	162.79	162.99	8.47	175.29	175.49	9.12	187.79	187.99	9.77
150.49	150.68	7.83	162.99	163.18	8.48	175.49	175.68	9.13	187.99	188.18	9.78
150.68	150.87	7.84	163.18	163.37	8.49	175.68	175.87	9.14	188.18	188.37	9.79
150.87	151.06	7.85	163.37	163.56	8.50	175.87	176.06	9.15	188.37	188.56	9.80
151.06	151.25	7.86	163.56	163.75	8.51	176.06	176.25	9.16	188.56	188.75	9.81
151.25	151.45	7.87	163.75	163.95	8.52	176.25	176.45	9.17	188.75	188.95	9.82
151.45	151.64	7.88	163.95	164.14	8.53	176.45	176.64	9.18	188.95	189.14	9.83
151.64	151.83	7.89	164.14	164.33	8.54	176.64	176.83	9.19	189.14	189.33	9.84
157.60	157.79	8.20	170.10	170.29	8.85	182.60	182.79	9.50	195.10	195.29	10.15
157.79	157.99	8.21	170.29	170.49	8.86	182.79	182.99	9.51	195.29	195.49	10.16
157.99	158.18	8.22	170.49	170.68	8.87	182.99	183.18	9.52	195.49	195.68	10.17
158.18	158.37	8.23	170.68	170.87	8.88	183.18	183.37	9.53	195.68	195.87	10.18
158.37	158.56	8.24	170.87	171.06	8.89	183.37	183.56	9.54	195.87	196.06	10.19
158.56	158.75	8.25	171.06	171.25	8.90	183.56	183.75	9.55	196.06	196.25	10.20
158.75	158.95	8.26	171.25	171.45	8.91	183.75	183.95	9.56	196.25	196.45	10.21
158.95	159.14	8.27	171.45	171.64	8.92	183.95	184.14	9.57	196.45	196.64	10.22
159.14	159.33	8.28	171.64	171.83	8.93	184.14	184.33	9.58	196.64	196.83	10.23
159.33	159.52	8.29	171.83	172.02	8.94	184.33	184.52	9.59	196.83	197.02	10.24
159.52	159.72	8.30	172.02	172.22	8.95	184.52	184.72	9.60	197.02	197.22	10.25
159.72	159.91	8.31	172.22	172.41	8.96	184.72	184.91	9.61	197.22	197.41	10.26
159.91	160.10	8.32	172.41	172.60	8.97	184.91	185.10	9.62	197.41	197.60	10.27
160.10	160.29	8.33	172.60	172.79	8.98	185.10	185.29	9.63	197.60	197.79	10.28
160.29	160.49	8.34	172.79	172.99	8.99	185.29	185.49	9.64	197.79	197.99	10.29
160.49	160.68	8.35	172.99	173.18	9.00	185.49	185.68	9.65	197.99	198.18	10.30
160.68	160.87	8.36	173.18	173.37	9.01	185.68	185.87	9.66	198.18	198.37	10.31
160.87	161.06	8.37	173.37	173.56	9.02	185.87	186.06	9.67	198.37	198.56	10.32
161.06	161.25	8.38	173.56	173.75	9.03	186.06	186.25	9.68	198.56	198.75	10.33
161.25	161.45	8.39	173.75	173.95	9.04	186.25	186.45	9.69	198.75	198.95	10.34
161.45	161.64	8.40	173.95	174.14	9.05	186.45	186.64	9.70	198.95	199.14	10.35
161.64	161.83	8.41	174.14	174.33	9.06	186.64	186.83	9.71	199.14	199.33	10.36
161.83	162.02	8.42	174.33	174.52	9.07	186.83	187.02	9.72	199.33	199.52	10.37
162.02	162.22	8.43	174.52	174.72	9.08	187.02	187.22	9.73	199.52	199.72	10.38
162.22	162.41	8.44	174.72	174.91	9.09	187.22	187.41	9.74	199.72	199.91	10.39
200.87	201.06	10.45	213.37	213.56	11.10	225.87	226.06	11.75	238.37	238.56	12.40
201.06	201.25	10.46	213.56	213.75	11.11	226.06	226.25	11.76	238.56	238.75	12.41
201.25	201.45	10.47	213.75	213.95	11.12	226.25	226.45	11.77	238.75	238.95	12.42
201.45	201.64	10.48	213.95	214.14	11.13	226.45	226.64	11.78	238.95	239.14	12.43
201.64	201.83	10.49	214.14	214.33	11.14	226.64	226.83	11.79	239.14	239.33	12.44
201.83	202.02	10.50	214.33	214.52	11.15	226.83	227.02	11.80	239.33	239.52	12.45
202.02	202.22	10.51	214.52	214.72	11.16	227.02	227.22	11.81	239.52	239.72	12.46
202.22	202.41	10.52	214.72	214.91	11.17	227.22	227.41	11.82	239.72	239.91	12.47
202.41	202.60	10.53	214.91	215.10	11.18	227.41	227.60	11.83	239.91	240.10	12.48
202.60	202.79	10.54	215.10	215.29	11.19	227.60	227.79	11.84	240.10	240.29	12.49
202.79	202.99	10.55	215.29	215.49	11.20	227.79	227.99	11.85	240.29	240.49	12.50
202.99	203.18	10.56	215.49	215.68	11.21	227.99	228.18	11.86	240.49	240.68	12.51
203.18	203.37	10.57	215.68	215.87	11.22	228.18	228.37	11.87	240.68	240.87	12.52
203.37	203.56	10.58	215.87	216.06	11.23	228.37	228.56	11.88	240.87	241.06	12.53
203.56	203.75	10.59	216.06	216.25	11.24	228.56	228.75	11.89	241.06	241.25	12.54
203.75	203.95	10.60	216.25	216.45	11.25	228.75	228.95	11.90	241.25	241.45	12.55
203.95	204.14	10.61	216.45	216.64	11.26	228.95	229.14	11.91	241.45	241.64	12.56
204.14	204.33	10.62	216.64	216.83	11.27	229.14	229.33	11.92	241.64	241.83	12.57
204.33	204.52	10.63	216.83	217.02	11.28	229.33	229.52	11.93	241.83	242.02	12.58
204.52	204.72	10.64	217.02	217.22	11.29	229.52	229.72	11.94	242.02	242.22	12.59
208.56	208.75	10.85	221.06	221.25	11.50	233.56	233.75	12.15	246.06	246.25	12.80
208.75	208.95	10.86	221.25	221.45	11.51	233.75	233.95	12.16	246.25	246.45	12.81
208.95	209.14	10.87	221.45	221.64	11.52	233.95	234.14	12.17	246.45	246.64	12.82
209.14	209.33	10.88	221.64	221.83	11.53	234.14	234.33	12.18	246.64	246.83	12.83
209.33	209.52	10.89	221.83	222.02	11.54	234.33	234.52	12.19	246.83	247.02	12.84
209.52	209.72	10.90	222.02	222.22	11.55	234.52	234.72	12.20	247.02	247.22	12.85
209.72	209.91	10.91	222.22	222.41	11.56	234.72	234.91	12.21	247.22	247.41	12.86
209.91	210.10	10.92	222.41	222.60	11.57	234.91	235.10	12.22	247.41	247.60	12.87
210.10	210.29	10.93	222.60	222.79	11.58	235.10	235.29	12.23	247.60	247.79	12.88
210.29	210.49	10.94	222.79	222.99	11.59	235.29	235.49	12.24	247.79	247.99	12.89

Continued on the following page

Wages		Tax to be withheld	Wages		Tax to be withheld	Wages		Tax to be withheld	Wages		Tax to be withheld
At least	But less than		At least	But less than		At least	But less than		At least	But less than	
211.45	211.64	$11.00	223.95	$224.14	11.65	$236.45	236.64	12.30	248.95	249.14	12.95
211.64	211.83	11.01	224.14	224.33	11.66	236.64	236.83	12.31	249.14	249.33	12.96
211.83	212.02	11.02	224.33	224.52	11.67	236.83	237.02	12.32	249.33	249.52	12.97
212.02	212.22	11.03	224.52	224.72	11.68	237.02	237.22	12.33	249.52	249.72	12.98
212.22	212.41	11.04	224.72	224.91	11.69	237.22	237.41	12.34	249.72	249.91	12.99
250.87	251.06	13.05	263.37	263.56	13.70	275.87	276.06	14.35	288.37	288.56	15.00
251.06	251.25	13.06	263.56	263.75	13.71	276.06	276.25	14.36	288.56	288.75	15.01
251.25	251.45	13.07	263.75	263.95	13.72	276.25	276.45	14.37	288.75	288.95	15.02
251.45	251.64	13.08	263.95	264.14	13.73	276.45	276.64	14.38	288.95	289.14	15.03
251.64	251.83	13.09	264.14	264.33	13.74	276.64	276.83	14.39	289.14	289.33	15.04
251.83	252.02	13.10	264.33	264.52	13.75	276.83	277.02	14.40	289.33	289.52	15.05
252.02	252.22	13.11	264.52	264.72	13.76	277.02	277.22	14.41	289.52	289.72	15.06
252.22	252.41	13.12	264.72	264.91	13.77	277.22	277.41	14.42	289.72	289.91	15.07
252.41	252.60	13.13	264.91	265.10	13.78	277.41	277.60	14.43	289.91	290.10	15.08
252.60	252.79	13.14	265.10	265.29	13.79	277.60	277.79	14.44	290.10	290.29	15.09

Federal Income Tax Tables
SINGLE Persons — WEEKLY Payroll Period

And the wages are—		And the number of withholding exemptions claimed is—										
At least	But less than	0	1	2	3	4	5	6	7	8	9	10 or more
		The amount of income tax to be withheld shall be—										
$80	$82	$11.00	$8.50	$6.00	$3.60	$1.50	$0	$0	$0	$0	$0	$0
82	84	11.40	8.90	6.40	4.00	1.90	0	0	0	0	0	0
84	86	11.80	9.30	6.80	4.30	2.20	.30	0	0	0	0	0
86	88	12.20	9.70	7.20	4.70	2.50	.60	0	0	0	0	0
88	90	12.60	10.10	7.60	5.10	2.90	.90	0	0	0	0	0
90	92	13.00	10.50	8.00	5.50	3.20	1.20	0	0	0	0	0
92	94	13.40	10.90	8.40	5.90	3.60	1.40	0	0	0	0	0
94	96	13.80	11.30	8.80	6.30	3.90	1.80	0	0	0	0	0
96	98	14.20	11.70	9.20	6.70	4.20	2.10	.30	0	0	0	0
98	100	14.60	12.10	9.60	7.10	4.60	2.50	.50	0	0	0	0
100	105	15.20	12.80	10.30	7.80	5.30	3.10	1.00	0	0	0	0
105	110	16.10	13.80	11.30	8.80	6.30	3.90	1.80	0	0	0	0
110	115	17.00	14.80	12.30	9.80	7.30	4.80	2.60	.70	0	0	0
115	120	17.90	15.70	13.30	10.80	8.30	5.80	3.50	1.40	0	0	0
120	125	18.80	16.60	14.30	11.80	9.30	6.80	4.30	2.20	.30	0	0
125	130	19.70	17.50	15.20	12.80	10.30	7.80	5.30	3.10	1.00	0	0
130	135	20.60	18.40	16.10	13.80	11.30	8.80	6.30	3.90	1.80	0	0
135	140	21.60	19.30	17.00	14.80	12.30	9.80	7.30	4.80	2.60	.70	0
140	145	22.60	20.20	17.90	15.70	13.30	10.80	8.30	5.80	3.50	1.40	0
145	150	23.70	21.10	18.80	16.60	14.30	11.80	9.30	6.80	4.30	2.20	.30
150	160	25.30	22.60	20.20	17.90	15.70	13.30	10.80	8.30	5.80	3.50	1.40
160	170	27.40	24.70	22.10	19.70	17.50	15.20	12.80	10.30	7.80	5.30	3.10
170	180	29.50	26.80	24.20	21.60	19.30	17.00	14.80	12.30	9.80	7.30	4.80
180	190	31.60	28.90	26.30	23.70	21.10	18.80	16.60	14.30	11.80	9.30	6.80
190	200	33.70	31.00	28.40	25.80	23.20	20.60	18.40	16.10	13.80	11.30	8.80
200	210	35.80	33.10	30.50	27.90	25.30	22.60	20.20	17.90	15.70	13.30	10.80
210	220	38.00	35.20	32.60	30.00	27.40	24.70	22.10	19.70	17.50	15.20	12.80
220	230	40.40	37.40	34.70	32.10	29.50	26.80	24.20	21.60	19.30	17.00	14.80
230	240	42.80	39.80	36.80	34.20	31.60	28.90	26.30	23.70	21.10	18.80	16.60
240	250	45.20	42.20	39.20	36.30	33.70	31.00	28.40	25.80	23.20	20.60	18.40
250	260	47.60	44.60	41.60	38.60	35.80	33.10	30.50	27.90	25.30	22.60	20.20
260	270	50.00	47.00	44.00	41.00	38.00	35.20	32.60	30.00	27.40	24.70	22.10
270	280	52.40	49.40	46.40	43.40	40.40	37.40	34.70	32.10	29.50	26.80	24.20
280	290	54.80	51.80	48.80	45.80	42.80	39.80	36.80	34.20	31.60	28.90	26.30
290	300	57.20	54.20	51.20	48.20	45.20	42.20	39.20	36.30	33.70	31.00	28.40
300	310	59.60	56.60	53.60	50.60	47.60	44.60	41.60	38.60	35.80	33.10	30.50
310	320	62.00	59.00	56.00	53.00	50.00	47.00	44.00	41.00	38.00	35.20	32.60
320	330	64.40	61.40	58.40	55.40	52.40	49.40	46.40	43.40	40.40	37.40	34.70
330	340	66.80	63.80	60.80	57.80	54.80	51.80	48.80	45.80	42.80	39.80	36.80
340	350	69.20	66.20	63.20	60.20	57.20	54.20	51.20	48.20	45.20	42.20	39.20
350	360	71.60	68.60	65.60	62.60	59.60	56.60	53.60	50.60	47.60	44.60	41.60
		24 percent of the excess over $360 plus—										
$360 and over		72.80	69.80	66.80	63.80	60.80	57.80	54.80	51.80	48.80	45.80	42.80

MARRIED Persons — WEEKLY Payroll Period

And the wages are—		And the number of withholding exemptions claimed is—										
At least	But less than	0	1	2	3	4	5	6	7	8	9	10 or more
		The amount of income tax to be withheld shall be—										
$100	$105	$13.10	$11.10	$9.10	$7.00	$4.80	$2.80	$1.00	$0	$0	$0	$0
105	110	13.90	11.90	9.90	7.80	5.70	3.60	1.70	0	0	0	0
110	115	14.70	12.70	10.70	8.70	6.50	4.40	2.40	.70	0	0	0
115	120	15.50	13.50	11.50	9.50	7.40	5.30	3.10	1.40	0	0	0
120	125	16.30	14.30	12.30	10.30	8.20	6.10	4.00	2.10	.30	0	0
125	130	17.10	15.10	13.10	11.10	9.10	7.00	4.80	2.80	1.00	0	0
130	135	17.90	15.90	13.90	11.90	9.90	7.80	5.70	3.60	1.70	0	0
135	140	18.70	16.70	14.70	12.70	10.70	8.70	6.50	4.40	2.40	.70	0
140	145	19.50	17.50	15.50	13.50	11.50	9.50	7.40	5.30	3.10	1.40	0
145	150	20.30	18.30	16.30	14.30	12.30	10.30	8.20	6.10	4.00	2.10	.30
150	160	21.50	19.50	17.50	15.50	13.50	11.50	9.50	7.40	5.30	3.10	1.40
160	170	23.10	21.10	19.10	17.10	15.10	13.10	11.10	9.10	7.00	4.80	2.80
170	180	25.00	22.70	20.70	18.70	16.70	14.70	12.70	10.70	8.70	6.50	4.40
180	190	26.90	24.50	22.30	20.30	18.30	16.30	14.30	12.30	10.30	8.20	6.10
190	200	28.80	26.40	24.10	21.90	19.90	17.90	15.90	13.90	11.90	9.90	7.80
200	210	30.70	28.30	26.00	23.60	21.50	19.50	17.50	15.50	13.50	11.50	9.50
210	220	32.60	30.20	27.90	25.50	23.10	21.10	19.10	17.10	15.10	13.10	11.10
220	230	34.50	32.10	29.80	27.40	25.00	22.70	20.70	18.70	16.70	14.70	12.70
230	240	36.40	34.00	31.70	29.30	26.90	24.50	22.30	20.30	18.30	16.30	14.30
240	250	38.30	35.90	33.60	31.20	28.80	26.40	24.10	21.90	19.90	17.90	15.90
250	260	40.20	37.80	35.50	33.10	30.70	28.30	26.00	23.60	21.50	19.50	17.50
260	270	42.10	39.70	37.40	35.00	32.60	30.20	27.90	25.50	23.10	21.10	19.10
270	280	44.10	41.60	39.30	36.90	34.50	32.10	29.80	27.40	25.00	22.70	20.70
280	290	46.20	43.60	41.20	38.80	36.40	34.00	31.70	29.30	26.90	24.50	22.30
290	300	48.30	45.70	43.10	40.70	38.30	35.90	33.60	31.20	28.80	26.40	24.10
300	310	50.40	47.80	45.20	42.60	40.20	37.80	35.50	33.10	30.70	28.30	26.00
310	320	52.50	49.90	47.30	44.70	42.10	39.70	37.40	35.00	32.60	30.20	27.90
320	330	54.60	52.00	49.40	46.80	44.10	41.60	39.30	36.90	34.50	32.10	29.80
330	340	56.70	54.10	51.50	48.90	46.20	43.60	41.20	38.80	36.40	34.00	31.70
340	350	58.80	56.20	53.60	51.00	48.30	45.70	43.10	40.70	38.30	35.90	33.60
350	360	60.90	58.30	55.70	53.10	50.40	47.80	45.20	42.60	40.20	37.80	35.50
360	370	63.00	60.40	57.80	55.20	52.50	49.90	47.30	44.70	42.10	39.70	37.40
370	380	65.10	62.50	59.90	57.30	54.60	52.00	49.40	46.80	44.10	41.60	39.30
380	390	67.30	64.60	62.00	59.40	56.70	54.10	51.50	48.90	46.20	43.60	41.20
390	400	69.80	66.70	64.10	61.50	58.80	56.20	53.60	51.00	48.30	45.70	43.10
400	410	72.30	69.10	66.20	63.60	60.90	58.30	55.70	53.10	50.40	47.80	45.20
410	420	74.80	71.60	68.50	65.70	63.00	60.40	57.80	55.20	52.50	49.90	47.30
420	430	77.30	74.10	71.00	67.90	65.10	62.50	59.90	57.30	54.60	52.00	49.40
430	440	79.80	76.60	73.50	70.40	67.30	64.60	62.00	59.40	56.70	54.10	51.50
440	450	82.30	79.10	76.00	72.90	69.80	66.70	64.10	61.50	58.80	56.20	53.60
450	460	84.80	81.60	78.50	75.40	72.30	69.10	66.20	63.60	60.90	58.30	55.70
460	470	87.30	84.10	81.00	77.90	74.80	71.60	68.50	65.70	63.00	60.40	57.80
470	480	89.80	86.60	83.50	80.40	77.30	74.10	71.00	67.90	65.10	62.50	59.90
480	490	92.30	89.10	86.00	82.90	79.80	76.60	73.50	70.40	67.30	64.60	62.00
490	500	94.80	91.60	88.50	85.40	82.30	79.10	76.00	72.90	69.80	66.70	64.10
500	510	97.30	94.10	91.00	87.90	84.80	81.60	78.50	75.40	72.30	69.10	66.20
510	520	99.80	96.60	93.50	90.40	87.30	84.10	81.00	77.90	74.80	71.60	68.50
520	530	102.30	99.10	96.00	92.90	89.80	86.60	83.50	80.40	77.30	74.10	71.00
		25 percent of the excess over $530 plus—										
$530 and over		103.50	100.40	97.30	94.10	91.00	87.90	84.80	81.60	78.50	75.40	72.30

 EMPLOYEE COMPENSATION: HOURLY-RATE PLAN

Under the hourly-rate plan, the employee's earnings are based on the number of hours he works at a specified rate per hour. To find the employee's gross earnings, it is necessary to multiply his hourly rate by the number of hours worked.

Example | $3.25, rate of pay per hour
×   40, hours worked during the week
$130.00, gross earnings

Overtime Pay

The federal Fair Labor Standards Act requires all enterprises engaged in interstate commerce (doing business outside the state in which they are located) to pay their employees a certain minimum wage per hour. In addition, it requires employers to pay a minimum of $1\frac{1}{2}$ times the regular hourly rate for all hours worked over 40 hours a week. Thus, if the regular rate is $3, the overtime rate must be at least $4.50. (Most firms abide by this regulation even though they are not engaged in interstate commerce.)

Each employer is also required by the federal Fair Labor Standards Act to keep a complete record of the hours each employee works. Some use a time book for this purpose. Others require each employee to "punch a time clock": each employee has a time card that he inserts into a time clock when he arrives and again when he leaves. At the end of the pay period, the payroll clerk gathers all the cards and computes for each worker the total hours worked and the gross earnings. The following is an illustration of a time card.

Name __Howard Pollock__   Employee No. __28__

Week Ending ____October 12, 19—____

Days	Regular				Overtime		Hours
	In	Out	In	Out	In	Out	
Mon.	9⁵⁸	12⁰²	12⁵⁴	5³¹			6½
Tues.	8⁰⁴	12⁰⁰	1⁰⁰	5⁰¹	6³⁰	9⁰⁰	10½
Wed.	8⁰⁰	12⁰¹	12⁵⁸	6⁰¹			9
Thurs.	7⁵⁹	12⁰²	12⁵⁶	5¹⁶			8¼
Fri.	8⁰⁰	11⁵⁹	12⁵⁸	4⁰⁰	5³⁰	9³⁰	11
Sat.	7⁵⁵	1⁰⁰					5
Sun.							

	Hours	Rate	Earnings
Regular	40	$4.00	$160.00
Overtime	10¼	$6.00	61.50
Total Hours	50¼	Gross Earnings	$221.50

Time is usually computed to the nearest quarter hour. Thus, if the starting time is 9:00 and the employee punches in at 9:06, his time is computed from 9:00. If he punches in at 9:09, his time is computed from 9:15. The strictness with which this rule is observed varies.

Example

PROBLEM George Ross, an employee of the Robert Mays Company, worked 9 hours on Monday, $8\frac{1}{2}$ hours on Tuesday, 9 hours on Wednesday, 8 hours on Thursday, 6 hours on Friday, and 4 hours on Saturday. The regular time is 8 hours daily, 5 days a week. If he was paid $2.40 an hour for work done during regular time, and time and a half for overtime work, find the regular time worked and the overtime worked; and the regular-time, overtime, and total earnings.

The Robert Mays Company considers every hour worked on Saturday and every hour over 8 on weekdays as overtime. In this case, the overtime worked is not to be used to complete any day during which less than 8 hours were worked.

	Regular Hours	Overtime Hours
Monday	8	1
Tuesday	8	$\frac{1}{2}$
Wednesday	8	1
Thursday	8	0
Friday	6	0
Saturday	0	4
Total	38	$6\frac{1}{2}$

SOLUTION To find the regular-time pay, multiply the rate per hour by the number of hours of regular time worked.

38 (hours) × $2.40 (per hour) = $91.20, regular-time earnings

To find the overtime earnings, multiply the rate per hour by $1\frac{1}{2}$ and multiply this product by the number of hours of overtime worked, or multiply the number of hours of overtime worked by $1\frac{1}{2}$ and multiply this product by the rate per hour.

$ 2.40, regular-time rate per hour
× $1\frac{1}{2}$
$ 3.60, overtime rate per hour
× $6\frac{1}{2}$, number of hours overtime
$23.40, overtime earnings

or

$6\frac{1}{2}$, number of hours overtime
× $1\frac{1}{2}$
$9\frac{3}{4}$, number of hours paid for overtime

$ 2.40, regular-time rate per hour
× $9\frac{3}{4}$
$23.40, overtime earnings

$ 91.20, regular-time earnings
+ 23.40, overtime earnings
$114.60, total earnings

Another way of finding total earnings for those who have worked overtime is to multiply the total time by the regular rate, and then add to it the bonus pay granted for overtime worked.

$44\frac{1}{2} - 38 = 6\frac{1}{2}$, hours overtime worked

$44\frac{1}{2}$ x $2.40   = $106.80, regular rate earnings

$3\frac{1}{4}$ ($\frac{1}{2}$ of $6\frac{1}{2}$) x $2.40 = $\underline{7.80}$, bonus, or excess earnings
                                        for overtime

                      $114.60, total earnings

Practice Drills

Complete the following payroll computations for the week ending March 28, 19—. Consider all hours over 40 worked each week as overtime. The overtime rate is $1\frac{1}{2}$ times the regular rate.

Employee	Rate	Hrs.	Regular Hours	Regular Earnings	Overtime Hours	Overtime Earnings	Total Earnings
1. Klein, B. A.	$4.00	42	_____	$_____	_____	$_____	$_____
2. Maher, E. J.	2.85	46	_____	_____	_____	_____	_____
3. Ogus, C. W.	3.25	$40\frac{1}{2}$	_____	_____	_____	_____	_____
4. Ryan, D. F.	3.40	48	_____	_____	_____	_____	_____
5. Wiss, G. H.	2.60	$46\frac{1}{2}$	_____	_____	_____	_____	_____
6. Young, M. E.	3.95	$48\frac{1}{2}$	_____	_____	_____	_____	_____
		Totals		$_____		$_____	$_____

ANSWERS
1. $160 + $12 = $172
3. $130.00 + $2.44 = $132.44
5. $104.00 + $25.35 = $129.35
Total regular earnings, $802.00
Total earnings, $958.60

2. $114.00 + $25.65 = $139.65
4. $136.00 + $40.80 = $176.80
6. $158.00 + $50.36 = $208.36
Total overtime earnings, $156.60

Payroll Register

Each pay period the payroll information on every employee is summarized in a payroll register. The payroll register shows the name and marital status of the employee, the number of exemptions, the hours worked (regular and overtime), the deductions for federal income tax, social security tax, etc., and the net pay, as shown below.

PAYROLL REGISTER

For the Week Beginning *April 22, 19—*   and Ending *April 28, 19—*   Paid *May 1, 19—*

No.	Name	Marital Status	No. of Exemptions	HOURS	Regular	Overtime	Total	Withholding	FICA	Insurance	Other	Total	Amount	Check No.
1	Gilbert Cohen	m	4	40	185 00		185 00	18 30	9 62	3 00		30 92	154 08	689
2	Leroy Williams	m	3	40	160 00		160 00	17 10	8 32	3 00		28 42	131 58	690
3	Carol Fraser	m	1	42	120 00	9 00	129 00	15 10	6 71	3 00		24 81	104 19	691

APPLICATION PROBLEMS

1. Complete the following partial payroll register.

Employee	Hours Worked					Reg. Hours	Reg. Rate	Total Earnings
	M	T	W	T	F			
Allen, P.	8	7	8	8	8	_____	$3.50	$_____
Dukes, J.	7	7	8	8	7	_____	3.10	_____
Manes, H.	8	8	8	...	8	_____	3.86	_____
Konig, I.	7½	8	9	8	4	_____	3.40	_____
Ratner, R.	8	7¼	8	5	7½	_____	3.16	_____
Dee, F.	8	5	8	...	8	_____	3.25	_____
							Total	$_____

2. Complete the following partial payroll register. Consider all hours over 40 worked each week as overtime. Overtime rate is $1\frac{1}{2}$ times regular rate.

Employee	Hours Worked					Reg. Hrs.	Reg. Rate	Reg. Earnings	Over. Hrs.	Over. Rate	Over. Earnings	Total Earnings
	M	T	W	T	F							
Adams	8	8	9	8½	8	___	$3.40	$___	___	$___	$___	$___
Cohen	8	8	8	8	9½	___	2.80	___	___	___	___	___
Perez	8	8	9	9	8	___	3.64	___	___	___	___	___
Fly	8	7½	8½	9	9	___	3.34	___	___	___	___	___
Jones	8	8	9	8¼	8	___	3.50	___	___	___	___	___
Toren	8	8¾	9	8	8½	___	3.06	___	___	___	___	___
Hogan	8	8	8	9	8¼	___	3.56	___	___	___	___	___
Drouin	10	8	8	9	8¾	___	3.80	___	___	___	___	___
							Totals	$___			$___	$___

69 EMPLOYEE COMPENSATION: PIECE-RATE PLAN

The piece-rate plan of compensation takes two basic forms: the *straight piece-work plan* and the *differential piece-work plan*.

Straight Piece-Work Plan

The *straight* piece-work plan provides for the payment of a fixed amount for each article produced, irrespective of the time required to produce it. Under this system, a person who produces 60 articles in a week would receive the same rate per article as he would receive if he produced only 40 articles. Of course, his earnings would be greater.

To find the week's wages due an employee under the straight piece-work plan, multiply the total number of articles produced during the week by the rate per article.

Example

PROBLEM Find the gross earnings for the week.

Employee	M.	T.	W.	Th.	F.	Rate
Fox	31	32	31	28	36	$1.40
Polk	24	27	21	25	24	1.77

SOLUTION Add the total number of pieces produced by each employee (Fox, 158; Polk, 121), then multiply by the piece rate.

Fox: 158 pieces × $1.40 = $221.20, gross earnings
Polk: 121 pieces × $1.77 = $214.17, gross earnings

Practice Drill

Prepare and complete a payroll register, like that illustrated, from the information given. Find the deductions by using the appropriate tables.

Em-ployee	Exemp-tions	Total Articles	Rate	Gross Earnings	Deductions			Net Earnings
					Soc. Sec. Tax	Federal Income Tax	Total Deduc-tions	

Employee	Exemp.	Marital Status	Articles Produced					Rate
			M.	T.	W.	Th.	F.	
Adler, P.	2	M	28	29	32	34	27	$1.56
Carr, H.	1	S	29	33	27	28	30	1.63
Leach, B.	4	M	32	36	35	34	38	1.58
Reiss, O.	3	M	26	29	28	28	30	$1.57\frac{1}{2}$
Stabile, L.	5	M	28	32	32	35	31	$1.59\frac{1}{4}$
Warner, S.	3	S	25	30	31	26	29	$1.62\frac{1}{2}$

ANSWERS   net earnings: Adler, $72.40; Carr, $76.14; Leach, $90.53; Reiss, $72.21; Stabile, $86.47; Warner, $77.15

Differential Piece-Work Plan

Under the *differential* piece-work plan, the rate per article varies with the number produced by an employee in a given time, usually one day.

There are many variations of the differential piece-work plan. Often an employer will fix a quota as the number of daily or weekly units of production expected of an average employee. He will then establish a rate for each unit produced up to the set standard, and a higher rate for production above this amount. In some firms, if the quota is exceeded, the higher rate applies to all the units produced by the worker.

In industrial plants where expensive machinery is used and obsolescence, depreciation, and other overhead expenses are constant, this wage system pays off for both the employer and the employee. The employer gets a higher return on his investment through greater production, and the employee is rewarded through an increase in his pay envelope.

Following is a schedule of differential rates in force in one company.

SCHEDULE OF DIFFERENTIAL RATES

Articles Produced per Day	Rate per Article
23 or less	$1.02
24-25	1.05½
26-27	1.09
28-29	1.12½
30-31	1.16
32-33	1.19½
34-35	1.23
36-37	1.26½
38 (and up)	1.30 (and up)

According to this schedule, a man who produced 37 articles in one day would be paid $1.26½ for each article. His earnings that day would amount to 37 × $1.26½, or $46.81. If he produced only 30 articles, he would receive $1.16 for each article, or $34.80.

Practice Drill | Using the schedule of differential rates given, determine how much an employee would earn in one week if he produced the following number of articles daily: Monday, 36; Tuesday, 42; Wednesday, 19; Thursday, 32; Friday, 38.

ANSWER $207.16

APPLICATION PROBLEMS

1. Compute the gross earnings of the following employees for the week under the straight piece-work plan.

	Employee	Articles Produced	Rate
a.	Brady, H.	100	$1.20
b.	Clark, J.	104	1.07½
c.	DeLeo, A.	115	1.25

	Employee	Articles Produced	Rate
d.	Farber, T.	92	$1.11\frac{1}{4}$
e.	Grew, B.	120	.70
f.	King, H.	112	1.12
g.	Lima, J.	106	1.40
h.	Payne, W.	107	1.15
i.	Reich, W.	100	$.97\frac{1}{2}$
j.	Young, C.	96	1.20

2. Compute the daily gross earnings for each of the following employees, using the schedule of differential rates on page 166. Then find the total daily gross earnings and the total gross earnings for the week.

	Employee	Articles Produced				
		M.	T.	W.	Th.	F.
a.	Ortiz	30	34	33	36	31
b.	Rosen	26	31	29	30	32
c.	Bennett	33	35	37	32	34
d.	White	34	32	28	29	33
e.	Branca	37	13	35	35	34
f.	Jonas	33	28	27	31	30
g.	Hecht	30	42	32	35	38
h.	Arnez	41	39	38	37	38
i.	Carson	39	40	35	29	37
j.	Kane	28	40	29	31	30
k.	Roberts	26	35	36	27	28
l.	Amir	33	34	27	26	40

70 EMPLOYEE COMPENSATION: BONUS AND PREMIUM-WAGE PLAN

The bonus-wage plan, based on increased production, is widely used in industry. This plan guarantees a minimum wage plus incentive bonus based on the number of units produced in excess of a set quota. This provides for payment of a fixed rate per hour if production is below a certain number of units or a bonus if production is at or above the quota.

The premium-wage plan based on time saved guarantees the worker a minimum wage plus a share of any time he saves. A quota for each employee or job is set at about 60% to 70% of average production.

Bonus-Wage Plan Based on Increased Production

The bonus provided by this plan is in the form of a percent (110% to 150%) multiplied by the rate per hour multiplied by the hours of work accomplished.

To find the hours of work accomplished, divide the number of units produced in one day by the set quota, and then multiply the quotient by the hours worked. For example, if a quota is 40 units for an 8-hour day and an employee produces 50 units in one day, the hours of work accomplished are found as follows.

$$Hours\ Worked\ \times\ \frac{Units\ Produced}{Unit\ Quota}\ =\ Hours\ of\ Work\ Accomplished$$

$$8 \times \frac{\overset{5}{\cancel{50}}}{\underset{4}{\cancel{40}}} = \frac{40}{4} = 10$$

An employee has a quota of 40 units for an 8-hour day, and receives a rate equal to 140% times the hourly rate of $3 if production is at or above quota. If he produces 50 units in a day, his daily earnings are determined as follows.

$$Daily\ Earnings\ =\ Bonus\ Percent\ \times\ Rate\ per\ Hour\ \times\ Hours\ of\ Work\ Accomplished$$

$$= 1.4 \times \$3 \times \left(8 \times \frac{\overset{10}{\cancel{50}}}{\underset{5}{\cancel{40}}} \right)$$

$$= 1.4 \times \$3 \times 10 = \$42$$

Example

PROBLEM Hillis is paid $2.95 an hour for an 8-hour day, with the average number of daily units of production fixed at 64. If the daily production per employee equals or exceeds the established number, a rate equal to 125% times the hourly rate is paid. Hillis completed 60 units on Monday, 64 units on Tuesday, and 72 units on Wednesday. Find his daily earnings and his total earnings for the 3 days.

SOLUTION

Monday	= 8 × $2.95	= $23.60
Tuesday	= 1.25 × $2.95 × 8	= 29.50

$$Wednesday = 1.25 \times \$2.95 \times \left(\overset{1}{\cancel{8}} \times \frac{\overset{9}{\cancel{72}}}{\underset{\cancel{8}}{\cancel{64}}} \right) = \underline{33.19}$$

$$\$86.29,\ total\ earnings$$

Practice
Drill

Fred Allan is paid $3.10 an hour for an 8-hour day. His daily produc-tion quota is 75 units. A rate equal to 150% times the hourly rate is paid if daily production equals or exceeds the quota. Find Allan's daily earnings and his total wages for the week if he produced the following number of units: Monday, 70; Tuesday, 72; Wednesday, 75; Thursday, 78; Friday, 84.

ANSWERS   Monday, $24.80; Tuesday, $24.80; Wednesday, $37.20; Thursday, $38.69; Friday, $41.66; total wages, $167.15

$$1.5 \times 3.10 \times (8 \times 75) =$$

Premium-Wage Plan Based on Time Saved

The bonus provided by this plan is in the form of a fixed rate per hour if production is kept at or below the quota. If the quota is exceeded, the earnings of the employee are equal to the rate per hour multiplied by the hours worked, plus a percent (25% to 75%) of the rate per hour multiplied by the hours saved. The hours saved are equal to the hours of work accomplished, less the hours worked.

Example

PROBLEM Ronald Woodruff was paid $2.90 an hour and worked a 40-hour week. His quota was 70 units per week, and he was credited with 60% of the hours saved. Find his total weekly earnings if he com-pleted 84 units.

SOLUTION

$40 \times \dfrac{84}{70} = 48$, hours of work accomplished

$48 - 40 = 8$, hours saved
$40 \times \$2.90 = \$116$, guaranteed minimum
60% of $\$2.90 = \$1.74$; $\$1.74 \times 8 = \$13.92$, premium

or

60% of 8 (hours saved) $= 4.8$; $4.8 \times \$2.90 = \$13.92$, premium
$\$116 + \$13.92 = \$129.92$, total weekly earnings

Practice
Drill

Henry Dullafont worked a 40-hour week at $3.40 an hour. He was ex-pected to meet a weekly quota of 56 units and would be credited with 65% of the hours saved. Find his total weekly earnings if he produced 72 units.

ANSWER $161.26

APPLICATION PROBLEMS

1. Find the daily and total weekly earnings for each of the following employees. The employees work an 8-hour day and are paid 150% of the hourly rate if the production is *above* the established daily quota.

Employee	Units of Production					Rate per Hour	Daily Quota
	M.	T.	W.	Th.	F.		
A.H.	40	42	35	51	43	$3.25	42
B.J.	52	51	50	49	55	3.65	50
F.T.	100	112	115	108	97	3.85	110
L.M.	110	112	106	83	98	3.75	100
P.K.	71	70	75	73	74	3.35	70
V.B.	27	27	29	30	24	4.05	25

2. Compute the gross earnings of each of the employees in problem 1 if the wage-payment plan provided for pay at 125% of the hourly rate when production was at quota or above. Find the total earnings of each for the week.

3. Find the total weekly minimum wage and the total weekly earnings earned by each of the following employees. The employees work a 40-hour week and are credited with 40% of the hours saved.

Employee	Weekly Units of Production	Rate per Hour	Weekly Quota
C.T.	72	$3.80	64
H.B.	45	3.50	40
M.M.	105	3.40	80
O.S.	75	3.15	75
C.H.	90	3.25	100
I.L.	85	3.75	68

71 EMPLOYEE COMPENSATION: COMMISSION AND PROFIT-SHARING PLAN

A commission is usually expressed as a percent of sales, and many salesmen count on commission revenue as an important part of their income. Typical of those who receive commissions of one type or another are life insurance salesmen, retail store clerks, real estate agents, and automobile salesmen.

Another type of employee compensation is the profit-sharing plan where certain employees, or all employees, share in the profits earned by the company during the year. Usually, the employee's share of the profits is based on his earnings (the higher his salary the greater his share) although in a few cases all employees receive the same amount regardless of earnings or length of service.

Straight-Commission Plan

Some salespeople receive only a straight commission with no base salary. In this case, their total earnings are computed as a percent of their sales.

Example

PROBLEM   Gregg Mason is a salesman for the Mayflower Wholesale Lumber Company. His earnings are computed at 2% of the total sales he makes each week. During the week of May 16, Mason's total sales (cash and credit) were $10,760. How much did he earn that week?

SOLUTION $10,760 × 2% = $215.20, earnings for the week

Salary-Plus-Commission Plan

Other salesmen receive a base salary plus a commission on sales.

Example

PROBLEM   Sarah Palfret works in the Now Dress and Boutique Shop. In addition to waiting on customers, she helps with the store records, display of stock, and supervision of other employees. Miss Palfret earns a basic salary of $75 a week and in addition is paid 3% of the sales she makes. During the week of October 9, her sales, as indicated by the sales tickets she filled out, amounted to $1,960. What were her gross earnings?

SOLUTION $75.00, base salary
                  + 58.80, commission (3% of $1,960)
                   $133.80, gross earnings

Salary-Bonus Plan

The salary-bonus plan is similar to the salary-plus-commission plan in that the employee receives a regular salary plus a bonus based on a quota. If the employee reaches or exceeds the quota, he receives a bonus, which may be either a set percent of total sales or a percent that graduates as sales increase.

Examples

PROBLEM 1   Charles Fry is a salesman for the Gold Award Company. His base salary is $9,600 a year, and his yearly sales quota is $200,000. If he reaches this quota, he receives no bonus, but if he goes over $200,000, he is paid 4% on the amount that exceeds the quota. At the end of the year Fry had sales of $275,000. What were his annual earnings?

SOLUTION $ 9,600, base salary
                     + 3,000, commission (4% of $75,000)
                      $12,600, gross earnings

PROBLEM 2   Hilda Kahn sells advertising space for the *Suburban Sophisticate* magazine. She receives a base salary of $7,500 a year. Her bonus plan operates on a graduated scale of percent based on increased sales: she receives 5% of all sales up to $10,000; 10% of all sales over $10,000 but under $15,000; and 15% of all sales over $15,000. During the year just ended Miss Kahn's sales amounted to $18,000. What were her total gross earnings?

SOLUTION

$7,500, base salary
  500, 5% of $10,000
  500, 10% of $5,000
+ 450, 15% of $3,000
$8,950, gross earnings

Practice Drills

1. Maureen Lipscomb receives a base salary of $7,200 a year. In addition, she receives 6% of the sales she makes over $140,000 during the year. At the end of the year, Miss Lipscomb's sales totaled $168,670. What was the amount of her bonus check?

2. Claude Kelly receives a monthly guaranteed salary of $600 and, in addition, 5% of all sales up to and including $6,000, 8% on the next $3,000, and 10% on everything above $9,000. During the month of February, Claude's sales were $7,100. What were his earnings for the month?

ANSWERS   1. $1,720.20   2. $988

Profit-Sharing Plans

A typical profit-sharing plan works this way: The company management decides at the beginning of the year that 3%, say, of its *net operating profit (NOP)* will be set aside as a fund for giving bonuses to certain top executives. This amount is equated to bonus points, and each executive who is to share in the plan is allotted so many points. At the end of the year the executive's "bonus points" are multiplied by 3% of the actual NOP in order to arrive at his share of the profits.

Example

PROBLEM   The Kendrick Advertising Agency has decided to set aside 3% of its NOP for the coming year as a profit-sharing plan for its 5 top executives. The anticipated profit, based on a sales forecast and estimated expenses, is $900,000; and $27,000 (3% of $900,000) will be divided into 500 bonus points worth $54 a point as follows:

Hargraves	200 points
Jenkins	100 points
Gabroski	75 points
Valeriano	65 points
Moshe	60 points

How much will each executive receive as a share of the profits if the company earns the profit it has budgeted?

SOLUTION

Hargraves:	200 points × $54	= $10,800
Jenkins:	100 points × $54	= 5,400
Gabroski:	75 points × $54	= 4,050
Valeriano:	65 points × $54	= 3,510
Moshe:	60 points × $54	= 3,240
		$27,000

Practice Drills

The Laytham Manufacturing Company has a profit-sharing plan for ten of its employees, including executives, department heads, and foremen. Each year the company sets aside 6% of its NOP for distribution among these key employees who are assigned bonus points as follows: Goforth, 100; Maraschal, 75; Livesay, 75; Kraus, 75; Mourney, 75; Hoffman, 75; Rosburg, 60; Phelps, 60; Levinthal, 55; O'Hara, 50.

The NOP for the current year, according to the auditors' final report, was $455,000.

1. How much is each point worth?
2. How much will each employee receive in the profit-sharing plan for the year?

ANSWERS 1. 1 point = $39   2. Goforth, $3,900; Maraschal, Livesay, Kraus, Mourney, and Hoffman, $2,925 each; Rosburg and Phelps, $2,340 each; Levinthal, $2,145; O'Hara, $1,950

APPLICATION PROBLEMS

1. Gilbert Winfree is a salesman of sheet steel for the Great States Steel Company. Although the company pays for Winfree's travel and miscellaneous expenses, his actual earnings come entirely from commissions on the sales he makes. His commission rate is 2%. During the past year, Winfree had sales amounting to $800,000. How much did he earn in commissions?

2. Arnold Terrera is employed by a correspondence school. It is his job to talk to those who have responded to the school's advertisements and attempt to sell them a home-study course in interior decorating. The course costs $500, and Arnold earns 15% commission on each tuition he sells. He receives no base salary. For all tuitions in excess of 10 each month, however, Arnold receives 20% commission. His sales for the year are shown in the following table. What was the total amount he earned in commissions?

Month	Tuitions Sold	Commission Earned	Month	Tuitions Sold	Commission Earned
January	6	$_____	July	5	$_____
February	9	_____	August	6	_____
March	10	_____	September	4	_____
April	7	_____	October	12	_____
May	5	_____	November	14	_____
June	7	_____	December	11	_____
	Total	$_____		Total	$_____
			Total Commission Earned		$_____

3. The Rockville Consultants Group has a profit-sharing compensation plan for its top 7 consultants. In the coming year, the company has budgeted its net operating profit at $1,140,000, and the Executive Committee has agreed to set aside 3% of this amount for profit sharing. Total bonus points allotted for this plan are 500, although only 430 will be distributed to the 7 consultants; the remaining points will be reserved for other consultants who may come under the plan during the year. Salaries and bonus points for the executives are set for the year as shown below. (Each bonus point is worth 3% of the NOP divided by 500.) Find the bonus earnings to be paid to each consultant. Then find the total earnings of each.

	Name	Salary	Bonus Points	Bonus	Total Earnings
a.	Albee	$35,000	200	$_____	$_____
b.	Kirkwood	29,500	50	_____	_____
c.	Parisi	26,000	45	_____	_____
d.	Kaufman	25,500	35	_____	_____
e.	Hecht	29,000	40	_____	_____
f.	O'Brian	23,500	25	_____	_____
g.	Bartholomew	24,000	35	_____	_____

PROBLEMS FOR PART NINE

Wage & Salary Administration

67

1. Using the weekly federal income tax tables on pages 159-160, find the tax to be deducted weekly from the earnings of each of the following employees.

Employee	Earnings	Exemptions	Status
J. Riggs	$240.50	1	Single
R. Kane	$197.75	4	Married
L. Ganges	$333.33	3	Single
K. Potts	$225.00	2	Married

2. Using the social security tax table on pages 158-159, find the amount to be deducted for social security tax from the weekly earnings of the following.

Frieda Cutter, $170.25

K. D. Fisk, $197.50

Maria Mancini, $240.90

Archibald Ramsing, $222.02

Lonnie Brandeis, $201.20

Juanita Chavez, $188.80

68

Find the gross earnings under the following conditions for each of the employees listed below.

a. The overtime rate per hour is the same as the regular rate.

b. The overtime rate is $1\frac{1}{2}$ times the regular rate, and every hour over 40 worked in 1 week is considered overtime.

c. The overtime rate is $1\frac{1}{2}$ times the regular rate, and every hour over 8 worked in 1 day is considered overtime.

Employee	Rate per Hour	M.	T.	W.	Th.	F.
1. Pindar, J.	$3.25	8	9	10	4	8
2. Budlong, R.	3.75	7	8	8	8	9
3. Marcus, S.	3.60	8	8	8	8	8
4. Lomax, A.	4.00	8	....	8	8	8
5. Osborne, N.	3.50	8	10	10	9	10
6. Cutchall, P.	3.80	8	10	9	4	4
7. Heinsohn, D.	3.25	9	9	....	10	10
8. Klein, F.	3.40	8	8	7	6	9
9. Ianezzi, W.	4.10	10	8	9	10	....
10. Yengel, G.	3.95	8	8	4	10	11

In the table header, "Hours Worked" spans the columns M., T., W., Th., F.

1. Find the daily and weekly gross earnings of each employee under the straight piece-work plan. Find the total for each column.

Employee	M.	T.	W.	Th.	F.	Rate per Article
	Articles Produced					
Cardozo, E.	18	22	21	24	15	$1.50
Phelps, C.	23	19	18	23	26	1.68
Potter, G.	21	20	22	21	24	1.44
Pucci, A.	17	26	27	18	19	1.52
Rogoff, D.	15	18	20	19	17	1.56
Ruh, F.	26	20	23	25	19	$1.39\frac{1}{2}$
Swift, Z.	21	19	18	28	26	1.50
Taussig, T.	29	28	30	27	26	$1.52\frac{1}{2}$
Zweig, R.	24	25	26	21	23	$1.47\frac{1}{2}$

2. Using the schedule of differential rates on page 166, compute the daily and weekly earnings for the following employees. Find the total for each column.

Employee	M.	T.	W.	Th.	F.
	Articles Produced				
Abt, Charles T.	36	41	40	32	12
Cox, James	27	31	22	38	22
Eulan, John J.	36	36	36	35	37
Folsom, Altus	42	41	41	40	39
Lowery, E.	26	25	24	25	26
Tarter, B. A.	33	34	27	27	37
Varney, Lloyd	21	19	19	22	23
Weisberg, L. T.	37	38	41	42	44
Yorick, J. J.	27	31	32	33	33
Zeiss, S. S.	30	30	31	31	37

1. Find the amounts earned daily by the following employees and their total earnings for the week. Each employee works an 8-hour day and is paid 150% of the hourly rate if the production is above the established daily quota.

Employee	M.	T.	W.	Th.	F.	Rate per Hour	Daily Quota
	Articles Produced						
Cripps, E.	80	82	91	77	65	$3.80	75
Long, J. D.	75	77	77	81	73	3.60	75
Mays, F.	97	100	110	105	101	3.50	100
Hawkins, R.	40	44	36	44	44	4.00	40
Dakin, T.	65	65	64	60	57	3.40	60
Maestro, B.	47	47	51	51	51	3.25	50

2. Compute the daily and weekly gross earnings of each of the employees in problem 1 if the wage-payment plan provides for 125% of the hourly rate if production is at quota or above.

3. Find the total weekly minimum earnings and the total weekly earnings of each of the following employees. The employees work a 40-hour week and are credited with 40% of the hours saved.

Employee	Rate per Hour	Weekly Quota	Weekly Units of Production
Glaser, Sol	$2.85	80	88
Frome, E. R.	3.00	80	92
Lysander, Kay	3.10	60	70
Crump, Edward	3.20	65	70
Kroft, Norman	3.20	90	110
Hunsiker, F. J.	3.05	75	84

1. The salesmen employed by Manchester Accessories, Inc. work entirely on commission. They pay their own travel expenses and receive $2\frac{1}{2}$% of all the sales they make. During August the sales in southern Oklahoma for the three sales representatives were as follows: Cartright, $60,448.20; Dooley, $48,916.65; Brinkman, $37,777.40. How much did each salesman earn in commissions in August?

2. Marcella Oberon sells cookware to housewives. Each set of cookware is priced at $200 on which Miss Oberon receives $40, or 20%. However, for sales above 20 sets each month, she receives an additional 6%. For the first six months of the current year, Miss Oberon's sales were as follows: January, 24; February, 20; March, 18; April, 21; May, 23; June, 19. What were Miss Oberon's earnings during this time?

3. Kemper Plastics Manufacturing Company has a profit-sharing plan, which is based on 8% of the net profits each year, for all of its 20 employees. The net profit for last year amounted to $372,600. Each employee receives a share of the profits according to the number of points assigned to him (based on his annual gross earnings). The total points issued are 1,300, distributed as follows: Ketcham, 100; Melrose, 100; Lanier, 90; Grossman, 90; Fabrizzi, 85; Arnold, 75; Youngquist, 75; Bellman, 75; Poteet, 70; Quito, 70; Cable, 70; Troseth, 60; Hicks, 50; Turner, 50; Garcia, 45; Thornton, 45; Lequeux, 40; Baroody, 40; Doblier, 40; Klein, 30.
a. What is the value per point?
b. How much will each employee receive as his share under the profit-sharing plan?

PART TEN
Depreciation Computations

Depreciation is the loss incurred through the decline in the value of property. Some property deteriorates primarily because of use, such as a mimeograph machine whose constant use has rendered it incapable of producing legible copies. Other property decreases in value because of obsolescence. The difference between the original cost and the accumulated depreciation is the *book value* of an asset.

The most common methods used to compute depreciation (all approved in principle by the Internal Revenue Service) are as follows.

Straight-line method   The straight-line method is the simplest and most common method of computing depreciation. It is called "straight line" because an equal amount of the cost of the asset is charged off each year over the life of the asset.

Decreasing-rate method   This method is based on the principle that assets depreciate more the first year than in later years; thus, each year of the asset's life the rate of depreciation decreases.

Declining-balance method   The principle of the declining-balance method is similar to that in the decreasing-rate method: assets have a greater decrease in value in their early life than in their later life. This method, however, is computed annually at a fixed rate on the decreasing value of the property rather than on a declining percentage rate.

Production-unit method   The production-unit method is based on the principle of depreciating an asset according to how much use it gets rather than on the age of the asset. That is, two postage meters purchased at the same time at the same price will vary in the amount of depreciation according to the number of pieces of mail each one processes.

Sum-of-the-years-digits method   By this method, the rate of depreciation decreases each year by means of a reducing-fraction method. It is popular with many businesses because it permits a quicker recovery of an investment and results in yearly savings on income taxes.

72 STRAIGHT-LINE METHOD

To compute depreciation by the straight-line method, follow these steps.

1. Determine the probable life of the machine.
2. Determine the scrap value of the machine at the end of its usefulness.
3. Divide the difference between the cost and the scrap value of the machine by its probable life, to find the amount of annual depreciation to be charged.
4. Find the rate of depreciation by dividing the annual depreciation charge by the original cost.

Example

PROBLEM It is estimated that machinery costing $7,500 will have a resale value of $1,500 at the end of 12 years. Find the rate percent to be charged off annually as an expense.

SOLUTION
$7,500 − $1,500 = $6,000, total depreciation
$6,000 ÷ 12 = $500, annual depreciation
500 ÷ 7,500 = $6\frac{2}{3}\%$, annual rate of depreciation

Practice Drill

Equipment that cost $10,400 will have a trade-in value of $3,200 at the end of 9 years. Find the annual depreciation and the annual rate percent of depreciation.

ANSWERS $800; 7.69+%

APPLICATION PROBLEMS

1. The owner of an apartment house estimated the annual depreciation as $2\frac{3}{4}\%$ of the cost. Find the amount charged yearly for depreciation if the original cost of the building is $374,000.

2. A photocopying machine that cost $1,350 is expected to have a life of 6 years and a resale value of 12% of its original cost. Find the resale value of the machine, the annual depreciation charge, and the rate of depreciation.

73 DECREASING-RATE METHOD

In the decreasing-rate method, depreciation is computed on the original value of the property at a decreasing rate each year. The principle behind this method is that various articles, such as automobiles and machinery, depreciate more the first year of purchase than later years.

The decreasing-rate method is advantageous when a firm wants to carry depreciable assets on its books at their resale value. The fact that an article is secondhand, regardless of how long or how much it has been used, results in a depreciation in its value during its first year or two that is at great variance with its actual depreciation. Obsolescence and change in style or type are often responsible for this difference between use value and resale value.

The amount or rate to be deducted from the value of an asset annually depends on the article, the policy of the firm, and the resale and trade-in market.

Example | **PROBLEM**   It is the policy of Jack's Fireball Delivery Service to trade its delivery trucks in every 4 years. The cost of each truck is $2,760 and the average trade-in allowance is $680. Show the annual depreciation charge and the value at which each truck is carried during each year of its use if the following arbitrary rates of depreciation are used: first year, $37\frac{1}{2}$%; second year, 30%; third year, 20%; fourth year, $12\frac{1}{2}$%.

SOLUTION

$2,760 − $680 = $2,080, total depreciation, on which the annual
depreciation is computed

Year	Rate	Depreciation Charge	Book, or Carrying, Value (Including $680 Trade-in)
1	$37\frac{1}{2}$%	$ 780	$1,980
2	30%	624	1,356
3	20%	416	940
4	$12\frac{1}{2}$%	260	680, trade-in value

Total depreciation $2,080

Practice Drill | The furniture and fixtures of the Downtowner Stationery Store were valued at $18,500 for depreciation purposes. Based on this evaluation, the store used the following yearly decreasing depreciation rates: first year, 20%; second year, 18%; third year, 15%; fourth year, 12%; and fifth and succeeding years, 10%. Find the book value of the property at the end of each of the first 5 years.

ANSWERS   first year, $14,800; second year, $11,470; third year, $8,695; fourth year, $6,475; fifth year, $4,625

APPLICATION PROBLEMS

1. A shipping firm uses the following rates in computing annual depreciation charges on its fleet of trucks: first year, 35%; second year, 20%; third year, $17\frac{1}{2}$%; and fourth year, 15%. If class A trucks cost $3,975, class B cost $4,680, and class C cost $5,890, find the book value of each class of trucks at the end of each of the 4 years of use.

2. The total value of property belonging to Yankton Builders Consulting Service, on which depreciation was computed, was $137,800. Based on the original valuation, the following rates were used: first year, 20%; second year, 15%; third year, 12%; fourth year, 8%; and fifth and succeeding years, 5%. Find the book value of the property at the end of each of the first 6 years.

3. Among the property of the business in problem 2 were a collating machine valued at $3,385 and office furniture that cost $6,819. What would be the book value of the collating machine during the fifth year and the office furniture during the eighth year?

74 DECLINING-BALANCE METHOD

With the declining-balance method of depreciation (also called the *fixed-rate method*), depreciation is computed annually at a fixed rate on the decreasing value of the property. In computing depreciation by the declining-balance method, follow these steps.
1. Find the depreciation charge for the first year by taking the fixed rate based on the original amount.
2. Subtract the first year's depreciation from the original amount to find the amount on which the second year's depreciation will be computed.

This procedure is followed annually during the life of the property, with each year's depreciation charge decreasing as the value decreases. The value remaining after the property has outlived its usefulness should equal its scrap value.

Example | **PROBLEM** Depreciation on an air-conditioning unit that cost $1,720 was computed at the rate of $12\frac{1}{2}$% a year on the decreasing value. Find the book value of the unit at the end of 5 years.

SOLUTION

$12\frac{1}{2}\% = \frac{1}{8}$

$\frac{1}{8}$ of \$1,720 = \$215, depreciation first year
\$1,720 − \$215 = \$1,505, value at end of first year

$\frac{1}{8}$ of \$1,505 = \$188.13, depreciation second year
\$1,505 − \$188.13 = \$1,316.87, value at end of second year

$\frac{1}{8}$ of \$1,316.87 = \$164.61, depreciation third year
\$1,316.87 − \$164.61 = \$1,152.26, value at end of third year

$\frac{1}{8}$ of \$1,152.26 = \$144.03, depreciation fourth year
\$1,152.26 − \$144.03 = \$1,008.23, value at end of fourth year

$\frac{1}{8}$ of \$1,008.23 = \$126.03, depreciation fifth year
\$1,008.23 − \$126.03 = \$882.20, value at end of fifth year

Practice Drill Love's Furniture Store provides for the replacement of its delivery equipment by annually putting aside $16\frac{2}{3}\%$ of the decreasing value of the equipment. If the original value of a delivery truck was \$6,400, how much was set aside each year for the first 3 years for the replacement of the truck?

ANSWER   first year, \$1,066.67; second year, \$888.88; third year, \$740.74

APPLICATION PROBLEMS

1. The depreciation charge on store fixtures costing \$6,800 was computed at $6\frac{2}{3}\%$ on the decreasing value annually. Find the amount at which the fixtures were carried on the books at the end of the fifth year.

2. Machinery and equipment costing \$23,800 were installed in a new manufacturing plant. In order to provide for ultimate replacements, a Depreciation Reserve account was set up, to which there was transferred annually $12\frac{1}{2}\%$ of the decreasing value of the property. Find the book value of the property at the beginning of the seventh year.

75 PRODUCTION-UNIT METHOD

The production-unit method of depreciation is used where it can be estimated with reasonable accuracy how many units of production or how many hours of use a machine will produce during its total life. This method is often called the *use method* of depreciation. The depreciation is computed as a fraction or percent of the total depreciation, based on the hours of use or on the actual number of units produced during the year.

To estimate the annual depreciation of a machine by the production-unit method, do the following:

1. Find the total depreciation.
2. Find the percent of the total depreciation to be charged.
3. Find the depreciation charge.

Example

PROBLEM A machine is estimated to have a production potential of 10,000 units during its useful life. The machine cost $34,600 and will have a scrap value of $1,800. What is the depreciation charge for a year during which the machine turned out 940 units?

SOLUTION

$34,600 − $1,800 = $32,800, total depreciation

$\frac{940}{10,000}$ = .094 or 9.4%, percent of total production

9.4% of $32,800 = $3,083.20, depreciation charge

Practice Drill

A duplicating machine costing $680 was guaranteed by its manufacturer to operate satisfactorily for 4,200 hours and to have a trade-in value of $150. How much should be charged to depreciation for a year in which the machine was used 715 hours?

ANSWER $90.22

APPLICATION PROBLEMS

1. Compute the depreciation charge based on the number of units of production.

	Cost	Scrap Value	Maximum Units of Production	Annual Units of Production	Depreciation Charge
a.	$4,500	$ 500	6,000	750	$_____
b.	9,000	2,500	50,000	10,000	_____
c.	884	None	100,000	22,500	_____

2. It is expected that a machine will have to be replaced after producing 60,000 units. The machine cost $26,800 and will have a scrap value of $1,500. Find the depreciation cost during each of the first three years of use if 4,800 units, 6,400 units, and 7,000 units, respectively, are produced. Find the book value of the machine at the end of the third year.

76   SUM-OF-THE-YEARS-DIGITS METHOD

The sum-of-the-years-digits method of depreciation (also known as the *reducing-fraction method*) is used by many businessmen because it allows more for depreciation on articles likely to depreciate rapidly during the first few years of use. This results in a quicker recovery of an investment and in yearly savings of income taxes. Although the sum-of-the-years-digits method is accepted by the Internal Revenue Service for tax purposes, it may be used only if the property has a predicted useful life of three years or more and was acquired (or constructed, reconstructed, or erected) after December 13, 1953. By this method, the rate of depreciation decreases each year, the exact rate depending on the estimated life of the article.

To compute the depreciation, first determine the constant denominator of the fractions to be used as multipliers. This constant denominator, or base, is the sum of all the years of estimated useful life of the article. Thus, if the useful life is 3 years, the fractions to be applied to the total amount to be depreciated will have a constant denominator of $3 + 2 + 1$, or 6.

The declining numerators of the fractions used as multipliers are one smaller each year and begin with the original number of years of estimated life. Thus, if the life of the article is 3 years, the declining numerators will be 3, 2, and 1 for each of the successive 3 years. The depreciation for the first year will be $\frac{3}{6}$ of the total depreciation; for the second year, $\frac{2}{6}$ of the total; and for the third year, $\frac{1}{6}$ of the total.

Example

PROBLEM   A company car that cost \$4,600 will have a trade-in value of \$1,000 in 5 years. Construct a depreciation schedule using the sum-of-the-years-digits method.

SOLUTION

$1 + 2 + 3 + 4 + 5 = 15$, sum of the years digits
\$4,600 (cost) — \$1,000 (trade-in value) = \$3,600, total depreciation

Year	Depreciation	Book Value at End of Year
First	$\frac{5}{15}$ of \$3,600 = \$1,200	\$4,600 — \$1,200 = \$3,400
Second	$\frac{4}{15}$ of \$3,600 = \$960	\$3,400 — \$960 = \$2,440
Third	$\frac{3}{15}$ of \$3,600 = \$720	\$2,440 — \$720 = \$1,720
Fourth	$\frac{2}{15}$ of \$3,600 = \$480	\$1,720 — \$480 = \$1,240
Fifth	$\frac{1}{15}$ of \$3,600 = \$240	\$1,240 — \$240 = \$1,000*

* Trade-in value.

Since the denominator of the fractions used in this method is always the sum of an arithmetic progression, another way to find the denominator is as follows: multiply the total useful life of the article by the total plus 1; then divide the product by 2.

$$\frac{5 \times (5 + 1)}{2} = \frac{5 \times 6}{2} = \frac{30}{2} = 15$$

Practice Drill

A machine costing $1,760 has an estimated life of 4 years and a trade-in value of $350. Find the annual depreciation by the sum-of-the-years-digits method.

ANSWER first year, $564; second year, $423; third year, $282; fourth year, $141

APPLICATION PROBLEMS

1. Find the depreciation of each of the following for the year shown.

	Article	Cost	Salvage or Trade-in Value	Useful Life	Depreciation Year	Amount
a.	Typewriter stand	$175	$25	6 years	3d	$_____
b.	Air conditioner	312	40	5 years	2d	_____
c.	Tape recorder	148	30	10 years	6th	_____
d.	Table	365	60	20 years	10th	_____
e.	Rug	620	None	6 years	3d	_____
f.	Desk lamp	133	15	10 years	5th	_____
g.	Bookcase	290	35	20 years	8th	_____

2. An oil burner that cost $850 was estimated to have a life of 10 years and a salvage value of $60 at the end of that time. Find the depreciation for the first 3 years by the sum-of-the-years-digits method.

77 INTERNAL REVENUE SERVICE REGULATIONS

Recent regulations of the Internal Revenue Service (I.R.S.) make two important provisions in computing depreciation. The first concerns *computing maximum percent allowable;* the second, *computing additional first-year depreciation allowance.*

Computing Maximum Percent Allowable

Federal income tax regulations for the computation of depreciation by the declining-balance method provide that the maximum percent allowable shall not be more than twice the rate that would be used in the straight-line method. For example, if the straight-line method is applied to an article with an expected useful life of 10 years, the depreciation is $\frac{1}{10}$ (10%) of the cost (minus salvage value) each year. The maximum declining-balance rate allowable for income tax purposes on the same item is twice 10%, or 20% (the salvage value is ignored).

Example

PROBLEM Machinery that cost $15,000 was to be written off in 6 years. Find the depreciation and book value for each year by the declining-balance method, using the maximum percent allowable.

SOLUTION The straight-line method rate is $16\frac{2}{3}$%. Two times the straight-line method rate is $33\frac{1}{3}$% or 2 × $16\frac{2}{3}$%, maximum percent allowable.

Year	Annual Depreciation	Depreciation to Date	Book Value at End of Year
0			$15,000.00
1	$5,000 ($\frac{1}{3}$ of $15,000)	$ 5,000.00	10,000.00
2	3,333.33 ($\frac{1}{3}$ of $10,000)	8,333.33	6,666.67
3	2,222.22 ($\frac{1}{3}$ of $6,666.67)	10,555.55	4,444.45
4	1,481.48 ($\frac{1}{3}$ of $4,444.45)	12,027.03	2,962.97
5	987.66 ($\frac{1}{3}$ of $2,962.97)	13,024.69	1,975.31
6	658.44 ($\frac{1}{3}$ of $1,975.31)	13,683.13	1,316.87*

*$1,316.87 = trade-in, or salvage, value

Practice Drill

Delivery equipment costing $8,400 was traded in at the end of 4 years of use when the equipment was replaced. Using the declining-balance method and the maximum rate allowable, find the book value at the end of 4 years.

ANSWER $525

Computing Additional First-Year Depreciation Allowance

I.R.S. permits an additional first-year allowance for depreciation on machinery and equipment only of 20% of the original cost. This extra 20% depreciation is in addition to the depreciation claimed by any of the standard methods. The articles must have a life of at least six years and must have cost no more than $10,000. The depreciation must be claimed during the first year of ownership.

The 20% additional depreciation allowance plus the trade-in, or salvage, value must be deducted from the original cost to find the amount on which the depreciation by the straight-line or the sum-of-the-years-digits method is computed. When the declining-balance method is used, only the additional first-year depreciation allowance is subtracted from the cost. The remaining balance is then multiplied by the annual depreciation rate.

Example

PROBLEM   The owner of a new diner paid $8,400 for electronic equipment that had an estimated useful life of 6 years and a trade-in value of $1,200. Find the additional 20% first-year depreciation allowance and the maximum annual depreciation rate.

SOLUTIONS   Find the additional first-year depreciation.

20% of 8,400 (original cost) = $1,680

The additional first-year depreciation allowance of $1,680 may be taken regardless of the method used.

STRAIGHT-LINE METHOD

1. Deduct the $1,680 additional first-year depreciation allowance and the $1,200 trade-in value from the cost.

$8,400 − $2,880 ($1,680 + $1,200) = $5,520, balance to be depreciated

2. Divide $5,520 by 6 (years of useful life).

$5,520 ÷ 6 = $920, annual ordinary depreciation

The total first-year depreciation is $1,680 (additional depreciation) + $920 (annual ordinary depreciation), or $2,600. The depreciation each year after the first year is $920.

DECLINING-BALANCE METHOD

1. Deduct the additional first-year depreciation ($1,680) from the cost ($8,400).

$8,400 − $1,680 = $6,720, balance to be depreciated

2. The annual ordinary depreciation rate is $33\frac{1}{3}$% (2 times straight-line rate of $16\frac{2}{3}$%).

$33\frac{1}{3}$% of $6,720 = $2,240, normal first-year depreciation
$1,680 + $2,240 = $3,920, total first-year depreciation
$8,400 − $3,920 = $4,480, balance to be used in computing second year's depreciation

The depreciation for the second and succeeding years will be $33\frac{1}{3}$% of the balance remaining after each preceding year's depreciation has been deducted. Thus, the second year's depreciation will be $33\frac{1}{3}$% of $4,480, or $1,493.33, and so on.

SUM-OF-THE-YEARS-DIGITS METHOD

1. Deduct the additional first-year depreciation and the trade-in value from the cost.

$$\$8,400 - \$2,880 \ (\$1,680 + \$1,200) = \$5,520$$

2. The sum of the digits $(1 + 2 + 3 + 4 + 5 + 6)$ is 21. The ordinary depreciation for 1st year is $\frac{6}{21}$, or $\frac{2}{7}$, of \$5,520, or \$1,577.14, and so on.

Practice
Drill

A delivery truck costing \$5,600 is depreciated by the sum-of-the-years-digits method. If the trade-in value after 6 years of use is estimated at \$800 and the additional 20% first-year depreciation allowance permitted by I.R.S. is taken, find the book value at the end of two years.

ANSWER \$2,552.38

APPLICATION PROBLEMS

1. The machinery used by Plastics, Inc. is usually replaced after 5 years of use. The firm provides for this by setting aside annually 40% of the decreasing value of the machinery. This is the maximum percent permitted under I.R.S. regulations. If the original cost of the machinery was \$28,600, how much was in the replacement fund at the end of the second year?

2. Air-conditioning equipment having an estimated life of 10 years was installed in a building at a cost of \$24,000. It is depreciated annually by the declining-balance method. Using the maximum percent allowable, find the book value of the equipment at the end of 3 years.

3. A bookkeeping machine costing \$3,200 was to be written off in 6 years. It was estimated that the machine would be worth \$500 on a trade-in at the end of that time. Find the depreciation and the book value of each year, using the declining-balance method and taking the maximum percent allowable.

4. Store fixtures purchased for a retail establishment cost \$9,750. Assuming an estimated life of 10 years and a trade-in value of \$1,600, find the annual depreciation for each of the first three years by the straight-line method, including the 20% additional first-year depreciation allowance.

5. It cost \$9,890 to furnish a dental office with sophisticated equipment. The equipment was to be written off in 8 years. At that time it was estimated that it will have a scrap value of approximately \$1,500. Find the depreciation for the first year by the straight-line method, by the declining-balance method (using the maximum rate allowed by the I.R.S.), and by the sum-of-the-years-digits method claiming the additional 20% first-year allowance.

PROBLEMS FOR PART TEN

Depreciation Computations

72

1. A posting machine that cost $2,140 has an estimated life of 12 years. It is expected to have a scrap value of $400 at the end of that period. Compute the annual depreciation rate based on the original value and show the carrying, or book, value of the machine every year during its use.

2. A printing press that cost $220,000 has an estimated life of 20 years. At the end of that time, it is felt that the scrap value of the press will be $30,000. Find the amount that should be deducted annually for depreciation expense and the rate percent of depreciation.

73

1. It is the policy of Allied Parcel Service to trade in its delivery trucks every 4 years. If the cost of each truck is $8,850 and the trade-in allowance is estimated at $1,800, show the annual depreciation charge and the value at which each truck is carried during each year of its use if the following arbitrary rates of depreciation are used: first year, 40%; second year, 30%; third year, 20%; fourth year, 10%.

2. The total value of the RCC Corporation's property, on which depreciation was computed, was $482,800. The rates used, based on the original valuation, were: first year, 15%; second year, 12%; third year, 10%; fourth year, 10%; fifth year, 8%; sixth and succeeding years, 5%. Find the book value of the property at the end of each of the first eight years.

74

1. Depreciation on a lathe that cost $3,225 was computed at the rate of $16\frac{2}{3}\%$ a year on the decreasing value. Find the book value at the end of four years.

2. A depreciation rate on a factory crane costing $24,800 was 8% on the decreasing value for 7 years. Find the annual depreciation and the carrying, or book, value each year.

75

1. The life of an air-conditioning unit used in a retail store is estimated to be 4,800 hours. If the unit cost $1,650 and is used 8 hours a day, 6 days a week, for approximately 16 weeks a year, how much annual depreciation should be charged? The unit has no scrap value at the end of its estimated life.

2. A lathe is expected to wear out after 28,000 hours of normal use. The lathe cost $11,600 and will have a salvage value of $1,200. Find the depreciation cost for a year in which it was used 7 hours a day and 5 days a week for 50 weeks.

76

1. A floor-waxing machine was purchased for use in an office building. The machine cost $434, and it is expected that a trade-in allowance of $50 will be given after 6 years of use. Compute the depreciation expense for each of the 6 years, using the sum-of-the-years-digits method.

2. A lathe cost $9,675 and has an estimated life of 5 years. Assuming that it will have a salvage value of $750 at the end of this time, how much will the annual depreciation expense be? Use the sum-of-the-years-digits method.

77

1. Using the declining-balance method of computing depreciation and the maximum rate allowed by I.R.S., find the book value after 3 years of use of a cutting machine that cost $2,430. It is estimated that the machine will have to be replaced at the end of 8 years.

2. Compute the depreciation and the book value at the end of each of the first four years of use of a power drill that cost $1,895. It is expected that the drill will be used six years. Prepare a declining-balance depreciation schedule, using the maximum rate allowed.

3. A billing machine cost $6,090. It is estimated that the machine will have a use value of 8 years, at the end of which time it will be practically worthless because of obsolescence. Its scrap value is computed at $350. Find the annual depreciation by the straight-line method, including the 20% additional first-year depreciation allowance.

4. A planer originally costing $4,550 is to be written off in 6 years. The scrap value of the machine is estimated at $600. Prepare depreciation schedules showing the annual depreciation and the book value at the end of each of the 6 years if the depreciation is computed by the declining-balance method (using the maximum rate allowable) and by the sum-of-the-years-digits method. The additional first-year depreciation allowance is applied to each method.

$$6090 \div .20 = 1218$$
$$\times 565.25 = 1st \ year \ depr$$
$$-350$$
$$5740$$
$$1218$$
$$4522 \div 8 = 565.25$$

PART ELEVEN

Accounting Processes

Accountants can easily identify the department or division of a company to which most expenses are to be charged. For example, the salaries of salesmen and the cost of advertising and promotion are selling expenses and are charged to the sales department. But there are certain types of expenses that are not so easily allocated, such as the amount to be charged to the sporting goods department of a large department store for rent, heat, light, and water. General expenses such as those mentioned are called *operating expenses,* or *overhead.* They are charged to various departments in a business in several ways, four of which are discussed in this part: according to space each department or division occupies, according to sales volume (especially applicable to a retail store), according to direct labor cost (applicable to manufacturing firms), and according to prime cost (also applicable principally to manufacturing firms).

Another operation that has specific application to accounting is computing the profit or loss of an enterprise each fiscal period. In a merchandising business, this means finding net sales, cost of goods sold, gross profit, and net income. After profits or losses are computed, financial statements are prepared.

It is one thing to prepare financial statements, such as income statements and balance sheets, and another thing to interpret them. An entrepreneur cannot measure the progress of his business merely by studying current figures. He must make comparisons with previous periods in terms of sales volume, expenses, gross profit, assets, and liabilities — not only in dollar amounts but also in percentages and ratios — if he is to have a really accurate picture of his operation and the current status of the business.

One of the most important figures in any enterprise is the one showing its cash position. The amount of cash shown on a business firm's records must obviously agree with the amount shown on the records of the bank where the money is kept. Differences must be reconciled, and this reconciliation is usually performed monthly when the bank statement is received.

78　OVERHEAD DISTRIBUTION

To determine the cost of manufacturing merchandise, it is necessary to add a share of the general expenses, or overhead, to the cost of materials and labor. Various methods are used for distributing overhead among the various departments of a business.

Finding Distribution Based on Space Occupied

One of the most popular methods used in distributing overhead among the various departments of a business is according to the space occupied. This is a legitimate way to allocate expenses, since a great many expenses, for example, rent, property taxes, interest on mortgage, heat, depreciation of building, fire insurance, cleaning and maintenance, and so on, have a direct bearing on the amount of space each department consumes.

The following example illustrates how overhead is distributed according to square feet occupied by each unit or department in a factory.

Example | **PROBLEM**　Find the share of the monthly overhead of $3,160 charged to each of the following departments of a metal-container manufacturing company on the basis of the square feet of space occupied.

Department	Space
Raw Materials	2,500 sq. ft.
Manufacturing	5,000 sq. ft.
Storage	2,000 sq. ft.
Administrative	500 sq. ft.

SOLUTION　The total number of square feet occupied by all departments is 10,000.

$$\frac{2,500}{10,000} = \tfrac{1}{4} \qquad \tfrac{1}{4} \text{ of } \$3,160 = \$ \ \ 790, \text{ Raw Materials Dept.}$$

$$\frac{5,000}{10,000} = \tfrac{1}{2} \qquad \tfrac{1}{2} \text{ of } \$3,160 = \ \ 1,580, \text{ Manufacturing Dept.}$$

$$\frac{2,000}{10,000} = \tfrac{1}{5} \qquad \tfrac{1}{5} \text{ of } \$3,160 = \ \ \ \ 632, \text{ Storage Dept.}$$

$$\frac{500}{10,000} = \tfrac{1}{20} \qquad \tfrac{1}{20} \text{ of } \$3,160 = \ \underline{\ \ \ 158}, \text{ Administrative Dept.}$$

$3,160, total overhead

Practice Drills

The books of a business disclosed the following manufacturing costs.

Materials	$39,811
Labor costs	24,538
Other expenses (overhead)	11,742
Total manufacturing cost	$76,091

1. What percent of the total manufacturing cost is each of these costs?
2. The materials and labor costs are the direct costs of manufacturing. Other expenses represent overhead. What percent of the material costs, of the labor costs, and of the total direct costs (materials and labor) is the overhead?

ANSWERS   1. materials, 52.32%; labor costs, 32.25%; other expenses, 15.43%
2. materials, 29.49%; labor costs, 47.85%; total direct costs, 18.24%

Finding Distribution Based on Sales

In many retail establishments, operating expenses are distributed according to the sales volume in each department.

Example

PROBLEM Pirelli's Department Store had operating expenses (rent, utilities, janitorial service, etc.) of $16,000 for August. The total sales of the entire store for the month were $188,000. Of this amount, the bookstore produced $6,000 in sales. Find the amount of overhead to be charged to the bookstore for the month.

SOLUTION $\dfrac{\$6,000}{\$188,000} = .03191$

$.03191 \times \$16,000 = \$510.56$, overhead

Practice Drill

The Economy Food Store had sales of $168,000 for the month of April. Of this amount, $14,000 in sales were made by the Produce Department. Operating expenses for the period came to $8,800. Assuming that operating expenses are distributed according to the sales of each department, find the Produce Department's share for April.

ANSWER $733.33

Finding Distribution Based on Cost of Direct Labor

A common method of distributing overhead in factories is according to the percent of direct labor costs (wages paid to workers who contribute directly to the making of the company's products — machinists, lathe operators, inspectors, *et al.*) that is the total overhead.

To determine the overhead rate to be charged to each department:
1. Find the rate percent that total overhead is of the total direct labor cost by dividing the total overhead by the total direct labor cost.
2. Multiply the rate percent by the direct labor costs of each department.

Example

PROBLEM The Extruded Plastics Company distributes overhead to each of its six departments according to the ratio of total overhead to the total direct labor costs. During January, the total overhead for the factory amounted to $20,000; the total direct labor costs, $140,000. Find the rate percent to be applied to each department. Then find the amount to be charged to the Quality Control Department whose direct labor costs for the month were $16,000.

SOLUTION $\dfrac{\$20,000}{\$140,000}$ = .1429, or 14.29%, rate to be applied to each department

$16,000 × .1429 = $2,286.40, amount to be charged to the Quality Control Department

Practice
Drills

The King-Tex Press, a publishing house, distributes overhead to its various departments according to the percent the total overhead is of the total direct labor costs. During the month of September, the total overhead was $36,000, and the total direct labor costs were $180,000.
1. Find the overhead percent of direct labor cost to be applied to each department.
2. Find the amount of overhead to be charged to the Bindery Department, which has a direct labor cost of $18,000.

ANSWERS   1. 20%   2. $3,600

Finding Distribution Based on Total Prime Cost

Some manufacturers distribute overhead according to the ratio of total overhead to the total prime cost. *Prime cost* is the sum of the costs of total direct labor and the total material used in manufacturing the product (the primary costs of production).

In determining the overhead rate to be charged to each department, do the following:

1. Add the total direct labor costs to the cost of materials to find the prime cost.
2. Find the rate percent of the total overhead to the total prime cost by dividing the total overhead by the prime cost.
3. Multiply the rate percent by the prime cost of each department.

Example

PROBLEM Johnstown Mills manufactures cotton fabrics. Overhead is allocated to each department according to the ratio of total overhead to the total prime cost. During February, total direct labor costs came to $216,000 and the cost of materials to $84,000. The total overhead for the month was $45,000. Find the overhead percent of prime cost to be charged to each department. Then find the amount of overhead to be charged to the Design Department with a prime cost of $18,500.

SOLUTION $216,000 + $84,000 = $300,000, prime cost

$$\frac{\$45,000}{\$300,000} = .15 \text{ or } 15\%, \text{ percent of prime cost to be charged to each department}$$

$18,500 × .15 = $2,775, overhead to be charged to Design Department

Practice Drills

Loomis Paper Company distributes overhead to each department in the factory according to the ratio of the total overhead to the total prime cost. During the month of October, the total direct labor costs came to $80,000 and the cost of materials to $24,000. The total overhead for the month was $10,000.

1. Find the overhead percent of the prime cost to be charged to each department. $9.621\% = \frac{10,000}{104,000}$
2. Find the amount of overhead to be charged to the Processing Department with a prime cost of $14,000.

ANSWERS   1. .0962 or 9.62%   2. $1,346.80

APPLICATION PROBLEMS

1. Find the rate percent of overhead to be charged to each of the following departments of a radio manufacturer if it is computed on the basis of the number of square feet of space occupied by each department.

Department	Space (Square Feet)	Percent of Overhead
Raw Materials	1,800	_____
Parts Manufacturing	6,400	_____
Assembling	3,200	_____
Finished Goods	2,500	_____
Offices	1,100	_____

2. The sales, in round numbers, of the departments of a small specialty store during a recent month are shown in the following table. The general and administrative expenses for the month amounted to $4,500. A portion of these expenses is charged to each department on the basis of its percent of total store sales. Compute the distribution.

Department	Sales	Overhead
Notions	$ 3,000	$_____
Dresses and Suits	18,000	_____
Shoes	5,000	_____
Lingerie	2,500	_____
Costume Jewelry	1,500	_____

3. The Jacobi Pump Company distributes overhead to each of its nine departments according to the ratio of total overhead to the total direct labor costs. During July the total overhead costs for the factory amounted to $120,000, and the total direct labor costs to $270,000.
a. Find the rate percent to be applied to each department.
b. Find the amount to be charged to the Inspection Department whose direct labor costs for the month were $54,000.

4. Overhead in the Universal Lithograph Corporation is allocated to each department according to the ratio of total overhead to the total prime cost. During the month of August, total direct labor costs came to $70,000 and the cost of materials to $16,000. The total overhead for the month was $6,000.
a. Find the overhead percent of prime cost to be charged to each department.
b. Find the amount of overhead to be charged to the Cartography Department with a prime cost of $7,500.

79 DETERMINING PROFIT OR LOSS

"Profit" means "gain." In business *net profit* (or *net income*) is the net gain of an owner after all his costs and expenses have been paid out of his sales revenue. If his sales revenue is less than his costs and expenses, a *net loss* (or *loss*) results. The results of operations are summarized in the income statement, which may be prepared monthly, quarterly, and/or yearly.

Net Sales

In determining net profit, the first step is to find the net sales. *Net sales* is the income received from the sale of merchandise, minus goods that have been returned by customers and minus discounts that have been allowed customers.

Example

Sales		$235,600
Less: Sales Returns and Allowances	$7,700	
Sales Discounts	9,640	17,340
Net Sales		$218,260

Cost of Goods Sold

The next step in finding net income for a business is to determine what the goods that were sold cost the firm. The cost of goods sold is found as follows.

1. Determine the value of the inventory of goods on hand at the beginning of the period for which profits are being computed.

2. To this beginning inventory, add purchases made during the period, minus the cost of goods that were returned for credit and minus discounts taken on purchases. The amount obtained is called goods available for sale.

3. From the goods available for sale subtract the merchandise inventory at the end of the period for which profits are being computed. (In the example it is assumed that profits are being computed on operations from January 1 to December 31 in the same year.)

Example

Merchandise Inventory, January 1		$ 57,800
Purchases	$112,300	
Less: Purchases Returns and Allow.	$3,450	
Purchases Discount	+1,550	5,000
Net Purchases		107,300
Cost of Goods Available for Sale		$165,100
Less Merchandise Inventory, December 31		43,300
Cost of Goods Sold		$121,800

Gross Profit on Sales

Once the net sales and cost of sales have been determined, the business owner needs merely to subtract the cost of goods sold from net sales to find his gross profit on sales.

Example

Net Sales	$218,260
Less Cost of Goods Sold	121,800
Gross Profit on Sales	$ 96,460

Net Income from Operations

Although gross profit is very meaningful to the businessman, he must determine his net income from operations before he will know whether his business is performing satisfactorily. To find net income from operations, he totals his expenses of operation and subtracts the amount from his gross profit on sales. Expenses of operation include such overhead as salaries, supplies used, insurance expense, rent, depreciation, and utilities.

Example

Gross Profit on Sales..		$96,460
Operating Expenses:		
Bad Debts...	$ 2,600	
Depreciation — Building............................	2,900	
Depreciation — Delivery Equipment..........	3,200	
Depreciation — Office Equipment............	1,400	
Insurance...	760	
Miscellaneous Expense............................	280	
Payroll Taxes..	4,200	
Salaries	43,600	
Supplies Used..	360	
Utilities	+ 1,140	
Total Operating Expenses...		−60,440
Net Income from Operations.......................................		$36,020

Other Income and Expenses

Income that is not derived from the regular operations of the business is classified as *nonoperating income* or, more commonly, *other income.* Examples are interest earned on notes receivable and income from tenants who pay rent for use of the company's building.

Likewise, expenses that are not the result of business operations are classified as other expenses. Interest paid on bank loans is an example.

Other income and expenses must be considered in arriving at the firm's net income or loss for the period. The other income items are added, and from this amount is deducted the total of the other expenses. The difference is added to or subtracted from (if expenses exceed income) the net income from operations to arrive at net income or loss.

Example			
Net Income from Operations			$36,020
Other Income:			
Interest Income	$ 460		
Rental Income	+ 975		
Total Other Income	$1,435		
Other Expenses:			
Interest Expense	− 864	+ 571	
Net Income			$36,591

Practice Drill

Find the net sales, cost of goods sold, net income from operations, and net income for the Jamestown Distributing Corporation.

Sales, $72,100; sales returns and allowances, $1,485; sales discounts, $113.

Beginning inventory, $18,250; purchases, $44,130; purchases returns and allowances, $855; purchases discount, $225; ending inventory, $14,000.

Operating expenses: Bad debts, $350; depreciation — building, $500; delivery equipment, $900; office equipment, $450; insurance, $210; miscellaneous expense, $55; payroll taxes, $1,025; salaries, $14,125; supplies used, $103; utilities, $245.

Interest income, $135; rental income, $240; interest expense, $120.

ANSWERS $70,502, net sales; $47,300, cost of goods sold; $5,239, net income from operations; $5,494, net income.

APPLICATION PROBLEMS

1. From the following information, find the net sales, cost of goods sold, gross profit on sales, and net income or loss for the Wilson Office Supply Company.

Sales, $25,264.82; sales returns and allowances, $410.03; sales discounts, $206.40.

Merchandise inventory, January 1, current year, $5,000; purchases, $16,045.50; purchases returns and allowances, $215; purchases discount, $114.16; merchandise inventory, December 31, current year, $8,000.

Operating expenses: rent, $1,700; miscellaneous expenses, $525.15; salaries, $8,877.82; shipping expenses, $150.10; bad debts, $125; depreciation, $400; supplies used, $225; insurance, $70.

2. Complete the following summary of income and expenses of the Home Department Store for the year ending December 31. Assume that this is a new business and there was no inventory at the beginning of the year.

Dept.	Net Sales	Purchases	Closing Inventory	Cost of Goods Sold	Gross Profit	Operating Expenses	Net Income
A	$ 7,768	$ 10,645	$ 7,078	$3,567	$4,201	$1,569	$2,632
B	14,847	15,640	11,664	_____	_____	4,278	_____
C	42,583	62,878	42,473	_____	_____	9,597	_____
D	98,809	166,816	97,649	_____	_____	8,989	_____
E	8,644	8,090	6,025	_____	_____	4,045	_____
F	37,508	45,276	29,644	_____	_____	9,643	_____
G	24,865	25,860	17,867	_____	_____	5,520	_____
H	32,766	32,758	24,676	_____	_____	3,861	_____
I	7,299	6,982	4,348	_____	_____	2,929	_____
J	24,568	28,761	19,433	_____	_____	6,877	_____
Totals $_____	$_____	$_____	$_____	$_____	$_____	$_____

80 INCOME STATEMENT ANALYSIS

Comparing the results of operations of one period with another provides answers to such questions as, "Are sales increasing at a satisfactory rate? What is the trend regarding expenses—are any getting out of line when compared to those of earlier periods? Are our profits improving?"

Comparisons of operations may be according to averages for a certain number of years, percents of increase or decrease in individual income and expense items, and the percent of net sales that each item represents.

Average Income and Expenses

In the following example, notice that the results of operations are compared for a 3-year period. The totals for the entire period are then taken and the average for 3 years is determined. This 3-year period can then be easily compared with any previous 3-year period.

Example | **PROBLEM** The results of operations of the Stewart Electronics Company are shown on the following income statement. Complete the statement.

SOLUTION

STEWART ELECTRONIC COMPANY
COMPARATIVE INCOME STATEMENT

	First Year	Second Year	Third Year	Total for 3-Year Period	Yearly Average
Sales..............................	$88,263	$98,614	$117,197	$304,074	$101,358
Less Cost of Goods Sold					
Beginning Inventory	$23,017	$18,559	$ 20,640	$ 62,216	$ 20,739
Add Purchases	48,990	54,077	67,129	170,196	56,732
Add Freight In........................	3,243	3,816	4,467	11,526	3,842
Cost of Goods Avail. for Sale..	$75,250	$76,452	$ 92,236	$243,938	$ 81,313
Less Ending Inventory	15,056	18,922	13,679	47,657	15,886
Cost of Goods Sold	$60,194	$57,530	$ 78,557	$196,281	$ 65,427
Gross Profit	$28,069	$41,084	$ 38,640	$107,793	$ 35,931
Less Expenses	4,016	7,129	5,341	16,486	5,495
Net Income from Operations	$24,053	$33,955	$ 33,299	$ 91,307	$ 30,436

Percent of Increase or Decrease

A second method of analyzing the results of operations is according to the percent of increase or decrease of individual items for one year as compared with another.

Example | **PROBLEM** Following is a comparative condensed income statement for a 2-year period for Hudson Supply Company. Complete the statement. (Compute using the previous year's amounts as 100%, or base. Measure the current year's amounts against the earlier period. Each percent should be computed to the nearest tenth. Show all decreases in parentheses.)

SOLUTION

HUDSON SUPPLY COMPANY
COMPARATIVE CONDENSED INCOME STATEMENT
YEARS ENDED THIS YEAR AND LAST YEAR

	Amounts		Increase or Decrease During This Year	
	This Year	Last Year	Amount	Percent
Income				
Net Sales	$816,519	$722,810	$ 93,709	13.0
Cost of Goods Sold				
Stock, Beginning of Year	$ 24,818	$ 36,219	$(11,401)	(31.5)
Purchases	562,533	499,086	63,447	12.7
Goods Available for Sale	$587,351	$535,305	$ 52,046	9.7
Stock, End of Year	30,008	42,814	(12,806)	(29.9)
Cost of Goods Sold	$557,343	$492,491	$ 64,852	13.2
Gross Profit	$259,176	$230,319	$ 28,857	12.5
Operating Expenses				
Selling Expenses	$ 89,514	$ 68,623	$ 20,891	30.4
Administrative Expenses	58,912	43,819	15,093	34.4
Miscellaneous Expenses	63,876	77,946	(14,070)	(18.1)
Total Operating Expenses	$212,302	$190,388	$ 21,914	11.4
Net Income from Operations	$ 46,874	$ 39,931	$ 6,943	17.4

Note: The amounts shown in parentheses are decreases.

Percent of Net Sales

A third method of analyzing results of operations is to find the percent of net sales each item on the income statement represents.

Example | **PROBLEM**   Complete the following income statement, indicating the percent of net sales each item represents. Compute each percent to the nearest hundredth.

SOLUTION

ETON CLOTHIERS
INCOME STATEMENT
YEAR ENDED DECEMBER 31, 19X7

			Percent of Net Sales
Income:			
Sales	$206,684		112.15
Less Sales Returns and			
Allowances	22,392		12.15
Net Sales		$184,292	100.00
Cost of Goods Sold:			
Merchandise Inventory,			
Jan. 1	$ 38,675		
Purchases $110,218			
Add Freight In ... 5,809			
Total	116,027		
Cost of Goods Avail. for Sale.... $154,702			
Less Merchandise Inventory,			
Dec. 31	41,658		
Cost of Goods Sold		113,044	61.34
Gross Profit on Sales		$ 71,248	38.66
Operating Expenses:			
Office Expenses	$ 4,381		2.38
Selling Expenses	15,024		8.15
Delivery Expenses.................	1,175		.64
Miscellaneous Expenses	2,218		1.20
Total Operating Expenses		$ 22,798	12.37
Net Income from Operations		$ 48,450	26.29

APPLICATION PROBLEMS

1. The following comparative income statement provides income and expense amounts for the current period and for the preceding period. Complete the statement and determine the increase or decrease in each item during the current period.

DIXON NOVELTY COMPANY
COMPARATIVE INCOME STATEMENT
YEARS ENDED CURRENT AND LAST

	Amounts		Amount of Increase or Decrease During Current Year
	Current	Last	
Income			
Sales	$186,545	$180,986	$ 5,559
Less Cost of Goods Sold			
Finished Goods Inventory, Jan. 1	$ 18,819	$ 21,008	$ (2,189)*
Add Cost of Goods Manufactured	157,312	163,912	(6600)
Total Available Goods	$176131	$184920	$(8789)
Less Finished Goods Inv., Dec. 31	23,409	31,176	(7767)
Cost of Goods Sold	$152722	$153744	$( )
Gross Profit	$ 33823	$27242	$
Less Operating Expenses	9,709	8,815	
Net Income Before Income Taxes	$ 24114	$ 18427	$

*Decreases are shown in parentheses.

2. The books of Tilton Decorators for the year 19X7 showed the following information: net sales, $164,000; purchases, $110,386; merchandise inventory at beginning of year, $28,614; inventory of goods at end of year, $17,500; and operating expenses, $13,760.

a. Prepare an income statement showing the net profit.

b. Using net sales as a basis or 100%, find the percent of net sales to which the cost of goods sold is equal and to which the gross profit is equal.

c. Determine what percent the operating expenses are of the net sales and of the gross profit.

d. Compute the percent that the net profit is of the net sales.

3. Last year the sales of the Miltown Company totaled $396,814. Expenses incurred during the year included the following: rent, $14,500; advertising, $8,995; salaries, $37,503; insurance, $5,741; and taxes, $7,708. What percent of sales was each item of expense? (Compute to the nearest tenth of a percent.)

81 BALANCE SHEET ANALYSIS

Comparing the condition of the business—that is, the assets and liabilities—for one year with another year provides meaningful answers to such questions as "Have current assets increased or decreased over the previous period? How do current liabilities compare? How can these changes in dollar amounts and percents be explained? Are accounts receivable increasing disproportionately? Are current and fixed liabilities increasing too rapidly?"

Determining Increase or Decrease

One method of analyzing a firm's condition is to determine the amount of increase or decrease in assets and liabilities in the current year as compared with the previous year.

Example | **PROBLEM**   Complete the following comparative balance sheet.

SOLUTION

HOME PRODUCTS MANUFACTURING COMPANY
COMPARATIVE BALANCE SHEET
YEARS ENDED CURRENT AND PRECEDING

	Current Year	Preceding Year	Increase	Decrease
Assets				
Cash	$ 3,260	$ 5,168		$1,908
Notes Receivable	2,500	1,250	$1,250	
Accounts Receivable	5,975	11,216		5,241
Inventories	47,342	49,095		1,753
Store Equipment....................	6,412	6,123	289	
Office Equipment	2,085	1,764	321	
Delivery Equipment	11,616	5,616	6,000	
Total Assets	$79,190	$80,232	$7,860	$8,902
Liabilities and Stockholders' Equity				
Liabilities				
Notes Payable	$ 5,400	$ 3,500	$1,900	
Accounts Payable	12,878	8,852	4,026	
Interest Payable	209	94	115	
Total Liabilities	$18,487	$12,446	$6,041	
Stockholders' Equity				
Common Stock.................	$50,000	$50,000		
Retained Earnings	10,703	17,786		$7,083
Total Stockholders' Equity	$60,703	$67,786		$7,083
Total Liabilities and Stockholders' Equity	$79,190	$80,232	$6,041	$7,083

Determining Averages

A second method of analyzing individual balance sheet items is to find the averages, which can be used for comparative purposes.

Example | PROBLEM   Find the total of the balance sheet items for Oak Ridge Printing Shop for 19X1 and 19X2, the average for those years, and the increase or decrease in each item for 19X3 when compared with the 19X1-X2 averages.

SOLUTION

OAK RIDGE PRINTING SHOP
COMPARATIVE BALANCE SHEET

	19X1	19X2	Total for 2-Year Period	Yearly Average	19X3	19X3 Compared with Yearly Average Increase	Decrease
Assets							
Cash	$ 7,200	$ 1,876	$ 9,076	$ 4,538.00	$ 5,590	$ 1,052.00	
Notes Receivable	750	3,500	4,250	2,125.00	5,000	2,875.00	
Accounts Receivable	5,987	6,246	12,233	6,116.50	8,087	1,970.50	
Merchandise Inventory	18,400	21,684	40,084	20,042.00	19,271		$ 771.00
Furniture and Fixtures	3,875	4,108	7,983	3,991.50	4,663	671.50	
Equipment	12,058	14,619	26,677	13,338.50	16,186	2,847.50	
Total Assets	$48,270	$52,033	$100,303	$50,151.50	$58,797	$ 9,416.50	$ 771.00
Liabilities and Owner's Equity							
Liabilities							
Notes Payable	$ 4,263	$ 3,750	$ 8,013	$ 4,006.50	$ 1,990		$2,016.50
Accounts Payable	9,245	12,117	21,362	10,681.00	10,255		426.00
Interest Payable	118	103	221	110.50	81		29.50
Total Liabilities	$13,626	$15,970	$ 29,596	$14,798.00	$12,326		$2,472.00
Owner's Equity	34,644	36,063	70,707	35,353.50	46,471	11,117.50	
Total Liabilities and Owner's Equity	$48,270	$52,033	$100,303	$50,151.50	$58,797	$11,117.50	$2,472.00

*The difference between the totals of the Increase and Decrease columns should equal the difference between the totals of the Yearly Average and 19X3 columns of both Total Assets and Total Liabilities and Equity.

Determining Increase or Decrease and Percent of Change

A third method of analyzing balance sheet items is to find the amount of increase or decrease and the percent of increase or decrease in one year as compared with another year.

Example | **PROBLEM** Find the increase or decrease and the percent of increase or decrease in the balance sheet items of Superior Associates, Incorporated, for the current year as compared with the previous year. (Compute each percent to the nearest tenth.)

SOLUTION

SUPERIOR ASSOCIATES, INCORPORATED
COMPARATIVE BALANCE SHEET
YEARS ENDED THIS YEAR AND LAST YEAR

	End of This Year	End of Last Year	Increase	Decrease	Percent Change
Assets					
Current Assets					
Cash	$ 6,645	$ 5,316	$ 1,329		+ 25.0
Accounts Receivable	14,595	12,510	2,085		+ 16.7
Merchandise Inventory	62,304	93,456		$31,152	– 33.3
Supplies on Hand	3,798	3,376	422		+ 12.5
Total Current Assets	$ 87,342	$114,658	$ 3,836	$31,152	– 23.8
Fixed Assets					
Furniture and Fixtures	$ 5,270	$ 4,960	$ 310		+ 6.3
Plant and Equipment	45,122	32,816	12,306		+ 37.5
Total Fixed Assets	$ 50,392	$ 37,776	$12,616		+ 33.4
Total Assets	$137,734	$152,434	$16,452	$31,152	– 9.6
Liabilities and Stockholders' Equity					
Current Liabilities					
Notes Payable	$ 10,752	$ 9,600	$ 1,152		+ 12.0
Accounts Payable	15,048	18,812		3,764	– 20.0
Total Current Liabilities	$ 25,800	$ 28,412	$ 1,152	$ 3,764	– 9.2
Stockholders' Equity					
Common Stock	$100,000	$100,000			
Retained Earnings	11,934	24,022		$12,088	– 50.3
Total Stockholders' Equity	$111,934	$124,022		$12,088	– 9.7
Total Liabilities and Stockholders' Equity	$137,734	$152,434	$ 1,152	$15,852	– 9.6

Determining Percent of Total Assets

A fourth method of comparative balance sheet analysis is to find the percent of the total assets that each asset item represents and the percent of the total liabilities that each liability item represents.

Example | **PROBLEM** Find the percent each asset represents of the total assets and the percent each liability represents of the total liabilities in the Hester Cook Dress Salon's comparative balance sheet. (Compute each percent to the nearest tenth.)

SOLUTION

HESTER COOK DRESS SALON
COMPARATIVE BALANCE SHEET
DECEMBER 31, CURRENT YEAR AND LAST YEAR

	Dec. 31, Current Year	Dec. 31, Last Year	Percent of Total Current Year	Percent of Total Last Year
Assets				
Current Assets				
Cash	$ 2,106	$ 1,876	3.5	4.2
Notes Receivable	4,575	2,800	7.6	6.3
Accounts Receivable	5,592	4,260	9.3	9.6
Stock Inventory	35,815	25,495	59.4	57.3
Total Current Assets	$48,088	$34,431	79.8	77.4
Fixed Assets				
Furniture and Fixtures	$ 8,964	$ 7,200	14.9	16.2
Other Equipment	3,211	2,875	5.3	6.4
Total Fixed Assets	$12,175	$10,075	20.2	22.6
Total Assets	$60,263	$44,506	100.0	100.0
Liabilities and Owner's Equity				
Current Liabilities				
Accounts Payable	$ 1,749	$ 2,290	2.9	5.1
Other Liabilities	2,115	1,935	3.5	4.4
Total Current Liabilities	$ 3,864	$ 4,225	6.4	9.5
Owner's Equity				
Hester Cook, Investment, Jan. 1	$40,281	$25,967	66.8	58.3
Net Profit for Year	16,118	14,314	26.8	32.2
Hester Cook, Investment, Dec. 31	$56,399	$40,281	93.6	90.5
Total Liabilities and Owner's Equity	$60,263	$44,506	100.0	100.0

APPLICATION PROBLEMS

1. The assets of a business amount to $37,620, and its liabilities amount to $10,032. Find the ratio of assets to liabilities. (Compute to the nearest hundredth. To find the ratio, divide assets by liabilities.)

2. Complete the comparative balance sheet information for Daniels Building Supply Corporation.

	19X2	19X3	Increase or Decrease* Amt.	%	Percent of Total Assets 19X2	19X3
Assets						
Current Assets						
Cash	$ 53,615	$ 68,744				
Notes Receivable	12,520	9,760				
Accounts Receivable	93,110	112,400				
Merchandise Inventory	118,695	116,200				
Total Current Assets	$277,940	$357,104				
Fixed Assets						
Building and Equipment	$128,600	$146,200				
Store Equipment	15,970	18,666				
Delivery Equipment	8,310	3,428				
Total Fixed Assets	$152,880	$168,294				
Total Assets	$430,820	$525,398			100.0%	100.0%
Liabilities and Stockholders' Equity						
Current Liabilities						
Notes Payable	$ 25,000	$ 18,610				
Accounts Payable	64,115	78,690				
Income Tax Payable	4,090	6,425				
Total Current Liabilities	$ 93,205	$103,725				
Long-Term Liabilities						
Bonds Payable	$ 50,000	$ 62,000				
Mortgage Payable	72,000	67,440				
Total Long-Term Liabilities	$122,000	$129,440				
Stockholders' Equity						
Common Stock	$180,000	$220,000				
Retained Earnings	35,615	72,233				
Total Stockholders' Equity	$215,615	$292,233				
Total Liabilities and Stockholders' Equity	$430,820	$525,398			100.0%	100.0%

*Show decreases in parentheses.

3. The *working capital ratio*—a comparison of current assets with current liabilities—is a very important amount to accountants and financial analysts. Most businesses are expected to maintain at least a 2-to-1 ratio of current assets to current liabilities. The ratio is found by dividing current assets by current liabilities. What is the working capital ratio for Daniels Building Supply Corporation (in problem 2) for 19X2 and 19X3?

82 DETERMINING VALUE OF GOODWILL

Goodwill is the value of any benefits that may accrue to a business from its good reputation, its favorable location, its monopoly privilege, and similar advantages the business enjoys. It is the cash value of the future profits of a business that are in excess of a normal return on capital.

The appraisal method is frequently used in determining the value of goodwill, especially when a small business is being sold. This means simply that the buyer and seller get together and place on the business a value that is in excess of the value of the assets.

There are several methods of determining the value of goodwill, and three of the most-used methods—all based on profits of the firm—are discussed in this unit.

Capitalized Value of Future Excess Net Profits

Goodwill may be the capitalized value of the future excess net profits when profits over normal return continue indefinitely and in equal amounts. (The normal rate of return on capital invested is the average annual rate realized by similar businesses; it may vary from a low of 5% or 6% to a high of 15% or 20%.)

To determine the value of goodwill by this method, do the following.
1. Subtract from the average annual net profit the normal return on capital invested. The difference is the excess net profits.
2. Divide the excess net profits by the rate of return on capital invested in businesses of this type. The quotient is the capitalized value of the excess net profits, and it is the value placed on the goodwill.

Example | **PROBLEM** The books of a business about to be sold disclosed the average annual net profits as $32,850 and the net worth as $180,000. The normal rate of return on capital invested in businesses of this type is 15%. Compute the value to be placed on the goodwill if the excess net profits are capitalized at the same rate of return.

SOLUTION $32,850, average annual net profits
            <u>27,000,</u> 15% of $180,000 (normal income)

            $ 5,850, excess net profits
            Capitalized value of excess net profits of $5,850
            (valued at 15%) = $5,850 ÷ 15 = $390 (1%)

            100 × $390 = $39,000, value of goodwill

The amount $39,000 represents the capitalization of that portion of the profits which is not attributable to the tangible net assets.

Practice Drill

Determine the value to be placed on the goodwill of a business at the time it is sold. The records show the average annual net profits to be $48,600 and the net worth to be $320,000. The normal rate of return on capital invested in businesses of this type is 12%. Capitalize the excess net profits at the same rate of return.

ANSWER $85,000

Purchase Price of Profits

Goodwill may be estimated at several years' purchase price of the net or gross profits of any one year, or at several years' purchase price of the average profits of a number of years. To determine the value of goodwill by this method, do the following.

1. Find the net, gross, or average profits. To find the average profits of a number of years, add the profits and divide by the number of years.
2. Multiply the profits by the number of years' purchase price. The product is the value placed on the goodwill.

Example

PROBLEM   The amount paid for goodwill by the purchasers of a business was equal to 3 years' purchase price of the average profits for the preceding 5 years. Determine the value placed on the goodwill if the profits for the preceding 5 years were as follows: first year, $32,000; second year, $26,000; third year, $42,000; fourth year, $54,000; fifth year, $70,000.

SOLUTION   Total profits for 5 years = $224,000
           $224,000 ÷ 5 = $44,800, average profits for 5 years
           $44,800 × 3 = $134,400, value of goodwill

Practice Drill

The amount paid for a business included goodwill valued at 2 years' purchase price of the average profits for the preceding 3 years. The profits for the preceding 3 years were as follows: first year, $58,000; second year, $74,000; third year, $81,000. Find the value placed on the goodwill.

ANSWER $142,000

Profits Over Interest

The value of goodwill may also be computed at several years' purchase price of the amount remaining from average profits after an agreed rate of interest on invested capital has been deducted.

To compute the value of goodwill by this method, do the following.

1. Find the average profits.

2. Deduct from the average profits an agreed rate of interest on the capital invested.

3. Multiply the remainder, or excess, of the profits by the number of years' purchase price. The product is the value placed on the goodwill.

Examples

PROBLEM 1   A certain business was sold for cash. The terms of sale provided for the payment of 80¢ on the dollar for the net assets, plus a 5 years' purchase price of the excess of the average profits over the interest at 8% on the amount paid for the net assets. Compute the amount paid for the business, including goodwill, if the net assets were valued at $125,000 and the average profits amounted to $22,500.

SOLUTION
80¢ on the dollar = 80% of $1
80% of $125,000 (net assets) = $100,000, amount paid for net assets
8% of $100,000 = $8,000, interest return on assets
$22,500 − $8,000 = $14,500, excess profits
5 × $14,500 = $72,500, value of goodwill
$100,000 + $72,500 = $172,500, amount paid for business

PROBLEM 2   A business was sold on the following terms: Payment was to be made in cash for the full value of the net assets plus the goodwill. The net assets were valued at $85,000 and the average annual profits at $18,600. Find the value placed on the goodwill if the return on capital invested was computed at 12% and the excess profits were capitalized at the same rate.

SOLUTION
12% of $85,000 = $10,200, return on capital invested
$18,600 − $10,200 = $8,400, excess profits
$8,400 ÷ 12% = $70,000, value of goodwill

Practice
Drill

An infants' wear shop was sold on the following terms: Payment was to be made at 75¢ on the dollar for the net assets, plus a 3 years' purchase price of the excess average profits over the interest at 6% on the amount paid for the net assets. Find the amount paid for the business, including goodwill, if the net assets were valued at $42,000 and the average profits amounted to $8,400.

ANSWER $51,030

APPLICATION PROBLEMS

1. The following facts were agreed upon between the parties involved in the sale of a business.

Capital stock outstanding = $100,000
Valuation of surplus = $18,000
Average annual net profits expected to continue indefinitely = $32,000
Normal rate of return = 15%

a. Find the goodwill cost to the purchaser. (The profits in excess of the basic rate of return on capital are capitalized at 15%. This number is the value placed on the goodwill.)
b. Find the amount the purchaser paid for the business.

2. The parties to the sale of a business agreed upon the following terms: the consideration was to be 5 years' purchase price of the average profits for the preceding 4 years, plus the capital investment. Find the price at which the business was sold.

> Capital stock = $100,000
> Surplus = $35,200
> Profits of preceding 4 years:
> First year = $31,500
> Second year = $28,750
> Third year = $36,840
> Fourth year = $41,670

3. The amount paid for the goodwill of a corporation at the time of its sale was equal to the total profits for the preceding 4 years, less 8% interest on the actual capital invested during each of these 4 years. The earnings and invested capital disclosed by the records of the firm were as shown in the following table. How much was paid for the goodwill?

Year	Profits	Invested Capital	Interest on Capital
First	$47,375	$285,400	$_____
Second	46,950	324,700	_____
Third	53,815	349,200	_____
Fourth	62,260	298,500	_____
Totals	$_____		$ _1 6_ _____

4. The selling price of the goodwill of a business was fixed at the average annual earnings for the 3 years preceding its sale, capitalized on a 10% basis, after the following deductions were made from the average earnings: $3,250 profits received on lapsing contracts; $7,500 for the estimated value of services rendered by two retiring district managers; and 8% interest on the net worth, not including goodwill.

Find the goodwill valuation if the net worth amounted to $276,500 and the annual earnings for the preceding 3 years totaled $47,860, $41,095, and $53,450, respectively.

5. The capital invested in a business about to be sold was valued at $213,850. The profits for the preceding 5 years averaged $37,615. Suppose the capital investment was sold at 85% of its value and the goodwill was capitalized at 15%, based on the excess of the average earnings after 7% interest was allowed on capital. Find the selling price of the business, including the amount received for the goodwill.

83 RECONCILING BANK STATEMENTS

Before the accountant can draw up accurate statements showing his firm's current cash position, he must usually reconcile his checkbook records with the records maintained by the bank where the firm's money is deposited. The fact that the bank's records and the firm's records do not agree is not necessarily an indication that one of them has made an error; indeed, it is rare that discrepancies exist because mistakes have been made.

There are four basic reasons why a bank statement (usually issued at the end of each month) and the firm's checkbook record may not agree.
1. Checks issued by the firm to individuals and other companies may not have been cashed and hence do not show on the bank's records. These are called *outstanding checks*. In this instance, the balance shown by the bank will be larger than that in the firm's records.
2. Deposits are often mailed to the bank rather than made in person. When they are mailed, the firm adds the deposits to its balance; but if at the time the bank prepares its statement these deposits have not been received, its balance will obviously show a smaller amount than the firm's balance. Mail deposits that have not been recorded by the bank are called *deposits in transit*.
3. The bank sometimes makes service charges and other deductions for expenses of maintaining the firm's account. Frequently the firm has no record of these charges until the bank statement is received.
4. In some cases, a bank will provide a collection service for its customers. When collections are made by the bank from a firm's customers, the amounts are credited to the firm's account; and while the bank immediately records the collection as a deposit to the firm's account, the firm may not learn about it for several days.

The accountant uses the bank reconciliation statement to adjust these differences and bring the bank balance and the firm's checkbook balance into agreement.

Example

PROBLEM The bank statement received by Webster and Company showed a balance of $7,962.50 instead of $8,000 as shown on the checkbook stub. In an attempt to reconcile this difference, the firm's accountant checked the entries shown on the bank statement with the checkbook stubs. The amounts of the paid checks agreed with the stubs. However, his investigation revealed the following: a deposit in transit amounting to $900; five outstanding checks totaling $625 (No. 269, $43.80; No. 274, $175; No. 291, $227.50; No. 295, $100; and No. 298, $78.70); a bank service charge and collection fee totaling $2.25; and a special note-collection credit by the bank of $239.75. Record this information on a reconciliation statement.

SOLUTION

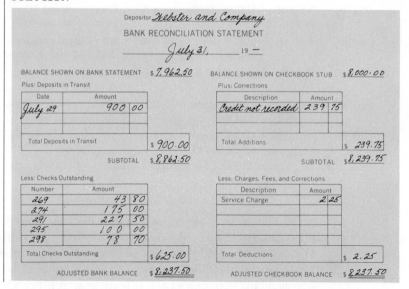

Depositor *Webster and Company*

BANK RECONCILIATION STATEMENT

July 31,   19 —

BALANCE SHOWN ON BANK STATEMENT	$7,962.50	BALANCE SHOWN ON CHECKBOOK STUB	$8,000.00

Plus: Deposits in Transit

Date	Amount
July 29	900 00

Total Deposits in Transit	$900.00

SUBTOTAL $8,862.50

Plus: Corrections

Description	Amount
Credit not recorded	239 75

Total Additions	$239.75

SUBTOTAL $8,239.75

Less: Checks Outstanding

Number	Amount
269	43 80
274	175 00
291	227 50
295	100 00
298	78 70

Total Checks Outstanding	$625.00

ADJUSTED BANK BALANCE $8,237.50

Less: Charges, Fees, and Corrections

Description	Amount
Service Charge	2 25

Total Deductions	$2.25

ADJUSTED CHECKBOOK BALANCE $8,237.50

Practice Drill

The bank statement of Claridge Clothes, Inc., shows a balance of $4,777.50 at the end of the month. A $540 deposit in transit is not shown on the statement, nor are three outstanding checks totaling $375 (No. 161, $43.50; No. 201, $118.75; and No. 208, $212.75). A special collection credit of $150 is listed by the bank as well as a $7.50 service charge. The balance shown on the checkbook stub is $4,800. Prepare a statement reconciling the differences between the bank statement and the checkbook stub.

ANSWER Correct balance: $4,942.50

APPLICATION PROBLEMS

1. Reconcile each of the following bank and checkbook balances. For
a and b, prepare statements similar to that shown in the example on
page 215.

	Bank State- ment Balance	Checkbook Balance	Outstanding Checks	Service Charge	Other Adjustments	Adjusted Bank and Checkbook Balance
a.	$1,088.20	$ 864.50	$48.70; $50.00	None	Deposit of $125 not entered on check stub.	$_____
b.	735.93	641.58	$36.50; $88.50	$3.65	$96.75 check entered on stub as $69.75.	_____
c.	5,024.93	4,919.86	$42.50; $65.00	2.25	Check for $8.86 entered on check stub as $8.68.	_____
d.	2,034.90	1,905.52	$127.56; $33.92	4.10	Check issued for $28 not recorded on check stub.	_____
e.	1,491.82	1,491.82	$12.74; $3.58; $46.39	.96	$61.75 late deposit not shown on bank statement.	_____
f.	9,952.98	7,498.94	$427.32; $695.47; $1,304.25	None	$125 check entered on stub as $152.	_____
g.	1,471.50	1,153.30	$84.36; $42.20; $262.00; $12.84	3.20	$80 late deposit not shown on bank statement.	_____
h.	1,016.62	941.22	$42.30; $23.00; $13.54; $16.80	4.24	$16 deposit entered twice on check stub.	_____

2. On March 31, a depositor's bank statement showed a balance of
$1,104.23. His checkbook balance was $780.03. Checks for $103.25 and
$145.35 were issued by the depositor but had not yet reached the bank.
The depositor also failed to record a late deposit of a check for $75.60.
Reconcile the depositor's bank balance against his checkbook balance.

3. On May 4, John Darrin received his statement from the bank, showing that his balance as of April 30 was $1,658.44. In going over the
statement, he discovered that he had issued two checks—one for $113.60
and one for $86.90—that had not yet been returned to his bank. In addi-
tion, the bank had added a service charge of $5. His checkbook balance
as of April 30 was $1,462.94. Reconcile the bank statement.

PROBLEMS FOR PART ELEVEN

Accounting Processes

78

1. The accountant for Younger's Department Store distributed the operating expenses on the basis of total area occupied by the various departments of the store. Complete the following overhead-distribution schedule.

Expenses	Area Occupied					
	Dress Dept. 40%	Shoe Dept. 15%	Acces-sories Dept. 10%	Cosmetics Dept. 11%	Lingerie Dept. 24%	Total 100%
Taxes	$_____	$_____	$_____	$_____	$_____	$24,640
Light	_____	_____	_____	_____	_____	2,875
Insurance	_____	_____	_____	_____	_____	6,418
Delivery	_____	_____	_____	_____	_____	7,964
Clerical	_____	_____	_____	_____	_____	18,652
Administration	_____	_____	_____	_____	_____	42,119
Totals	$_____	$_____	$_____	$_____	$_____	$_____

2. A new accountant for Younger's Department Store (problem 1) decided to change overhead distribution from the percentage of space each department occupied to the percentage of total sales each department produced. Sales for each department for the month were as follows: Dresses, $16,440; Shoes, $22,660; Accessories, $3,600; Cosmetics, $4,800; Lingerie, $14,500. Operating expenses for the month totaled $3,400. How much will each department be charged for overhead expenses?

3. Find the rate percent of overhead to be charged to each of the following departments of a radio manufacturing concern if computed on the basis of the number of square feet of space occupied by each department.

Department	Area (square feet)
Raw Materials	1,800
Parts Manufacturing	6,400
Assembling	3,200
Finished Goods	2,500
Offices	1,100

Complete the following chart by finding the amount of monthly overhead chargeable to each department.

Month	Overhead	Raw Materials	Parts Mfg.	Assembling	Finished Goods	Offices
Jan.	$6,350	$____	$____	$____	$____	$____
Feb.	5,675	____	____	____	____	____
Mar.	7,290	____	____	____	____	____
April	6,918	____	____	____	____	____
May	4,367	____	____	____	____	____
June	5,986	____	____	____	____	____

4. Goodwin's Glass and Mirror Company distributes overhead to each of its 4 departments according to the ratio of total overhead to the total direct labor costs. During September the total overhead amounted to $12,000; the total direct labor cost, $72,000.
a. Find the rate percent to be applied to each department.
b. Find the amount to be charged to the Glazing Department whose direct labor costs for the month were $16,000.

79

1. Find the cost of goods sold.
a. Beginning inventory, $8,261.30; purchases, $51,010.72; purchases discount, $251.75; purchases returns and allowances, $415.90; ending inventory, $7,163.80.
b. Purchases, $11,500; purchases returns, $250; purchases discount, $500; ending inventory, $9,500; beginning inventory, $7,500.

2. Find the net sales, cost of goods sold, gross profit on sales, and net income for the Triangle Desk Company.
Sales, $50,529.64; sales returns and allowances, $820.06; sales discounts, $412.80.
Merchandise inventory, January 1 of current year, $10,000; purchases, $32,091; purchases returns and allowances, $430; purchases discount, $228.32; merchandise inventory, December 31 of current year, $16,000.
Operating expenses: Rent, $3,400; bad debts, $2,105; depreciation—factory machines and equipment, $1,120, office furniture and equipment, $888; miscellaneous expenses, $1,050.30; salaries, $16,900; shipping expenses, $300.20; supplies used, $250; insurance, $140.
Other income and other expenses: Interest income, $285.20; rental income, $1,200; interest expense, $160.40.

80 1. Complete the missing entries in the following income statement.

LAIRD AND BURKE
INCOME STATEMENT
FISCAL YEAR ENDED JUNE 30, 19X7

			Percent of Net Sales
Income			
Sales	$183,740		
Sales Returns and Allowances..	7,740		
Net Sales		$_____	100.0
Cost of Goods Sold			
Merchandise, Beginning of Year.$	29,615		
Purchases...............................	115,890		
Cost of Goods Avail. for Sale..$_____			
Less Merchandise, End			
of Year	17,580		
Cost of Goods Sold		_____	_____
Gross Profit		$_____	_____
Operating Expenses			
Selling Expenses ....$	12,325		
Administrative Expenses	8,760		
Total Operating Expenses		_____	_____
Net Income from Operations		$_____	_____

2. The comparative income statement for a 2-year period (on page 220) shows for each item the change in dollar amounts and the percent of each change. Study the statement carefully until you understand the meaning of each item and the significance of every amount on the statement. Check the accuracy of the arithmetic in each step. Correct any errors; there is at least one error on the statement. Compute to the nearest tenth of a percent, and write your answers on a separate sheet of paper. Then answer the following questions.

a. In determining the percent of increase or decrease in each item, was 19X6 or 19X7 used as a base or was 100%? Why?
b. In both 19X7 and 19X6, determine the percent of net sales to which each of the following was equal.

        Cost of Goods Sold   Total Operating Expenses
        Gross Profit   Net Income

c. What percent of the gross profit was the net income in 19X7? In 19X6?
d. Did the business of the Eric Michael Herberts Company increase or decrease in 19X7? By what amount? By what percent of 19X6?

ERIC MICHAEL HERBERTS COMPANY
COMPARATIVE CONDENSED INCOME STATEMENT
YEARS ENDED DECEMBER 31, 19X7 AND 19X6

	Amounts		Increase or Decrease During 19X7	
	19X7	19X6	Amount	Percent
Income				
Sales	$621,320	$547,860	$73,460	13.4
Returns and Allowances	4,685	4,090	595	14.5
Net Sales	$616,635	$543,770	$72,865	13.4
Cost of Goods Sold				
Merchandise, Jan. 1	$ 19,125	$ 28,610	$ (9,485)*	(33.2)
Purchases	420,975	376,855	44,120	11.7
Total	$440,100	$405,465	$34,635	8.5
Merchandise, Dec. 31	24,865	43,705	(18,840)	(43.1)
Cost of Goods Sold	$415,235	$361,760	$53,475	14.8
Gross Profit	$201,400	$182,010	$19,390	10.7
Operating Expenses				
Salaries	$ 68,310	$ 49,765	$18,545	37.2
Advertising	24,615	26,805	(2,190)	(8.2)
Supplies	16,090	11,915	4,175	35.0
Insurance	3,780	3,810	(30)	(.8)
Taxes	2,655	3,175	(520)	(16.4)
Depreciation	3,240	3,560	(320)	(9.0)
Delivery Expenses	7,105	10,155	(3,050)	(30.0)
Miscellaneous	38,615	24,830	13,785	55.5
Total Operating Expenses	$164,410	$134,015	$30,395	22.7
Net Income	$ 36,990	$ 47,995	$(11,005)	(29.8)

*Decreases are shown in parentheses.

e. Although the net sales increased by $72,865 in 19X7 over 19X6 and the gross profit increased by $19,390, the net profit showed a decrease of $11,005. Why?

f. What percent of total operating expenses was each item of expense in 19X7? In 19X6?

81

1. Complete the following balance sheet by finding the totals of all columns.

a. What percent of the total assets is each asset?

b. What percent of the total liabilities and equity is each liability and the owner's equity on June 30?

LAIRD AND BURKE
BALANCE SHEET
JUNE 30, 19X7

Assets

Cash	$13,317
Notes Receivable	1,750
Accounts Receivable	24,755
Stock on Hand	32,814
Supplies on Hand	4,090
Furniture	8,896
Equipment	7,713
Total Assets	$

Liabilities and Owner's Equity

Liabilities

Notes Payable	$ 3,500
Accounts Payable	11,949
Interest Payable	217
Total Liabilities	$

Owner's Equity

Laird and Burke, Investment, July 1, 19X6	$50,679
Net Profit for Year	26,990
Laird and Burke, Investment, June 30, 19X7	
Total Liabilities and Owner's Equity	$

2. The current assets of Harmon and Company on December 31 were $87,300, and its current liabilities were $25,800. If the net sales for the year amounted to $322,875, what was the ratio of net sales to working capital? Compute to the nearest hundredth.

3. The owner's average equity in the Rialto Novelty Company for the year was $34,600 and his net income for the year was $3,979. Compute the return on the investment to the nearest tenth of a percent.

4. The current assets as shown on the balance sheet of Drew and Kessler amounted to $85,960; the current liabilities were $55,560. If the inventory was valued at $19,608, what percent of working capital was the inventory?

5. The fixed assets on the books of merchant William Dobbs were valued at $54,335. If Dobbs' equity in the business was $43,468, find the ratio of fixed assets to owner's equity. Compute to the nearest hundredth.

82

1. The net worth of a business, not including goodwill, is valued at $160,000. The goodwill account amounts to $38,000. Assume that the normal net profit rate for this line of business is 12% on capital, exclusive of goodwill, and the average annual net profits are $26,712. Prepare a chart showing how the goodwill can be written off against the excess profits earned annually. Show the number of years that it will take to close the goodwill account. Submit your solution on a form similar to the following.

Year	Goodwill at Beginning of Year	Average Net Annual Profit	Normal Net Profit Rate, 12%	Excess Profit Earned	Goodwill at End of Year
First	$38,000	$26,712	$19,200	$7,512	$30,488
Second	30,488	26,712	19,200	7,512	22,976

2. The assets of a business, not including goodwill, are worth $312,500. The liabilities amount to $106,750, the average annual net profits total $46,320, and the normal rate of return on net worth in businesses of this type is 9%. Assuming that the average net profits will continue to be the same amount indefinitely, find the value to be placed on the goodwill if the excess net profits are capitalized at the rate of 9%.

3. The total capital stock and surplus accounts of a business, exclusive of goodwill, amount to $270,000. The average annual rate of net profit on invested capital is 12%, and the average net income amounts to $43,500.
a. What is the normal income?
b. Find the profits in excess of the basic rate of return on capital.
c. What is the value of the goodwill if the excess profits are capitalized at 10%?

4. The books of a business about to be sold disclosed that the profits during each of the preceding 3 years were as follows: first year, $33,700; second year, $24,800; and third year, $40,250. The average net worth during the 3-year period amounted to $85,000. By the terms of the contract of sale, the goodwill was fixed at $1\frac{1}{2}$ times the total profits for the preceding 3 years, less 3 years' interest on the net worth at $7\frac{1}{2}$%. Find the value placed on the goodwill.

83

1. When reconciling his monthly bank statement, Harvey Young found that he had failed to record in his checkbook a deposit of $254.30. A check for $249 that he had mailed late in the month in payment of a bill had not yet been deposited by the person who received it. For issuing more checks than his deposits warranted, the bank had charged him $6 that month. His checkbook record showed a balance of $2,693.08; the bank's record was $3,190.38. Reconcile the bank statement.

2. On July 31, Clare Hill's checkbook balance was $726. Her bank statement on that day showed a balance of $594.20. Still outstanding was a check for $44.70. On the morning of July 31, she had mailed a deposit of $175 to the bank, but this had not been received in time to be recorded on the statement. A service charge of $1.50 was deducted from her account that month. Prepare a reconciliation statement, showing Clare's correct balance.

3. The December statement of Charles Mann's account showed a balance of $594.59. In reconciling this statement against his own checkbook balance of $496.13, Mann noticed that the bank had charged him $1.25 for issuing more checks than his monthly balance permitted. He also discovered that he had failed to record two items that month—a check for $169.32 that he had written while at work and a deposit of $167.84. A check for $101.19 that he had issued during the month had not yet been returned to his bank. Reconcile the bank and checkbook balances.

4. On June 30, a depositor's bank statement showed a balance of $1,634.08. His checkbook balance was $1,324.84. Checks for $83.25 and $117.94 had been issued but had not yet reached the bank. Comparing the bank statement with the checkbook, the depositor discovered that he had failed to record in his checkbook a canceled check for $95.45 and a deposit of $203.50. Reconcile the balances, showing the correct checkbook balance.

PART TWELVE
Taxes, Insurance & Real Estate

The subjects of taxes, insurance, and real estate are important not only in one's personal activities but in one's occupational activities as well. Everyone who spends money pays taxes; most people buy insurance and real estate. So these topics are of significance to the consumer. At the same time, they are equally important to the businessman. Most businesses collect, as well as pay, taxes; many own property that must be insured; and an increasing number of them purchase real estate, not only for occupancy but also for investment purposes.

Before making tax, insurance, and real estate computations, it is necessary to understand the following terms.

Sales taxes Sales taxes are taxes levied by state and local governments on consumer goods and services.

Excise taxes Excise taxes are sales taxes levied by the federal government, usually on goods considered unessential.

Property taxes Property taxes, or *real estate taxes,* are taxes on land and buildings levied by local governments.

Assessed valuation Assessed valuation is the estimate of the value of land and buildings made by the tax assessor for the purpose of determining property taxes.

Underwriter The underwriter, or the *insurer,* is the insurance company that draws up the insurance policy.

Premium The premium is the amount paid periodically by the insured to the insurer for insurance protection.

Indemnity	Indemnity is the amount paid by the insurer to the insured in the event of loss sustained by the insured.
Insurance policy	An insurance policy is a contractual agreement between the insurer and the insured specifying conditions under which the insurer will reimburse the insured for losses incurred.
Term insurance	Term insurance premiums are paid for a fixed period of time. For instance, in a 10-year term policy, the insured agrees to pay premiums for 10 years or until his death, whichever occurs first. If he is still living at the end of 10 years, he will no longer be insured nor will he or his beneficiary receive any money from the insurance company. If the insured should die at any time during the 10-year period, his beneficiary will receive the face value of the policy. Term insurance can be purchased for various periods of time; the most common use of term insurance is to cover people while they are traveling by plane.
Straight-life insurance	Under a straight-life (sometimes called *whole-life*) policy, the insured agrees to pay premiums for his entire life. At the time of his death, his beneficiary will receive the face value of the policy.
Limited-payment life insurance	Under a limited-payment policy, premiums are paid for a fixed period of time, say, 10, 20, or 30 years. If the insured dies before the end of the term, his beneficiary receives the face value of the policy. If he lives to the end of the term, he no longer makes payments but continues to be insured for the rest of his life. His beneficiary receives the face value of the policy upon the insured's death.
Endowment insurance	The holder of an endowment insurance policy also pays premiums for a fixed period of time. In a 20-year endowment policy, the insured agrees to pay premiums until his death or for 20 years, whichever occurs first. However, if the insured is still alive at the end of this period, he himself will receive the face value of the policy, but he will no longer be insured. If he should die during the 20-year period, his beneficiary will receive the face value of the policy.
Real estate	Real estate is land and its natural resources (water, oil, gas, etc.) as well as man-made improvements (buildings, fences, etc.) on the land.
Mortgage	A mortgage is a contract that represents a pledge of property for payment of a debt. Sometimes called a *deed of trust,* it can be taken out for land, buildings, machinery, equipment or other property.

84 TAXES

Local governments are responsible for various kinds of public services. These services include fire and police protection, schools, libraries, parks, roads, street lighting, garbage collection, health protection, and similar benefits. The major source of income to finance these services is taxes.

Sales Taxes

The general sales tax is a method used by an increasing number of states and cities to obtain revenue. The purchases that are taxed and the tax rates vary somewhat by state and city. For example, in some areas there is a tax on hotel rooms, meals eaten in a restaurant, and magazines; in other areas, a tax may be charged on a different set of consumer goods. In nearly all areas of the country, however, most consumer goods (clothing, automobiles, appliances, and so on) are taxed.

The rate of sales tax is always expressed as a percent. Typical state sales-tax percentages are 2%, 3%, 4%, and 5%. Local taxes, such as city taxes, are generally (though not always) quite a bit lower, usually ranging from $\frac{1}{4}$% to 3%.

The seller collects the tax when he makes a sale, and the total tax collections are sent periodically to the various government agencies levying the tax.

Generally, sales taxes are charged only on purchases made and delivered within a given tax area. Purchases to be delivered outside the tax area are not usually taxed. For example, if you reside in Connecticut and buy a stereo console in New York City to be delivered to your home in Connecticut, you don't have to pay the New York sales tax. If, however, you live in New York and make the same purchase for local delivery, you must pay the tax.

For purposes of speed and accuracy, retail clerks usually use a printed tax chart, like the one shown on page 227, which they keep near the cash register. It is based on the simple process of multiplying the percent of tax by the price of the item and rounding the result to the nearest penny.

Example | **PROBLEM** Laura Parmalee purchased a desk for $96.25 on which there was a sales tax of 3%. What was the total cost of the desk, assuming the purchase was made and delivered in the same tax area?

SOLUTION $96.25 × 3%   = $2.89, sales tax
$96.25 + $2.89 = $99.14, total cost

6% SALES AND USE TAX

Sale		Tax	Sale		Tax
.01 –	.10	.00	6.11 –	6.17	.37
.11 –	.17	.01	6.18 –	6.34	.38
.18 –	.34	.02	6.35 –	6.50	.39
.35 –	.50	.03	6.51 –	6.67	.40
.51 –	.67	.04	6.68 –	6.84	.41
.68 –	.84	.05	6.85 –	7.10	.42
.85 –	1.10	.06			
1.11 –	1.17	.07	7.11 –	7.17	.43
1.18 –	1.34	.08	7.18 –	7.34	.44
1.35 –	1.50	.09	7.35 –	7.50	.45
1.51 –	1.67	.10	7.51 –	7.67	.46
1.68 –	1.84	.11	7.68 –	7.84	.47
1.85 –	2.10	.12	7.85 –	8.10	.48
2.11 –	2.17	.13	8.11 –	8.17	.49
2.18 –	2.34	.14	8.18 –	8.34	.50
2.35 –	2.50	.15	8.35 –	8.50	.51
2.51 –	2.67	.16	8.51 –	8.67	.52
2.68 –	2.84	.17	8.68 –	8.84	.53
2.85 –	3.10	.18	8.85 –	9.10	.54
3.11 –	3.17	.19	9.11 –	9.17	.55
3.18 –	3.34	.20	9.18 –	9.34	.56
3.35 –	3.50	.21	9.35 –	9.50	.57
3.51 –	3.67	.22	9.51 –	9.67	.58
3.68 –	3.84	.23	9.68 –	9.84	.59
3.85 –	4.10	.24	9.85 –	10.00	.60
4.11 –	4.17	.25			
4.18 –	4.34	.26			
4.35 –	4.50	.27	10.00		.60
4.51 –	4.67	.28	20.00		1.20
4.68 –	4.84	.29	30.00		1.80
4.85 –	5.10	.30	40.00		2.40
5.11 –	5.17	.31	50.00		3.00
5.18 –	5.34	.32	60.00		3.60
5.35 –	5.50	.33	70.00		4.20
5.51 –	5.67	.34	80.00		4.80
5.68 –	5.84	.35	90.00		5.40
5.85 –	6.10	.36	100.00		6.00

Excise Taxes

Federal excise taxes are levied on certain types of merchandise to raise
revenue. Such tax levies are usually limited to merchandise that is not
considered absolutely essential; they are paid by the manufacturer, who
then adds them to the cost of the product. In some few cases, excise

taxes are paid directly by the retailer, who adds them to the selling price. Excise taxes that are based on the selling price rather than on the manufacturer's cost must be added to the selling price before the sales tax, if any, is computed.

Example

PROBLEM   Phil Coulter bought an automobile tire for $24 on which there was an excise tax of 13% and a sales tax of 5%. What was the total cost of the purchase?

SOLUTION

Selling price	= $24.00
$24.00 × 13%	= $3.12, excise tax
	$27.12
$27.12 × 5%	= $1.356, or $1.36, sales tax
$27.12 + $1.36	= $28.48, total cost

Practice Drills

Find the tax on the following purchases, using the sales tax chart on page 227. Assume that in item 3 there is also an excise tax of 5% and in item 5 there is an excise tax of 8%.

1. $5.35   2. $21.38   3. $51   4. $13.20   5. $44.50

ANSWERS   1. $.33   2. $1.29   3. $56.77   4. $.80   5. $50.94

Property Taxes

Property tax is levied on the assessed value of real property (buildings and land). The assessed value (frequently less than actual market value) is determined by the tax assessor.

Money collected from property taxes is distributed in accordance with a budget similar to the following.

CITY OF LANDERSVILLE
ANALYSIS OF 19X3 TAX DISTRIBUTION

Department	Percent of Tax
Police and Fire	23.17
Schools	29.84
Library	2.15
Health	4.93
Public Works	11.68
Debt and Reserves	6.46
Administration and General	10.59
County Tax	11.18

FINDING TAX RATE

The actual tax rate to be applied on real property varies from year to year according to the financial needs of the government. The tax rate is found by dividing the total city budget by the assessed valuation of community property.

Example

PROBLEM   A budget of $3,022,600 must be met in a city where property is assessed at $63,500,000. Find the tax rate on $1 assessed valuation and on $100 assessed valuation.

SOLUTION

$3,022,600 ÷ $63,500,000 = .0476, tax rate on $1 assessed valuation

or

$$\frac{\$3,022,600}{\$63,500,000} = \$63,500,000\overline{)\$3,022,600.0000}^{\quad.0476}$$

100 × $.0476 = $4.76, tax rate on $100 assessed valuation

Practice Drill

Real estate in a town in New Hampshire is valued at $18,365,000. If the property is assessed at 60% of its value and the revenue to be raised by taxation amounts to $1,135,000, find the tax rate on $1 assessed valuation, $100 assessed valuation, and $1,000 assessed valuation.

ANSWERS $.103 on $1, $10.30 on $100, $103 on $1,000

FINDING TAX DUE

To determine the amount of tax due on property if the tax rate is based on $100, use the following method.

1. Divide the value of the property by 100 to find the number of hundreds.

2. Multiply the number of hundreds of valuation by the tax rate per $100 to find the property tax.

Example

PROBLEM   Find the total tax paid by the owner of property assessed at $47,500 if the tax rate is $5.16 per $100.

SOLUTION   47,500 ÷ 100 = 475, number of hundreds
475 × $5.16 (tax rate per $100) = $2,451, property tax

Practice Drill

Property was assessed at $57,600. This assessed valuation was 75% of the actual value of the property. If the tax rate was $64.17 per $1,000, what was the actual value of the property? How much tax was paid by the owner?

ANSWERS $76,800, actual value; $3,696.19, taxes paid

APPLICATION PROBLEMS

1. Assume that the sales tax in an eastern state is 5%. Find the amount of tax to be collected on the following amounts. Round off to the nearest cent.

a. $27.70 *1.38*   c. $845 *42.25*   e. $124.49 *6.22*   g. $2.45 *.12*

b. $14.95 *.75*   d. $1.98 *.10*   f. $.64 *.03*   h. $6.60 *.33*

2. Milton Gabriel bought 4 tires for his car, which were priced at $26.50 each. There was an excise tax of 13% on each tire, and the local sales tax was 3%. What was the amount Mr. Gabriel paid?

3. Find the tax rate in each of the following on $1 assessed valuation, $100 assessed valuation, and $1,000 assessed valuation.

Assessed Valuation of Community Property	Total City Budget for Coming Year	Tax Rate Levied on:		
		$1	$100	$1,000
a. $12,480,000	$ 149,760.00	$_____	$_____	$_____
b. 10,590,000	222,390.00	_____	_____	_____
c. 15,304,000	183,648.00	_____	_____	_____
d. 87,900,000	5,713,500.00	_____	_____	_____
e. 42,820,125	2,141,006.25	_____	_____	_____
f. 19,168,150	1,296,779.40	_____	_____	_____

4. Carl Jordan paid $1,323 in taxes on property worth $56,000 and assessed at $\frac{3}{4}$% of its value. *75%*

a. Find the tax rate. *.0315*

b. If the total assessed valuation of the town property is $22,964,300, what is the total town budget?   *723,325.45*

c. If the town budget is 64% of the total budget to be raised, the county tax 22%, and the state tax the remainder, find the total tax to be collected for each purpose. $\frac{723,325.45}{.64}$

85 FIRE INSURANCE COST

Fire insurance provides protection against financial loss due directly to fire or smoke, to water or chemicals used to extinguish a fire, and to measures taken to prevent the fire from spreading, such as dynamiting or water-soaking the property.

Premium rates for insurance depend upon the risk that the insurance company takes. In the case of fire insurance, the risk of loss depends upon such factors as the materials used in the construction of the insured property; the proximity of the property to fire hydrants and fire hazards; the capabilities of the fire department in the locality; the use of built-in fire protection, such as a sprinkler system; the presence of guards or watchmen; and so on.

Premium rates for insurance against loss by fire or other causes are usually expressed as so much per $100 of property value insured or as a rate percent of the value of the property insured. Premiums must normally be paid in advance.

Computing Cost—Rate Given

To compute the premium on fire insurance when the amount of insurance protection desired and the premium rate are given, apply the principle *Premium rate × Insurance = Premium.*

Examples

PROBLEM 1   Find the annual premium on $4,750 of insurance at $\frac{7}{8}$%.

SOLUTION $\frac{7}{8}$% of $4,750 = $\frac{7}{8}$ of 1% of $4,750
1% of $4,750 = $47.50

$$\frac{7}{8} \text{ of } \overset{23.75}{\underset{4}{\$47.50}} = \frac{166.25}{4} = \$41.56, \text{ premium}$$

PROBLEM 2   Find the annual premium on $23,600 of insurance at 1%, less 10%.

SOLUTION   1% of $23,600 = $236.00
10% of $236   = $ 23.60
$236 − $23.60 = $212.40, premium

PROBLEM 3   Find the annual premium on $11,500 of insurance at 1.12\frac{1}{2}$ per $100.

SOLUTION $11,500 ÷ 100 = 115, number of hundreds
115 × 1.12\frac{1}{2}$ = $129.38, premium

Practice
Drills

1. Property valued at $9,700 was insured for 1 year at a premium rate of $\frac{3}{4}$%. Find the annual premium.

2. A house that cost $12,600 is insured for $\frac{3}{4}$ of its value at 68 cents per $100 per year. The household furniture, valued at $4,850, is insured for $\frac{4}{5}$ of its value at an annual rate of 1%, less 15%. Find the total cost of this insurance.

ANSWERS   1. $72.75   2. $64.26, premium on house; $32.98, premium on furniture; $97.24, total cost

Computing Cost With Rate Schedules

Premium rates on fire insurance vary from one state or community to another, depending on past experience and future loss estimated by the insurer (or underwriter). The most meaningful factors in determining these rates are the type of construction of the property to be insured (whether it is built of brick or wood and whether the roof is approved by the Board of Fire Underwriters), and the degree of fire protection available in the community in which the property is located.

Based on these factors, a large fire insurance company prepared rate schedules from which the following table was taken.

ANNUAL RATE CHARGE PER $100 OF FIRE INSURANCE

Building and Contents	Community							
	A	B	C	D	E	F	G	H
Brick:								
Building	.084	.090	.106	.165	.280	.395	.450	.485
Contents	.170	.185	.210	.300	.355	.502	.545	.580
Frame:								
Building	.115	.130	.142	.236	.341	.444	.515	.558
Contents	.230	.263	.294	.325	.409	.562	.602	.641

It is a common practice among fire insurance companies to allow lower premium rates on policies running for 2 or more years. Thus, for a 2-year policy, the rate is 1.85 times the annual rate; for a 3-year policy, it is 2.7 times the annual rate; for a 4-year policy, it is 3.55 times the annual rate, and for a 5-year policy, it is 4.4 times the annual rate.

Examples

PROBLEM 1 Frederick Fallon owns a brick house in Community D. He insures the house for $25,000 and the contents for $5,600. Find the yearly premium. If the insurance policy is issued for a 3-year period, what is the total premium? Refer to the rate schedule given.

SOLUTION Number of hundreds in $25,000 = 25,000 ÷ 100 = 250
Number of hundreds in $5,600 = 5,600 ÷ 100 = 56

Cost per $100 annually on brick building = $.165
Cost per $100 annually on contents = $.300

250 × $.165 = $41.25, insurance cost on building
56 × $.300 =   16.80, insurance cost on contents
                $58.05, total yearly premium

3-year premium = 2.7 times annual rate
2.7 × $58.05 = $156.735, or $156.74, total premium

PROBLEM 2   The owner of a frame house insured it for $18,000. He insured the contents for $6,750. Find the total premium if the policy was issued for a 5-year period. The house was located in Community C.

SOLUTION   18,000 ÷ 100 = 180, number of hundreds
6,750 ÷ 100 = 67½, number of hundreds
Annual rate on frame building = $.142
Annual rate on contents = $.294
180 × $.142 = $25.56, annual premium on building
67½ × .294 =   19.85, annual premium on contents
                    $45.41, total annual premium
4.4 × $45.41 = $199.80, 5-year premium

Practice Drills

1. A frame house in Community F is insured for $18,600, and the contents are insured for $6,200.
a. Find the total annual premium.
b. Find the total premium if the policy is issued for 2 years; for 3 years; for 4 years; and for 5 years.

2. A man owned a frame house valued at $19,900 and a brick house valued at $24,900. He insured each for a 3-year period. Find the premium on each property, both of which were located in Community G.

ANSWERS   1. a. $117.42   1. b. $217.23, 2 years; $317.03, 3 years; $416.84, 4 years;
$516.65, 5 years   2. $276.71, frame house; $302.54, brick house

APPLICATION PROBLEMS

1. Find the premium paid on the following fire insurance policies.

Amount of Insurance	Premium Rate	Premium Paid
a. $16,200	¾%	$_____
b. 24,500	80¢ per $100	_____
c. 7,500	⅞% less 5%	_____
d. 8,600	93¢ per $100	_____
e. 46,000	⅞%	_____
f. 8,400	1⅜%	_____
g. 13,750	$1.36 per $100	_____
h. 32,500	⅚% less 10%	_____

2. If the 5-year premium rate for insuring a house is 4.4 times the rate for 1 year, find the premium on a house insured for $11,750 for 5 years at an annual rate of ⅚%.

$11,750 × .01 = 117.50 × ⅚ = 97.92
                                          ×4.4
                                    43.848

3. Emerson owns a brick building in Community E. He insures the building for $24,000 and the contents for $6,250. Find the total premium.

$2 4000 \div 240 \times 28 =$

4. Using the table on page 232, find the premium on the following policies.

Amount of Insurance		Com-munity	Struc-ture	Annual Premium	Period in Years	Total Premium
Building	Contents					
a. $12,000	$3,000	B	Brick	$_____	3	$_____
b. 18,500	5,500	H	Brick	_____	2	_____
c. 25,000	4,700	F	Frame	_____	5	_____
d. 17,600	6,650	A	Frame	_____	4	_____
e. 32,500	5,900	G	Brick	_____	3	_____
f. 24,500	7,250	E	Frame	_____	5	_____

86 FIRE INSURANCE INDEMNITY

When the insured suffers a loss, the amount paid to him by the insurance company to cover the loss is called the *indemnity.*

Under an ordinary fire insurance policy, the insurance company will indemnify (compensate) the insured for any fire losses up to the amount of insurance carried but will never pay more than the actual loss suffered by the insured.

Examples | **PROBLEM 1**   A house valued at $18,500 is insured for $15,000. How much would be collected under an ordinary fire insurance policy in case of a $12,500 fire loss?

SOLUTION   The actual loss, $12,500, would be recovered from the insurance company since this amount is less than the insurance carried.

PROBLEM 2   If the house in problem 1 was insured for $12,000, and a $12,500 fire loss was suffered, how much would be collected under an ordinary fire insurance policy?

SOLUTION   Only $12,000 could be collected from the insurance company since the amount of loss is more than the insurance. Under this type of policy, the insurance company will pay either the actual loss suffered or the amount of insurance carried, whichever is lower. This is in agreement with the basic purpose of insurance—that is, protection, not profit.

Practice
Drills

Property worth $30,000 is insured for $24,000 under an ordinary fire insurance policy. Suppose there is a $5,000 loss.
1. How much can the owner collect from the insurance company?
2. If the property had been insured for $35,000, would the insured be entitled to a larger indemnity? Explain.

ANSWERS   1. $5,000   2. The insurance company will pay only the actual loss suffered or the amount of insurance carried, whichever is lower.

APPLICATION PROBLEMS

1. A house valued at $47,500 was insured for $35,000. How much would be collected under an ordinary fire insurance policy in case of a $23,000 fire loss?

2. If the house in problem 1 was insured for $30,000, and a $30,500 loss was suffered, how much would be collected under an ordinary fire insurance policy?

87 COINSURANCE

Statistics show that most fires result in only small partial losses. For this reason, property owners are inclined to insure their property for only enough to cover the probable losses. Insurance companies do not look with favor upon such practices because they then collect premiums on only part of the property that is insured.

To encourage property owners to adequately insure their property, insurance companies offer, at reduced premium rates, policies containing coinsurance clauses. Coinsurance is a form of insurance whereby property is insured for less than its full value, and the insured agrees to be responsible for the difference. With a coinsurance clause, the insurer is liable for the full amount of any fire loss up to the face of the policy if the property is insured for an amount not less than the specified minimum percent of its value, which is generally 80%. A policy specifying an 80% minimum is referred to as an 80% coinsurance policy. Policies providing financial protection against certain types of losses resulting from fire, such as loss of rent or income, are often issued with coinsurance clauses for minimums other than 80%. Such rate percents as 90%, 60%, and 70% are also common.

Coinsurance Clause Policy

To solve fire insurance problems based on the coinsurance clause policy, use the following formula.

$$\frac{Insurance}{Rate\ percent\ of\ property\ value}\ of\ Loss\ =\ Amount\ paid$$

$$\frac{I}{R\%\ of\ V}\ of\ L\ =\ A \qquad \text{which can be expressed as}$$

$$\frac{I}{R\ \times\ V}\ \times\ L\ =\ A$$

Example

PROBLEM Property valued at $15,000 was insured for $12,000. Fire caused a loss of $7,200. Find the amount of indemnity paid under a policy containing a 90% coinsurance clause.

SOLUTION

$$\frac{I}{90\%\ of\ V}\ of\ L\ =\ A$$

$$\frac{\overset{8}{\cancel{12,000}}}{\underset{\underset{9}{\cancel{13,500}}}{\cancel{.90\ \times\ 15,000}}}\ \times\ \overset{800}{\cancel{\$7,200}}\ =\ \$6,400,\ \text{amount paid}$$

Practice Drill

A building valued at $36,000 is insured for $\frac{7}{8}$ of its value; and its contents, valued at $16,200, are insured for 75% of their value. Find the amount recoverable from the insurance company under a 90% coinsurance clause policy if fire causes a loss of $16,000 to the building and a total loss to the contents.

ANSWER $15,555.56, amount recoverable on building; $13,500.00, on contents; $29,055.56, total

80% Average-Clause Policy

Under an 80% coinsurance, or average, clause policy, the insurance company will pay up to 80% of the value of the property that is insured. For instance, if a house valued at $25,000 is insured for $15,000, only $\dfrac{15,000}{80\%\ of\ 25,000}$, or $\dfrac{15,000}{20,000}$, or $\frac{3}{4}$ of the loss can be recovered by the insured, since only $\frac{3}{4}$ of the 80% of the value of the property was insured. If $20,000 insurance had been carried, the full loss up to $20,000 could be collected from the insurance company, as this amount is 80% of the value of the property.

The coinsurance clause in a policy does not mean that only the minimum amount of insurance required is the maximum amount collectible. If the property is insured for its full value, the full amount would be collected in case of a total loss. This type of policy only provides that not less than a specified minimum rate percent of the value of the property can be protected by insurance, and that the insured must bear the difference between the actual insurance carried and the minimum requirement. Here, as in the ordinary fire insurance policy, no more than the actual loss nor more than the actual amount of insurance carried can be collected.

Example

PROBLEM Property valued at $37,500 was insured for $27,000. Fire caused a loss of $26,250. Find the amount of indemnity paid under a policy containing an 80% average clause.

SOLUTION $\dfrac{I}{80\% \text{ of } V} \text{ of } L = A$

$$\dfrac{\overset{9}{\cancel{27{,}000}}}{\underset{\underset{10}{\cancel{30{,}000}}}{\cancel{.80} \times \cancel{37{,}500}}} \times \overset{2{,}625}{\cancel{26{,}250}} = \$23{,}625, \text{ amount paid}$$

Practice Drill

A house worth $20,000 is insured for $\frac{3}{5}$ of its value under an 80% coinsurance clause policy. In case of an $8,000 loss due to fire and water, how much would the insured recover under the policy?

ANSWER $6,000

APPLICATION PROBLEMS

1. Find the amount paid by the insurance company under an ordinary policy in each of problems **a** to **d** and under a policy containing an 80% average clause in each of problems **e** to **h**.

	Value of Property	Insurance	Fire Loss	Amount Paid by Insurance Company
a.	$15,000	$12,000	$10,000	$_____
b.	24,000	20,000	22,000	_____
c.	18,000	25,000	18,000	_____
d.	8,400	7,000	7,500	_____
e.	12,500	8,000	6,000	_____
f.	17,500	15,000	16,000	_____
g.	35,000	50,000	35,000	_____
h.	30,000	20,000	15,000	_____

2. A house valued at $50,000 is insured for $32,000. The contents, valued at $10,000, are insured for $\frac{3}{4}$ of their value. The policy contains an 80% average clause. Fire caused a loss of $14,400 on the house and an 80% loss on the contents. Find the amount collected from the insurance company on the house and on the contents.

88 REMITTANCES ON POLICIES CANCELED BY INSURER

Every fire insurance policy contains a cancellation clause that gives the insurer (underwriter) and the insured the right to cancel. When the underwriter cancels a policy he has written, he is required to give the insured at least 5 days' notice in advance.

When the decision to cancel is that of the insurance company, the company must refund to the insured a portion of the premium; in fact, the underwriter may not retain more than an exact pro rata portion of the premium for the length of time the policy has been in force. Exact days, based on a 365-day year, are used in computing the amount to be retained by the company and the amount refunded to the insured.

Examples

PROBLEM 1 The Abel Novelty Store insured its building on September 6 for one year. Because of unusual fire hazards, the insurance company notified the Abel Novelty Store the following April 12 that the policy would be canceled on April 25. If the one-year premium paid by Abel amounted to $160, how much could the insurance company retain? How much would the insured receive as a remittance?

SOLUTION

September 6 – April 25 = 231 days, number of days in which Abel was covered on the policy

$160 (annual premium) $\times \dfrac{231}{365}$ = $101.26, amount retained by underwriter

$160 − $101.26 = $58.74, amount refunded to Abel Novelty Store

PROBLEM 2 Rockwell Insurance Company issued a 3-year policy to Phil's Auto Supplies, receiving $240, the full premium. The policy became effective on July 15, 1973. Because Phil's Auto Supplies did not take the required fire precautions on its building, the insurance company decided to cancel the policy as of September 27, 1975. Find the premium retained by Rockwell Insurance Company and the refund given to Phil's Auto Supplies.

SOLUTION July 15, 1973, to September 27, 1975, equals 2 years and 74 days, or 804 days (the number of days the policy was in force).

$$\$240 \times \frac{804}{1,096^*} = \$176.06, \text{ amount retained by insurer}$$

$$\$240 - \$176.06 = \$63.94, \text{ amount refunded to insured}$$

*The 3-year policy on which the refund is based totaled 3 × 365 days, + 1 day (29 days in February, 1976), or 1,096 days.

Practice Drill

On October 19, an annual premium amounting to $48.72 was paid on a policy. The policy was canceled by the insurance company on the following May 14. Find the premium returned by the insurance company to the insured.

ANSWER $21.09

APPLICATION PROBLEMS

Assuming that the following policies were canceled by the insurance company, find the premium returned to the insured and retained by the company.

	Face of Policy	Annual Rate (%)	Premium Amount	Date of Policy	Date Canceled	Days in Force	Premium Returned	Premium Retained
1.	$40,000	$1\frac{1}{2}$	$ 600	Aug. 16	Oct. 14	59	$ 503.01	$ 96.99
2.	16,000	$\frac{7}{8}$	____	Feb. 6	Mar. 21	____	____	____
3.	90,000	$\frac{3}{4}$	____	Nov. 20	Apr. 16	____	____	____
4.	33,000	$\frac{5}{6}$	____	Jan. 27	Feb. 12	____	____	____
5.	18,500	$1\frac{1}{4}$	____	Apr. 3	Oct. 9	____	____	____

89 SHORT-TERM POLICIES AND CANCELLATION BY THE INSURED

From time to time insurance policies are purchased for less than a year. Such a situation would arise when, for example, a firm expects to occupy a building for three or four months while a new one is being constructed. In such cases, the insurance company will "short-rate" the policy; that is, charge a higher rate than would be charged if the policy were written for a full year. For example, a policy for six months costs 60% of the annual premium rather than 50%; a policy for three months costs 35% of the annual premium rather than 25% (the shorter the period, the higher the rate).

To determine premium charges for short-term policies, the standard short-rate table (page 240) is used.

STANDARD SHORT-RATE SCALE FOR COMPUTING PREMIUMS
FOR TERMS LESS THAN 1 YEAR

Days in Force	%	Days in Force	%	Days in Force	%
1	5	95– 98	37	219–223	69
2	6	99–102	38	224–228	70
3– 4	7	103–105	39	229–232	71
5– 6	8	106–109	40	233–237	72
7– 8	9	110–113	41	238–241	73
9– 10	10	114–116	42	242–246 (8 mo.)	74
11– 12	11	117–120 (4 mo.)	43	247–250	75
13– 14	12	121–124	44	251–255	76
15– 16	13	125–127	45	256–260	77
17– 18	14	128–131	46	261–264	78
19– 20	15	132–135	47	265–269	79
21– 22	16	136–138	48	270–273 (9 mo.)	80
23– 25	17	139–142	49	274–278	81
26– 29	18	143–146	50	279–282	82
30– 32 (1 mo.)	19	147–149	51	283–287	83
33– 36	20	150–153 (5 mo.)	52	288–291	84
37– 40	21	154–156	53	292–296	85
41– 43	22	157–160	54	297–301	86
44– 47	23	161–164	55	302–305 (10 mo.)	87
48– 51	24	165–167	56	306–310	88
52– 54	25	168–171	57	311–314	89
55– 58	26	172–175	58	315–319	90
59– 62 (2 mo.)	27	176–178	59	320–323	91
63– 65	28	179–182 (6 mo.)	60	324–328	92
66– 69	29	183–187	61	329–332	93
70– 73	30	188–191	62	333–337 (11 mo.)	94
74– 76	31	192–196	63	338–342	95
77– 80	32	197–200	64	343–346	96
81– 83	33	201–205	65	347–351	97
84– 87	34	206–209	66	352–355	98
88– 91 (3 mo.)	35	210–214 (7 mo.)	67	356–360	99
92– 94	36	215–218	68	361–365 (12 mo.)	100

Example

PROBLEM The Fairchild Plastics Company has been occupying an old factory building, carrying fire insurance on which the annual premium is $260. The policy expires three months before Fairchild will move into its new building, and the company wishes to take out a 3-month policy. Using the standard short-rate table, determine the premium on the new policy for 3 months.

SOLUTION The rate for 3 months, as shown in the standard short-rate table, is 35%.

35% of $260 = $91, premium for 3 months

The standard short-rate table is also used to determine the amount of refund to be given the insured when he cancels a one-year policy before it expires.

Example

PROBLEM On October 19, an annual premium amounting to $48.72 was paid on a policy. The policy was canceled by the insured on the following May 14. Find the amount of the premium returned to the insured.

SOLUTION The number of days by exact time from October 19 to May 14 is 207 days. According to the standard short-rate table, 66% of the annual premium is to be retained by the insurance company if the policy is canceled by the insured. A premium of 34% was returned.

34% of $48.72 = $16.56, premium returned

Practice Drill

On March 20, a builder insured a newly constructed house for $16,500 at $1.05 per $100. When he sold the house on August 1 of the same year, he canceled the policy. How much of the premium was returned to him?

ANSWER $91.83

APPLICATION PROBLEMS

Use the standard short-rate table on page 240 in solving the following problems.

1. Find the premium returned by the insurance company in each of the following cases, assuming that the policy was canceled by the insured.

Face of Policy	Annual Premium		Date of Policy	Date Canceled	Days in Force	Premium Returned
	Rate	Amount				
a. $35,000	$\frac{5}{6}$%	$_____	July 17	Sept. 15	90	$_____
b. 14,000	$1\frac{1}{2}$%	_____	Nov. 30	Feb. 13	_____	_____
c. 64,000	$\frac{7}{8}$%	_____	June 21	Sept. 19	_____	_____
d. 48,000	$\frac{5}{8}$%	_____	Mar. 5	Aug. 12	_____	_____
e. 18,000	$\frac{3}{4}$%	_____	Oct. 19	Jan. 22	_____	_____
f. 7,500	$1\frac{1}{8}$%	_____	Aug. 30	Nov. 18	_____	_____
g. 28,750	$1\frac{1}{4}$%	_____	Feb. 27	Dec. 9	_____	_____
h. 12,900	$\frac{4}{5}$%	_____	Apr. 3	Oct. 1	_____	_____

2. A house was insured for $21,750 at $\frac{5}{6}$% for 1 year. At the end of 7 months and 15 days, the policy was canceled by the insured. Find the amount of the annual premium returned.

3. Merchandise inventory was insured for $13,850 for 75 days at 96 cents per $100. Find the amount of premium paid.

90 AUTOMOBILE INSURANCE—BODILY-INJURY AND PROPERTY-DAMAGE

Bodily-injury liability insurance (often called *public-liability insurance*) protects the driver of a car against the cost of injuries that he might inflict on other people through the use of his car. The basic coverage limits for bodily-injury insurance are commonly known as 10-and-20, which stands for the amounts $10,000 and $20,000. The owner of a 10-and-20 liability policy is protected to a maximum payment of $10,000 for any one person, and to a maximum payment of $20,000 for any one accident in which he may have injured more than one person.

Higher limits of protection are also available for bodily-injury insurance, including 25-and-50, 50-and-100, 100-and-300, and so on. The principle of coverage on these bigger policies is the same as for 10-and-20 just described.

Property-damage liability insurance covers damages caused by the insured to anyone else's property, such as a house, a lawn, or an automobile. The basic maximum limit in property-damage insurance is $5,000; however, policies can be purchased with maximum limits of either $10,000 or $25,000.

Rates for both bodily-injury and property-damage insurance depend on the frequency with which accidents occur in the area in which the insured lives, the age of the principal driver, the purpose for which the car is used, and the number of accidents the drivers of the car have had.

In determining premium rates, each state is divided into territories according to the number of accidents; some states have as many as 40 or more territories. Base premiums are established for the territory in which the car is garaged.

In the table that follows, the base premium on a 10-and-20 bodily-injury policy in an 01 territory is $46 a year; in an 06 territory the base premium on the same policy is $19 a year.

BASE PREMIUMS FOR PRIVATE PASSENGER AUTOMOBILES

Limits	Territory Schedule							
	01	02	03	04	05	06	07	08
Bodily Injury								
10-and-20	$46	$25	$33	$37	$31	$19	$29	$47
25-and-50	55	30	39	44	37	23	35	56
50-and-100	60	33	43	48	40	25	38	61
100-and-300	65	35	47	52	44	27	41	66
Property Damage								
$ 5,000	$22	$20	$19	$23	$20	$20	$20	$24
10,000	23	21	20	24	21	21	21	25
25,000	24	22	21	25	22	22	22	26

As was stated earlier, several factors are considered in determining the cost of bodily-injury insurance and property-damage insurance, and the base premium in the table above is only one of these. The age of the driver, the purpose for which the car is used, and other factors must be considered. The table given below shows the factors that must be taken into account in determining the premium rate for young drivers.

Note that drivers under the age of 21 who have had a driver training course pay less for insurance than those in the same age bracket who have not taken such a course. Note also that a married male pays less than an unmarried male of the same age; that one pays less for insurance when a car is used for pleasure rather than for business; and that female drivers need pay less than male drivers in the youthful age group.

FACTORS FOR YOUTHFUL OPERATOR

Operator	Driver Training	Age	Pleasure Use	Work— Under 10 Miles	Work— 10 Miles or More	Business Use	Farm Use
Unmarried female	No	17*	1.55	1.65	1.95	2.05	1.30
		18	1.40	1.50	1.80	1.90	1.15
		19	1.25	1.35	1.65	1.75	1.00
		20	1.10	1.20	1.50	1.60	.85
	Yes	17*	1.40	1.50	1.80	1.90	1.15
		18	1.25	1.35	1.65	1.75	1.00
		19	1.15	1.25	1.55	1.65	.90
		20	1.05	1.15	1.45	1.55	.80

*Age 17 or less.   Continued on the following page.

FACTORS FOR YOUTHFUL OPERATOR

Operator	Driver Training	Age	Pleasure Use	Work— Under 10 Miles	Work— 10 Miles or More	Business Use	Farm Use
Married male	No	17*	1.80	1.90	2.20	2.30	1.55
		18	1.70	1.80	2.10	2.20	1.45
		19	1.60	1.70	2.00	2.10	1.35
		20	1.50	1.60	1.90	2.00	1.25
	Yes	17*	1.60	1.70	2.00	2.10	1.35
		18	1.55	1.65	1.95	2.05	1.30
		19	1.50	1.60	1.90	2.00	1.25
		20	1.45	1.55	1.85	1.95	1.20
	N/A†	21	1.40	1.50	1.80	1.90	1.15
		22	1.30	1.40	1.70	1.80	1.05
		23	1.20	1.30	1.60	1.70	.95
		24	1.10	1.20	1.50	1.60	.85
Unmarried male (not owner or principal operator)	No	17*	2.30	2.40	2.70	2.80	2.05
		18	2.10	2.20	2.50	2.60	1.85
		19	1.90	2.00	2.30	2.40	1.65
		20	1.70	1.80	2.10	2.20	1.45
	Yes	17*	2.05	2.15	2.45	2.55	1.80
		18	1.90	2.00	2.30	2.40	1.65
		19	1.75	1.85	2.15	2.25	1.50
		20	1.60	1.70	2.00	2.10	1.35
	N/A	21	1.55	1.65	1.95	2.05	1.30
		22	1.40	1.50	1.80	1.90	1.15
		23	1.25	1.35	1.65	1.75	1.00
		24	1.10	1.20	1.50	1.60	.85
Unmarried male (owner or principal operator)	No	17*	3.30	3.40	3.70	3.80	3.05
		18	3.10	3.20	3.50	3.60	2.85
		19	2.90	3.00	3.30	3.40	2.65
		20	2.70	2.80	3.10	3.20	2.45
	Yes	17*	2.70	2.80	3.10	3.20	2.45
		18	2.65	2.75	3.05	3.15	2.40
		19	2.60	2.70	3.00	3.10	2.35
		20	2.55	2.65	2.95	3.05	2.30
	N/A	21	2.50	2.60	2.90	3.00	2.25
		22	2.30	2.40	2.70	2.80	2.05
		23	2.10	2.20	2.50	2.60	1.85
		24	1.90	2.00	2.30	2.40	1.65
		25	1.70	1.80	2.10	2.20	1.45
		26	1.50	1.60	1.90	2.00	1.25
		27	1.35	1.45	1.75	1.85	1.10
		28	1.20	1.30	1.60	1.70	.95
		29	1.10	1.20	1.50	1.60	.85

*Age 17 or less.   †Not applicable.

When there is no youthful driver in the family, the insurance rates are considerably less, as shown by the following table.

FACTORS WHEN NO YOUTHFUL OPERATOR IS TO BE INSURED

Operator	Pleasure Use	Work— Under 10 Miles	Work— 10 Miles or More	Business Use	Farm Use
One or more, 65 or over	1.00	1.10	1.40	1.50	.75
One female, 30-64	.90	1.00	1.30	1.40	.65
All other	1.00	1.10	1.40	1.50	.75

Another important factor in determining premium costs is the accident rate of the operators. The table below shows the accident factor that must be included in the cost.

Driving Record No. of Accidents	Factor
0	0.00
1	0.30
2	0.70
3	1.20
4	1.80

If, for example, the driver had one accident in the previous year, his factor is .30 as compared with 1.20 for the driver who has had three accidents.

The information supplied in the foregoing tables — Base Premiums for Private Passenger Automobiles, Factors for Youthful Operator, Factors When No Youthful Operator Is To Be Insured, and Driving Record No. of Accidents — is used in arriving at the total premium in bodily-injury and property-damage policies.

Examples | **PROBLEM 1** Marcia Giancoli is 19 years old and has had a course in driver education. The car Marcia drives is garaged in an 04 territory. What will be the cost of a 10-and-20 bodily-injury policy if the car is used for pleasure and has been involved in 2 accidents during the previous year?

SOLUTION   Base premium = $37
Operator factor = 1.15
Accident factor = .70
Total factor = 1.15 + .70 = 1.85
Total premium = 1.85 × $37 = $68.45, or $68*

* All premium amounts are rounded off to the nearest dollar.

PROBLEM 2   Mike Winston is an unmarried male, 20 years old. Although he is not the principal operator of an automobile, he drives the family car to and from work each day, a distance of 8 miles for a round trip. During the past year, Mike had one accident. He has had no driver training. What premium will Mike pay on a $25,000 property-damage policy if the car is garaged in an 08 territory?

SOLUTION   Base premium = $26
Operator factor = 1.80
Accident factor = .30
Total factor = 1.80 + .30 = 2.10
Total premium = 2.10 × $26 = $54.60, or $55

PROBLEM 3   Phil and Marge Gilbert are a young married couple, both 22 years of age. Both drive their automobile, Phil using it for his job as a salesman. They live in an 05 territory and last year Phil had two accidents. What will be the premium on a 50-and-100 bodily-injury policy and a $25,000 property-damage policy?

SOLUTION   Base premium, bodily injury = $40
Base premium, property damage = $22
Operator factor = 1.80
Accident factor = .70
Total factor = 1.80 + .70 = 2.50
Bodily-injury premium = 2.50 × $40 = $100
Property-damage premium = 2.50 × $22 = $55
Total premium = $100 + $55 = $155

Practice Drills

1. Maria Blanco, 18, uses the family car for pleasure. The Blancos live in an 03 territory. What will be the cost of a 50-and-100 bodily-injury policy and a $25,000 property-damage policy, assuming that Maria has completed driver training and that she has had no accidents during the past year?

2. Jerry Gittelson, 18, has his own car, which he uses primarily for pleasure, although he drives to his part-time job 5 miles from his home. Jerry has not had driver training. He lives in an 01 territory and has had no accidents. What will be the premium on a 25-and-50 bodily-injury policy and a $10,000 property-damage policy?

ANSWERS   1. $80   2. $250

APPLICATION PROBLEMS

1. Find the cost of each of the following policies.

Operator	Driver Training	Use of Car	Terri-tory	Acci-dents	Policy	Cost
a. Male, 23, unmarried	....	Business	03	1	50-and-100 bodily-injury	$_____
b. Male, 24, married	....	Work (over 10 miles)	05	0	100-and-300 bodily-injury	_____
c. Female, 17, unmarried	Yes	Pleasure	08	2	$25,000 property-damage	_____
d. Female, 55	....	Business	01	0	100-and-300 bodily-injury and $25,000 property-damage	
e. Male, 29, unmarried	....	Work (less than 10 miles)	02	3	25-and-50 bodily-injury and $10,000 property-damage	_____

2. Mrs. Lydia Murphy injured an elderly man while driving her car. Mrs. Murphy, who carried a 10-and-20 bodily-injury policy, was sued for $50,000. How much would the insurance company have to pay on the policy if a judgment of $25,000 was awarded the injured man against Mrs. Murphy?

91 AUTOMOBILE INSURANCE — COLLISION AND COMPREHENSIVE

Collision insurance is designed to protect the insured against damage to his own car. Under this coverage, the insurance company pays the cost of repairs of any damage to the insured's car caused by collision of the car with another object. However, only part of the cost of the repairs is paid by the insurance company, because these policies always contain a deductible clause. A $50-deductible collision policy means that the insured will pay for the first $50 worth of damage to his car and the insurance company will pay the rest. For example, if the owner of a $50-deductible collision policy damages his car so that the cost of repairs is $228, the owner pays $50 of the cost, and the insurance company pays the remaining $178. Had the cost of the repairs been $50 or less, the insured would have had to cover the entire loss himself.

In the case of a $100-deductible collision policy, the owner will pay for the first $100 of the damage to his car, and the insurance company will pay the balance. It is also possible to purchase a $25-deductible collision coverage policy, but the cost is comparatively high.

All damage to an autombile other than collision (or upset) or mechanical failure is frequently grouped under a coverage called comprehensive insurance. The most important coverages in this group protect the owner against loss caused by fire or theft. Damage caused by lightning, transportation, windstorm, hail, earthquake, explosion, riot, falling parts, flood, malicious mischief, and vandalism is also covered under a comprehensive policy.

The cost of comprehensive and collision insurance depends not only on the factors that determine the cost of property-damage and bodily-injury insurance but on two other factors as well: the age of the automobile and the cost of the car when it was new.

The tables on page 249 show the cost of comprehensive, $50-deductible collision, and $100-deductible collision insurance. The "Car Symbol" heading refers to the group into which cars are placed according to the original cost of the car when it was purchased. The larger the car symbol number, the greater the original price of the car and the greater base premium on the policy.

Example

PROBLEM Rick Hyman, 23 and unmarried, owns a 4-year-old car, which is grouped as symbol 5. He uses the car for business and garages it in an 04 territory. What is the cost of both comprehensive and $100-deductible collision insurance if Rick had no accidents last year?

SOLUTION Comprehensive base premium = $29
$100-deductible base premium = $71
Operator factor = 2.60
Accident factor = 0
Comprehensive premium = 2.60 × $29 = $75
$100-deductible premium = 2.60 × $71 = $185
Total premium = $75 + $185 = $260

Practice Drill

Mary Jane Mastic, 20, purchased a new car a few months ago, which she drives only for pleasure. She has no accident record. Mary Jane lives in an 01 territory. What will be the cost of comprehensive and $50-deductible collision coverage for her? The car is in the symbol 3 category, and she has had no driver training.

ANSWER $140

BASE PREMIUMS FOR TERRITORIES 01, 02, 03, 04

Age Group and Type	Car Symbol						
	1	2	3	4	5	6	7
Comprehensive							
New	$21	$25	$30	$38	$48	$61	$77
2 or 3 years	18	21	26	32	41	52	66
4 or more years	13	15	18	23	29	37	46
$50-Deductible Collision							
	$70	$83	$97	$112	$129	$143	$156
2 or 3 years	61	73	85	98	113	125	137
4 or more years	52	63	73	84	96	107	117
$100-Deductible Collision							
New	$39	$55	$68	$81	$94	$106	$116
2 or 3 years	34	49	60	71	82	92	101
4 or more years	30	42	51	61	71	79	87

BASE PREMIUMS FOR TERRITORIES 05, 06, 07, 08

Age Group and Type	Car Symbol						
	1	2	3	4	5	6	7
Comprehensive							
New	$13	$15	$18	$23	$29	$37	$46
2 or 3 years	11	13	15	19	25	31	39
4 or more years	8	9	11	14	17	22	28
$50-Deductible Collision							
New	$40	$48	$56	$64	$74	$82	$90
2 or 3 years	35	42	49	56	65	72	79
4 or more years	30	36	42	48	56	62	67
$100-Deductible Collision							
New	$22	$31	$39	$46	$53	$59	$65
2 or 3 years	19	27	34	37	46	52	57
4 or more years	17	23	29	34	40	45	49

APPLICATION PROBLEMS

1. Find the cost of each of the following policies.

Operator	Use of Car	Acci-dents	Age Group	Car Symbol	Terri-tory	Policy	Cost
a. Male, 35	Business	1	New	2	07	$50-deductible	$_____
b. Female, 35 one operator	Business	1	New	2	04	$50-deductible	_____
c. Male, 23 owner, married	Pleasure	4	8	4	01	Comprehensive	_____
d. Female, 16, no driver education	Pleasure	0	2	1	01	$50-deductible	_____

2. Eric McKinley, age 37, uses his car to drive to and from work, 15 miles each way. It is classified as symbol 5, is garaged in an 02 territory, and is 4 years old. Assuming McKinley has a perfect driving record, how much will he have to pay for 50-and-100 bodily-injury, $25,000 property-damage, comprehensive, and $50-deductible collision insurance for his automobile?

92 LIFE INSURANCE

Life insurance premiums may be paid annually, semiannually, quarterly, monthly, or weekly. The more frequently the premiums are paid, the higher the premium rate because of the added cost of recordkeeping. If the premiums are paid more often than once a year, the cost is greater because of the increased bookkeeping expense. In fact, if the premiums are paid semiannually, the total amount paid each year is 3% more than if they are paid annually. If paid quarterly, the cost is 5% more than if paid annually; and if paid monthly, the cost is 6% more than the annual payments. To compute semiannual, quarterly, or monthly premiums, insurance companies use a table that is similar to the one shown on the top of page 251.

The *face value* of the policy is the amount of money the insurance company agrees to pay at the time of the death of the insured or, in some cases, after a fixed period of time. The person to whom this money is paid is called the *beneficiary*.

TO COMPUTE PERIODIC PREMIUM

If Period Is	Multiply Annual Premium By*
Semiannual	.515
Quarterly	.2625
Monthly	.08833

* These rates vary slightly between companies.

Computing Premiums on Life Insurance

Life insurance policies can be divided into four major kinds of coverage: term, straight-life, limited-payment, and endowment insurance. The table below shows typical rates charged by life insurance companies for the four major types of policies.

ANNUAL PREMIUMS PER $1,000 WORTH OF INSURANCE

Age at Issue	Term		Straight-Life	Limited-Payment		Endowment	
	10-Yr.	15-Yr.		20-Yr.	30-Yr.	20-Yr.	30-Yr.
15	....	....	$15.78	$28.13	$22.06	$49.44	$31.87
20	$ 7.74	$ 8.11	17.66	30.57	23.99	49.77	32.38
25	8.52	9.09	19.96	33.34	26.24	50.29	33.16
30	9.70	10.57	22.82	36.49	28.90	51.08	34.36
35	11.52	12.83	26.40	40.14	32.15	52.29	36.19
40	14.29	16.27	30.95	44.46	36.23	54.16	38.98
45	18.53	21.48	36.79	49.71	41.57	57.05	43.22
50	24.97	29.32	44.43	56.38	48.77	61.52	49.61
55	34.75	....	54.56	65.22	58.77	68.48	....
60	....	....	68.23	77.52	72.80	79.29	....

Examples

PROBLEM 1 Find the annual premium on an $8,000 30-year endowment policy issued at age 25 and on a $5,000 20-payment life policy issued at age 30.

SOLUTION

Premium for $1,000 30-year endowment policy at age 25 = $33.16
Premium for $8,000 policy = 8 × $33.16 = $265.28

Premium for $1,000 20-payment life policy at age 30 = $36.49
Premium for $5,000 policy = 5 × $36.49 = $182.45

PROBLEM 2   Find the quarterly premium on a $10,000 15-year term policy issued at age 35.

SOLUTION

The annual premium for $1,000 15-year term policy at age 35 is $12.83.
The annual premium for $10,000 policy (10 × $12.83) is $128.30.
The quarterly premium for $10,000 policy (.2625 × $128.30) is $33.68.

Practice Drills

1. Find the annual premium on a $12,000 20-year limited-payment policy issued at age 35.

2. Find the annual premium on a $7,000 15-year term policy issued at age 25.

3. Find the annual premium on a $15,000 30-year endowment policy issued at age 30.

4. Find the semiannual premium on a $10,000 straight-life policy issued at age 20.

5. Find the quarterly premium on an $8,000 10-year term policy issued at age 50.

ANSWERS   1. $481.68   2. $63.63   3. $515.40   4. $90.95°   5. $52.44°

°In computing premiums, the insurer converts any fraction of 1 cent (even if less than ½) to 1 cent.

APPLICATION PROBLEMS

1. Find the annual and periodic premiums on each of the following policies. (Refer to the annual premium table and the periodic premium table both on page 251.)

	Policy	Age at Issue	Face Value	Annual Premium	Payment Period	Periodic Premium
a.	30-year endowment	35	$ 2,000	$_____	Quarterly	$_____
b.	15-year term	40	10,000	_____	Semiannually	_____
c.	30-payment life	35	6,000	_____	Monthly	_____
d.	Whole-life	25	5,000	_____	Annually	_____
e.	10-year term	30	10,000	_____	Annually	_____
f.	20-year endowment	35	3,000	_____	Annually	_____
g.	30-payment life	30	15,000	_____	Annually	_____
h.	Whole-life	15	1,000	_____	Semiannually	_____
i.	20-payment life	45	5,000	_____	Quarterly	_____
j.	10-year term	50	25,000	_____	Monthly	_____

2. At age 40, Boris Cryzinski purchased a $10,000 20-year endowment policy. If he had purchased the policy at age 30, how much less would his annual premiums be?

3. L. T. Hogan purchased a $5,000 20-payment life policy at age 25. To how much would the premium amount if paid annually? semiannually? quarterly? monthly?

93 REAL ESTATE

Real estate (buildings, land, etc.) is often purchased for the purpose of making a profit on the investment. When property is purchased for investment purposes, a number of factors must be considered. To receive an income on his investment, the owner must find a tenant who will pay him rent for the use of the property. He must meet the costs of taxes, insurance, and maintenance and provide for depreciation.

Computing Net Return and Rate Percent Return

The net return and the rate percent return on a real estate investment can be computed by applying the formula $P \div B = R$ (*Percentage $\div$ Base $=$ Rate Percent Return*) in the following procedure.

1. Find the total annual rental.
2. Find the total expenses.
3. Subtract the expenses from the rental to arrive at the net return.
4. Subtract the amount of the mortgage from the value of the property to find the investment.
5. Find the answer to the question, "What percent of the amount invested by the owner is the net return?"

Example | **PROBLEM** An apartment house with an assessed value of $75,000 is mortgaged for $25,000 at 5% interest. The apartment house rents for $810 a month. Find the net return and the rate percent return on the investment if the tax rate is 4.6% and the other annual expenses amount to $660.

SOLUTION

Annual rental (12 x $810)..$9,720

Total expenses:

    Interest on mortgage (5% of

        $25,000)... $ 1,250

    Taxes (4.6% of $75,000)........................ 3,450

    Other expenses 660   5,360

Net return $4,360

Value of property... $75,000

Mortgage on property.................................. 25,000

Investment.. $50,000

    Percentage ÷ Base = Rate

      $4,360 ÷ $50,000 = 8.72%

$$\frac{\$4,360}{\$50,000} = \$4,360 \div \$50,000 = .0872 = 8.72\%, \text{ rate of return}$$

Practice Drill

A man bought property for $32,000 on the following terms: $8,500 cash and a $5\frac{1}{2}\%$ mortgage on the balance. His annual expenses are $800 for depreciation, $375 for maintenance, $109 for insurance, and $930 for taxes. If the property rents for $415 monthly, find the net return and the rate percent return.

ANSWERS $1,473.50, net return; 17.33%, rate percent return

Financing Home Ownership

Purchasing a home is considered an investment, although its return is measured somewhat differently. Home ownership gives the purchaser greater material comforts and conveniences at less cost over a period of time than can be achieved from paying rent.

    The typical homeowner purchases his home by borrowing the money from a bank or other lending institution, making his payments in "installments" much as he would pay rent.

COMPUTING AVERAGE MONTHLY PAYMENTS

To determine the monthly installments necessary to meet interest and principal payments on real estate loans, proceed as follows.

1. Add the beginning balance and the final balance; then divide this sum by 2 to find the average principal balance. (The final balance is the quotient obtained by dividing the beginning balance by the number of monthly installments to be made.)

2. Find the interest on the average principal balance.

3. Add the interest to the principal, and divide this total by the number of payments to be made. The quotient is the amount of the monthly payments.

Very often, instead of using the beginning balance and the balance for the last monthly payment, the beginning balance and the balance at the beginning of the last year are used to compute the average principal balance. This produces a higher monthly balance than that found by the method just outlined. Some mortgages provide for fixed payments, with variable amounts of each payment applied to principal and to interest. Mortgages may also provide for fixed payments on principal, with the actual interest computed on the unpaid balance. The interest is computed by the banker's 60-day interest method.

Example

PROBLEM   A lakefront cottage is purchased by Mr. Mario for $9,800 on the following terms: $1,400 down, with the balance to be paid in 10 years by monthly installments. The carrying charges are 8% on the unpaid balance, with payments to be applied first to the interest and then to the principal. Find the total amount of the average monthly payment.

SOLUTION

$9,800 - $1,400 = $8,400, beginning balance

$8,400 ÷ 120 (monthly installments) = $70, final balance

$$\frac{\$8,400 + \$70}{2} = \frac{\$8,470}{2} = \$4,235, \text{ average principal balance}$$

$4,235 × .08 × 10 = $3,388, total interest

$8,400 + $3,388 = $11,788, total amount to be paid

$11,788 ÷ 120 = $98.23, average monthly payment

Practice Drill

A house is purchased for $24,200. The terms are as follows: 20% down, with the balance on a 20-year $7\frac{1}{2}$% mortgage. The mortgage is to be repaid in monthly installments with interest payable on the unpaid balance. Find the amount of the average monthly payment.

ANSWER $141.42

USING A MORTGAGE-REPAYMENT TABLE

Most people who are paying mortgages on their homes prefer a plan that calls for the payment of the same amount each month. Each payment includes the interest due for the period plus a sum that is applied to the reduction of the mortgage debt. If paid regularly, these monthly payments will pay off the full mortgage debt by the time the last payment is made. The plans for such payments are available for all kinds and amounts of mortgage debts and for various time periods and rates. Following is a section of a typical mortgage repayment table.

MORTGAGE-REPAYMENT TABLE: MONTHLY PAYMENT ON $1 DEBT

Yrs.	Rate of Interest									
	4%	5%	6%	7%	7.5%	8%	8.5%	9%	9.5%	10%
5	$.0184	$.0189	$.0193	$.0198	$.0200	$.0203	$.0205	$.0208	$.0210	$.0212
10	.0101	.0106	.0111	.0116	.0119	.0121	.0124	.0127	.0129	.0132
15	.0074	.0079	.0084	.0090	.0093	.0096	.0098	.0101	.0104	.0107
20	.0061	.0066	.0072	.0078	.0081	.0084	.0087	.0090	.0093	.0097
25	.0053	.0058	.0064	.0071	.0074	.0077	.0081	.0084	.0087	.0091
30	.0048	.0054	.0060	.0067	.0070	.0073	.0077	.0080	.0084	.0088

This table shows what the monthly payments must be to repay a mortgage debt of $1. To find the total monthly payment, multiply the monthly payment due on $1 by the amount of the debt. Thus, if an $8,500 mortgage is to be repaid over 10 years in equal monthly payments, with interest on the unpaid balance at 5%, the monthly payment on a $1 debt, $.0106 as shown in the table, must be multiplied by 8,500. The product, $90.10, is the amount of each of the monthly payments.

Example

PROBLEM Perry Lynn bought a house for $22,500 on which he made a $5,000 down payment. The balance was secured by a mortgage on the house. Monthly payments were to be made which would provide for 6% interest on the unpaid balance and which would also pay off the mortgage in 20 years. Find the amount of each month's payment.

SOLUTION According to the mortgage-repayment table, the monthly payment on a $1 debt for 20 years at 6% is .0072. The monthly payment on a $17,500 debt ($22,500 − $5,000) will be 17,500 × $.0072, or $126.

Practice Drill

Kent's house, costing $30,500, has a $20,000 mortgage. The mortgage must be repaid in 25 years at 5% interest. Using the mortgage-repayment table, find the amount of each monthly payment.

ANSWER $116

APPLICATION PROBLEMS

1. Lasker bought a two-family house for $28,000 as an investment. The estimated annual expenses were as follows: taxes, $886; depreciation, $760; insurance, $154.80; and maintenance, $350. What must the monthly rental be on each of the two apartments in order for Lasker to realize a net return of 8% on his investment?

2. Find the net return on the investment and the rate percent return in each of the following problems.

	Value of Property	Amount of Mortgage	Interest Rate on Mortgage	Taxes	Other Expenses	Monthly Rental	Net Return	Rate Percent Return(%)
a.	$50,000	$30,000	6%	5.8%	$295	$540	$_____	_____
b.	40,000	25,000	5%	6.09%	380	620	_____	_____
c.	30,000	12,000	5%	5.7%	565	415	_____	_____
d.	25,000	10,000	7%	5.64%	420	385	_____	_____
e.	65,000	15,000	$5\frac{1}{2}$%	6.68%	255	700	_____	_____
f.	36,000	16,000	$7\frac{1}{2}$%	6.31%	310	550	_____	_____

3. As an investment, Manning purchased a building for $36,500, paying $16,500 cash and obtaining a $7\frac{1}{2}$% mortgage for the remainder. At the end of the first year, his records showed the following expenses in addition to the interest on the mortgage: depreciation, $730; insurance; $228; repairs, $340; taxes, $689; and miscellaneous, $116.
a. How much did it cost him to carry the building that year?
b. If he wishes to gain a net return of 5% on his actual cash investment, what monthly rental must he charge?

4. Using the average-balance method, find the amount of the monthly payment for principal and interest in each of the following problems.

	Value of Property	Down Payment	Balance Due	Years of Payments	Average Principal Balance	Carrying Charges	Interest	Average Monthly Payment
a.	$10,000	$2,000	$ 10,419	10	$ 40333	6%	$_____	$ 86.85
b.	8,000	1,200	_____	20	_____	6%	_____	_____
c.	24,000	8,000	_____	12	_____	6%	85556	_____
d.	15,000	2,500	_____	15	_____	5%	_____	_____
e.	11,500	3,500	_____	10	_____	4%	_____	_____
f.	9,500	2,300	_____	20	_____	$4\frac{1}{2}$%	_____	_____

5. A lot 80 feet × 125 feet is purchased for $1,340. A down payment of $80 is made, and the balance is payable in 36 equal monthly installments. Carrying charges of 5% on the unpaid balance are added to the monthly payments. Each payment is applied first to the interest and then to the principal. How much is the average monthly payment for principal and interest?

6. Using the mortgage-repayment table on page 256 find the amount of the monthly payment for principal and interest in each of the following problems.

	Value of Property	Down Payment	Balance Due	Years of Payments	Interest Rate	Payment on $1 Debt	Monthly Payment
a.	$10,000	$2,500	$_____	15	6%	$_____	$_____
b.	25,000	3,500	_____	10	5%	_____	_____
c.	7,800	2,400	_____	20	6%	_____	_____
d.	35,000	7,500	_____	30	4%	_____	_____
e.	18,750	3,250	_____	25	5%	_____	_____
f.	12,500	4,500	_____	5	6%	_____	_____

PROBLEMS FOR PART TWELVE

Taxes, Insurance & Real Estate

84

1. The state sales tax in a Pacific Coast state is 2% and the city tax in Metropolitanville in that state is 3%. Compute the sales tax to be collected on the following purchases.

a. $322.40   c. $4.49   e. $44.88   g. $11.50
b. $.33   d. $18.95   f. $6.65   h. $1,281.75

2. The taxable property in a town was assessed at $23,400,000. The budget for the year amounted to $612,000. What is the tax rate? How much would a property owner have to pay if his realty was assessed at $97,500? 612,000 ÷ 23,400,000 = ,025 × 97,500 =

3. Property worth $35,400 is assessed at 80% of its actual value for tax purposes. If the city tax is $5.12 per $100 valuation, the county tax $1.08 per $100 valuation, and the state tax 93¢ per $100 valuation, find the total tax paid by the property owner. 5.12 × 283.20
35,400 × .80 = 28,320   1.08 × 11
                                                 93 2 11

4. Property owned by a taxpayer is assessed at $24,380. The tax rate is $5.99 per $100 of assessed value, and all taxes are due in equal semi-annual installments on November 10 and April 10. Interest at 1% a month, or a fraction thereof, is charged on overdue payments. If the property owner waited until April 10 to pay both installments, find his total tax payment. 243.8 × 5.99 = 2 | 1460.36
730.18

85

1. Find the premium paid on each of the following fire insurance policies.

Amount of Insurance	Premium Rate	Premium Paid
a. $ 7,200	83¢ per $100	$ 59.76
b. 4,300	¾% less 10%	29.02
c. 15,000	⅘% less 20%	96.00
d. 27,500	$1.75 per $100	
e. 3,200	1⅚%	
f. 1,750	⅗% less 10%	
g. 19,900	$1.35 per $100	268.65

handwritten: 72×.83 = 59.76
43×¾ = 32.25×.10 = 3.23   3.23
.01833 ⁱ⁴⁄₆ 58.67
268.65

2. A house is insured for $18,500 for a 3-year period at 1¾%, and the contents are insured for $7,800 for the same period at $1.35 per $100. What is the total premium? If the 3-year rate is 2.7 times the rate for 1 year, what would the annual premium be at the yearly rate?

handwritten: 18500× .0175 = 323.75
7800 ÷ 100 = 78× 1.35 = 105.30 + 323.75 = 429.05 ÷ 2.7 = 158.91 ×2.7

86

1. A building of the Wentworth Novelty Company was insured for $125,000. How much would be collected under an ordinary fire insurance policy in case of a $100,000 fire loss?

2. If the building in problem 1 was insured for $140,000 and a $150,000 loss was suffered, how much would be collected under an ordinary fire insurance policy?

3. A building valued at $22,500 is insured under an ordinary policy for $18,000. The insurance is distributed as follows: Company A, $10,000; Company B, $5,000; and Company C, $3,000. The premium rate is 1⅞%. Find the net loss of each company if fire causes a loss of $13,500. *handwritten:* 10000/18000 × 13500 = Answer

87

1. Sewell, the proprietor of a gift shop, carried $24,000 insurance on his stock. The policy contained an 80% coinsurance clause. At the time when his inventory records disclosed that the value of his stock at cost was $55,000, a fire completely destroyed his business. What insurance settlement should he have received?

2. The Excel Appliance Company carried $32,000 fire insurance with a 90% coinsurance clause on its stock of merchandise. At the time when fire destroyed $12,600 worth of the stock, inventory records disclosed that the value of the total stock at cost was $40,000. What insurance settlement should the company receive?

3. In a department store completely destroyed by fire, the stock was insured as follows: Company A, $27,000; Company B, $36,000; Company C, $54,000; and Company D, $18,000. Assuming that the value of the stock at the time of the fire was $200,000, find the amount paid by each insurance company if each policy contained a 90% coinsurance clause.

4. A building valued at $50,000 is insured for $\frac{3}{5}$ of its value. Its contents, valued at $8,000, are insured for 75% of their value. Find the amount recoverable from the insurance company under a 90% coinsurance clause policy if fire causes a loss of $21,600 to the building and a total loss to the contents.

88

1. Assuming that the following policies were canceled by the insurance company, find the premium returned to the insured and the premium retained by the company.

	Face of Policy	Annual Rate	Date of Policy	Date Canceled
a.	$32,000	$\frac{7}{8}$%	June 18	Sept. 16
b.	6,000	$\frac{3}{4}$%	Oct. 12	Jan. 15
c.	7,000	$1\frac{1}{2}$%	Nov. 18	Feb. 1
d.	24,000	$\frac{5}{8}$%	Mar. 1	Aug. 8
e.	17,500	$\frac{5}{6}$%	July 12	Sept. 10

2. A building was insured on July 25 for $28,000 at $1\frac{5}{8}$% per year. On October 23, the policy was canceled by the insured.
a. Find the amount of premium returned by the insurance company.
b. If the insurance company had canceled the policy, how much of the premium would have been returned to the insured?

3. An annual premium of $296 was paid on a house insured for $18,500. The policy was written on June 25 and canceled when the house was sold on December 11.
a. Find the premium rate on the insurance.
b. Since the insured canceled the policy, how much of the premium was returned by the insurance company?
c. If the insurance company had canceled the policy, how much of the premium would have been returned?

4. On July 18, Cameron took out a 1-year $15,500 fire insurance policy on his frame house located in Community C. On November 5, the fire underwriter canceled the policy. What refund did Cameron receive? (Use the annual rate charge table on page 232.)

89 Use the standard short-rate table on page 240 to solve the following problems.

1. Find the premium returned by the insurance company in each of the following cases, assuming that the policy was canceled by the insured.

	Face of Policy	Annual Rate	Date of Policy	Date Canceled
a.	$ 50,000	$1\frac{1}{2}$%	Sept. 14	Nov. 18
b.	85,000	$1\frac{7}{8}$%	Apr. 2	Oct. 29
c.	22,500	$1\frac{1}{4}$%	Aug. 19	Dec. 22
d.	40,750	$\frac{3}{4}$%	Feb. 27	July 9
e.	110,000	$\frac{4}{5}$%	Jan. 12	Sept. 14

2. A factory was insured for $250,000 at $\frac{5}{6}$%. At the end of 6 months and 20 days the policy was canceled by the insured. Find the amount of the annual premium returned.

90 1. Two persons were injured by Birkner's car. The injured sued and were awarded $12,000 and $3,500. If Birkner carried a 5-and-10 bodily-injury policy, how much was paid to the injured parties by the insurance company?

2. Ryan carried 10-and-20 bodily-injury insurance and $5,000 property damage insurance. During a snowstorm, he hit a car driven by Mankin. Mankin and his daughter required medical attention. They sued and were awarded the following judgments: $12,500 and $7,500, respectively, for personal injuries; and $1,200 for damage to the car.
a. How much of this liability will the insurance company pay?
b. How much must Ryan pay?

3. Find the cost of each of the following policies.

	Operator	Driver Training	Use of Car	Territory	Accidents	Policy
a.	Male, 40	....	Business	03	2	50-and-100 bodily-injury
b.	Female, 18, unmarried	No	Work (more than 10 miles)	02	0	$10,000 property-damage
c.	Male, 19, unmarried, owner	Yes	Pleasure	04	1	10-and-20 bodily-injury
d.	Female, 41, only operator	....	Business	06	0	25-and-50 bodily-injury
e.	Male, 26, married, owner	....	Farm	01	2	$5,000 property-damage

91

1. In an accident, George Michaels damaged the car of Arlene Rudge to the extent of $388.80 and his own car to the extent of $870.40. How much did Michaels' insurance company have to pay if he carried $50-deductible collision insurance and $5,000 property-damage insurance?

2. Phil Lasser, 24 and married, is the owner of a 4-year-old car. He uses the car to drive to work, a distance each way of 5 miles. During the previous year, Phil had 2 accidents with his car. He lives in an 04 territory. How much would Phil save on both $100-deductible collision insurance and comprehensive insurance if he drove a car classified as symbol 2 rather than symbol 7?

3. Find the cost of the following policies.

Operator	Use of Car	Acci-dents	Age Group	Car Symbol	Terri-tory	Policy
a. Male, 67	Pleasure	1	1	3	02	$50-ded.
b. Female, 27, one operator	Business	0	2	1	06	Comp.
c. Male, 29, unmarried, owner	Farm	0	4	7	03	Comp.
d. Female, 19, married	Work (more than 10 miles)	2	New	5	03	$100-ded.
e. Male, 22, married, owner	Work (less than 10 miles)	1	3	4	01	$50-ded.

92

1. Using the annual premium table on page 251, find the annual premiums for the following life insurance policies.
a. 15-year term policy, $6,000, taken out at age 35
b. Straight-life policy, $20,000, taken out at age 30
c. Limited-payment policy, $5,000, taken out at age 20
d. Endowment policy, $14,000, taken out at age 40

2. What would the total premium on each of the policies in problem 1 be if the insured elected to pay the premium quarterly? semiannually? Refer to the periodic premium table on page 251.

3. How much less will a person pay each year if he purchases an $8,000 10-year term policy at age 20 than if he purchases an $8,000 straight-life policy at the same age?

4. At age 30, Carlson purchased a $25,000 straight-life policy. How much will he save annually on premiums if he makes annual instead of semiannual payments? How much will he save if he makes semiannual instead of monthly payments?

93

1. A tract of land cost an investor $84,000. After holding the land for 2 years, he sold the tract for $103,500. Miscellaneous expenses amounted to $398.40. If the land was assessed for tax purposes at 75% of its value ($84,000, cost to investor) and the tax rate was $5.16 per $100, find the profit on the investment.

2. On property that rents for $450 a month, the following annual expenses must be met: $610 for taxes, $175 for insurance, 6% interest on a $20,800 mortgage on the property, and $1,850 for maintenance and other expenses. How much can a purchaser pay for the property to net $7\frac{1}{2}$% on his investment? The purchaser is expected to assume the mortgage and pay the interest on it annually.

3. A $12,500 house is purchased on the following terms: $2,500 down, the balance to be paid in 20 years by monthly installments. The carrying charges are 6% on the unpaid balance. Find the amount of the average monthly payment for principal and interest.

4. A house is sold for $9,200 on the following terms: $1,200 down, and the balance secured by a 20-year 6% mortgage. Payments are to be made monthly. Each payment is to include interest on the unpaid balance plus a sum that will pay off the amount of the mortgage at the end of the 20-year period. Using the mortgage-repayment table on page 256, what will be the amount of each monthly payment?

PART THIRTEEN

Distributing Partnership Profits & Corporate Dividends

A *partnership* results when two or more parties agree to combine their assets, labor, and skill for the purpose of carrying on a lawful business, with the understanding that the profits and losses arising from the undertaking will be shared among them. The partnership contract specifies the amount and the form of the capital that each partner is to contribute, the duties and salaries of each, and the method of sharing profits and losses. If the partnership contract does not include an agreement as to the method by which profits are to be distributed, profits are shared equally, regardless of the ratio of the partners' respective investments or the time given to the enterprise by the individual partners. Losses that may be incurred are distributed in the profit-sharing ratio unless other provision is made in the contract. Partnership profits are generally distributed according to one of five different methods: equal distribution, arbitrary ratios, original investment, average investment, and arbitrary distribution.

A *corporation* is a type of business organization in which shares of stock are sold to investors who, if the business prospers, have an opportunity to share in the profits of the corporation. The organizers of a corporation (*incorporators*) invest a certain sum in the corporation, and each receives as evidence of his investment a printed statement called a stock certificate. The certificate shows the number of shares and the value (called *par value*) of each share. If the corporation prospers and its earnings are high, the demand for stock usually increases, resulting in an increase in price. If the earnings are low, the price of the stock will probably go down. The price for which the stock can be sold is called the *market price.* The holders of stock certificates are called *stockholders,* and the investments of stockholders make up the capital of a corporation (usually called *capital stock*). The par value of each share of capital stock is usually expressed in round amounts, such as $5 or $10 or multiples of these amounts, not exceeding $100. In some cases stock without par value (*no-par-value stock*) is issued. When this is first issued by a corporation, a certain price is fixed for the sale; after the stock is put on the market, its value is determined by the market price.

94 EQUAL DISTRIBUTION AND ARBITRARY RATIOS

There are several methods of profit distribution frequently provided in partnership agreements. Equal distribution and arbitrary ratios are two of the more common methods used.

Equal Distribution

In this type of agreement, the partners consent to divide the profits of the business equally. Where there is no provision in the contract for profit distribution, each partner shares equally regardless of his investment or the value of the services he renders the firm.

Example

PROBLEM   The partnership agreement of Hull, Carr, and Lyle made no provision for the division of profits. Hull contributed the building and equipment as his investment in the business. Carr invested $10,000 and Lyle, $25,000. The business was operated by Hull and Carr; Lyle took no active part in the management. The profits for the first year were $12,600. What was each partner's share?

SOLUTION $\frac{1}{3}$ of $12,600 = \$ 4,200$, Hull's share
$\frac{1}{3}$ of $12,600 = \quad 4,200$, Carr's share
$\frac{1}{3}$ of $12,600 = \underline{\quad 4,200}$, Lyle's share
$\qquad\qquad\qquad\quad \$12,600$

Practice Drill

Keller and Schiff formed a partnership in which Keller invested $19,000 and Schiff, $6,000. During the first year, Schiff took practically no part in the operation of the business because of illness. At the end of the year, the business showed a profit of $8,400. If the partnership agreement made no provision for the division of profits, to how much would each partner be entitled?

ANSWER $4,200, Keller; $4,200, Schiff

Arbitrary Ratios

By this type of agreement, profits are distributed among partners by arbitrary ratios. The term "arbitrary" here means simply that the partners agree on a certain division of profits and losses based on a number of factors. For example, one partner might get credit for having thought up the idea for the business, or for spending more time in the business than the other(s), or because he has more experience in that particular type of business, or because he has a greater clientele. Under this type of agreement, the amount each partner is to receive is expressed as a percent of the total profit.

Example

PROBLEM Young invested $10,000 in a partnership and Burke, $25,000. Because Young will spend more time than Burke in running the business, he is to receive 45% of the profits and Burke, 55%. How much was each entitled to if the business earned $13,250?

SOLUTION
45% of $13,250 = $ 5,962.50, Young's share
55% of $13,250 = $\underline{\quad 7,287.50}$, Burke's share
$13,250.00

Practice
Drill

Harper, Syms, and Classen entered into a partnership agreement that provided that Harper was to receive 25% of the net earnings of the business; Syms, $33\frac{1}{3}$%; and Classen, $41\frac{2}{3}$%. It further provided that Harper's investment in the business would be to contribute his knowledge and skill; Syms' investment would be $15,000 cash; and Classen's, $25,000 cash. How should earnings of $12,460 be divided among the partners?

ANSWER $3,115, Harper; $4,153.33, Syms; $5,191.67, Classen

APPLICATION PROBLEMS

1. Davis and Franks invested $10,000 and $5,000, respectively, in a partnership. Davis worked full time in the business. Franks devoted only half his time to partnership affairs. The profits for the first year amounted to $3,800. If the partnership agreement made no provision for the distribution of profits, to how much would Davis and Franks each be entitled?

2. Kowolski and O'Grady formed a partnership to establish the Haven Animal Hospital. Kowolski invested $60,000 in the venture and O'Grady invested $45,000; but because O'Grady would spend all his time at the hospital and Kowolski only about $\frac{1}{2}$ his time there, it was decided that O'Grady would receive 65% of the profits and Kowolski, 35%. At the end of the first year, the profits to be divided were $16,000; the second year, $37,500. How much did each partner receive at the end of the first and second years?

3. Meagher and McGrath entered into a partnership to operate a card and stationery business. McGrath invested $27,500 in the firm and Meagher contributed 30 clients. In drawing up the partnership agreement, the men decide that Meagher will receive $66\frac{2}{3}$% of the profits and McGrath $33\frac{1}{3}$%. The first year's profits were $21,778.60. Find how much each partner should have received.

95 ORIGINAL AND AVERAGE INVESTMENT

Original and average investment are two additional methods of profit distribution provided in partnership agreements. D_1 – Dec *Calandi Yea*

D_1 – *June 30 Fiscal*

Original Investment

By the original investment type of agreement, profits are distributed according to each partner's original investment or in the ratio of their capital accounts at the beginning of each year.

Examples | **PROBLEM 1** Egger, Worth, and Maher invested \$7,500, \$5,000, and \$2,500, respectively, in a small consulting business. The profits were to be shared in proportion to the original investments. Profits the first year amounted to \$6,000 and the second year to \$8,400. Each partner withdrew \$1,000 of his share of the profits each year. Find each partner's profit for the first and second years.

SOLUTION   \$7,500 + \$5,000 + \$2,500 = \$15,000, total investment

$$\frac{7,500}{15,000} = \frac{1}{2}$$

$\frac{1}{2}$ of \$6,000 = \$3,000, Egger's share

$$\frac{5,000}{15,000} = \frac{1}{3}$$

$\frac{1}{3}$ of \$6,000 = \$2,000, Worth's share

$$\frac{2,500}{15,000} = \frac{1}{6}$$

$\frac{1}{6}$ of \$6,000 = \$1,000, Maher's share

Although Egger's investment in the business at the beginning of the second year increased to \$9,500 (\$2,000 of his profit credit was not withdrawn) and Worth's to \$6,000 (\$1,000 of his profit credit was not withdrawn), by the terms of the agreement, the original profit distribution ratio of $\frac{1}{2}$, $\frac{1}{3}$, and $\frac{1}{6}$ remains.

$\frac{1}{2}$ of \$8,400 = \$4,200, Egger's share
$\frac{1}{3}$ of \$8,400 = \$2,800, Worth's share
$\frac{1}{6}$ of \$8,400 = \$1,400, Maher's share

PROBLEM 2 If the partnership agreement in problem 1 provided for the distribution of profits in the ratio of capital accounts at the beginning of each year, how much would each partner have been entitled to the first and second years?

SOLUTION   The division of profits the first year would be the same as in problem 1.

The second year, when profits amounted to $8,400, the capital accounts showed a total investment of $9,500 + $6,000 + $2,500, or $18,000.

$$\frac{9,500}{18,000} = \tfrac{19}{36}$$

$\tfrac{19}{36}$ of $8,400 = $4,433.33, Egger's share

$$\frac{6,000}{18,000} = \tfrac{1}{3}$$

$\tfrac{1}{3}$ of $8,400 = $2,800.00, Worth's share

$$\frac{2,500}{18,000} = \tfrac{5}{36}$$

$\tfrac{5}{36}$ of $8,400 = $1,166.67, Maher's share

Practice Drills

1. Tuck invested $12,500 in a business and Nevins, $7,500. The articles of copartnership provided for the distribution of profits in the ratio of the original investments. If profits the first year amounted to $9,086, find each partner's share.

2. The partnership agreement of Allen and Hill provided that Allen's investment in the business would be $9,600 and Hill's, $6,400; that profits were to be divided in proportion to the amount of each partner's investment at the beginning of each year; and that profits were to be left in the business the first year of operation. The profits the first year amounted to $5,200 and the second year to $11,500. Find each partner's share of the first year's profit and of the second year's profit.

ANSWERS 1. Tuck, $5,678.75; Nevins, $3,407.25   2. First year: $3,120, Allen; $2,080, Hill. Second year: $6,900, Allen; $4,600, Hill.

Average Investment

Some partnership agreements provide, at the time of organization, for the distribution of profits in the ratio of each partner's average investment in the business. The manner in which the profits are divided in this method is described in the following example.

Example

PROBLEM The partnership agreement of Grant and Horner provided for the distribution of profits in the ratio of average investment. Grant's investment at the beginning of last year amounted to $30,000 and Horner's to $20,000. On April 1, Grant received from a loan-investment company $5,000, which he invested in the business. On June 1, he withdrew from the business $15,000 with which to make a payment on an annuity. On March 1, Horner withdrew $5,000 from the business, which he repaid on November 1. If the business showed a profit of $14,000 at the end of the year, to how much was each partner entitled?

SOLUTION Grant's investment:

$30,000 for 12 months	=	$360,000 for 1 month
5,000 for 9 months	=	45,000 for 1 month
		$405,000 for 1 month
Withdrawal of $15,000 for 7 months	=	105,000 for 1 month
		$300,000 for 1 month

Horner's investment:

$20,000 for 12 months	=	$240,000 for 1 month
5,000 for 2 months	=	10,000 for 1 month
		$250,000 for 1 month
Withdrawal of $5,000 for 10 months	=	50,000 for 1 month
		$200,000 for 1 month

The profit-sharing ratio is $300,000 to $200,000, or 3 to 2. The profit is divided into 5 parts (3 + 2).

$$\tfrac{3}{5} \text{ of } \$14,000 = \$ \ 8,400, \text{ Grant's share}$$
$$\tfrac{2}{5} \text{ of } \$14,000 = \underline{\ \ \ 5,600}, \text{ Horner's share}$$
$$\$14,000$$

Practice Drill

At the beginning of last year, Markin's investment in a retail business amounted to $10,000; his partner Smith's investment amounted to $25,000. Profits were to be divided in the ratio of average investment. On April 1, Markin invested an additional $10,000 in the business. On June 1, Smith withdrew from the business $5,000, which he repaid on October 1. If the business showed net earnings of $14,400 for the year, to how much did each partner's share amount?

ANSWER $6,171.43, Markin; $8,228.57, Smith

APPLICATION PROBLEMS

1. Wallace invested $12,000 in a partnership with Wright who invested $18,000. At the end of the first year, the business showed a profit of $2,750; the second year, $9,600. The profits were to be shared according to the partners' investments at the beginning of each year. Find each partner's share of the profits each year if Wallace withdrew only half of his share of the profits the first year and Wright withdrew his full share of the profits both years.

2. King, Brewer, and York formed a partnership, investing $5,000, $10,000, and $15,000, respectively. The articles of copartnership provided that each partner's share in the capital of the business should be in proportion to his original investment. King died 8 years after the

business had been set up, which resulted in the automatic dissolution of the partnership. If the net worth of the business at that time amounted to $46,500, how much did King's estate, Brewer, and York each receive?

3. Hopkins and Smith, partners, share profits in proportion to their share in the average capital invested. Hopkins' investment in the business on January 1 amounted to $15,000. He invested an additional $5,000 on May 1 and $7,500 on August 1. Smith's investment on January 1 amounted to $22,000. He withdrew $4,000 on May 1 and invested $6,000 on October 1. Find each partner's share of a profit of $12,300 for the year.

4. Barr and Nichols were partners, having invested $8,000 and $10,000, respectively, in a retail business. The partnership agreement provided for the sharing of profits and losses in proportion to the investment of each partner at the beginning of each year. Profits the first year amounted to $4,500; the second year, to $6,800. Each year, Barr withdrew half of his share of the profits and Nichols withdrew his full share. To how much was each partner entitled the first year and the second year?

% ARBITRARY DISTRIBUTION

Arbitrary distribution is another of the common methods of profit distribution provided in partnership agreements.

Arbitrary Distribution

In the arbitrary distribution type of agreement, profits or losses are distributed equally or arbitrarily among the partners after payment of salaries and/or interest on capital investments.

Examples | **PROBLEM 1** The capital accounts of Hill and Ellis, partners, showed a balance on January 1 of $12,000 and $8,500, respectively. At the end of the year, the business showed a net profit of $6,500. The partnership agreement provided that each partner receive 6% interest on his investment, that the interest be deducted from the total profits, and that the balance of the profits be divided equally. Find each partner's share of the net profit.

SOLUTION
$12,000 (Hill's investment) × .06 = $ 720, Hill's share
$8,500 (Ellis's investment) × .06 =   510, Ellis's share
                                    $1,230

$6,500 (net profit) — $1,230 = $5,270, balance of profits
$5,270 ÷ 2 = $2,635, each partner's share after interest is deducted

$720 + $2,635 = $3,355, Hill's share
$510 + $2,635 = 3,145, Ellis's share
                $6,500

PROBLEM 2 The partnership agreement of Barr and Clark provided for an interest credit of 5% on investment before profit distribution. Profits or losses were to be shared equally. Barr's investment at the beginning of the year amounted to $28,750; Clark's, to $22,500. The business profits for the year amounted to $2,400. Show the profit distribution at the end of the year.

SOLUTION
$28,750 (Barr's investment) × .05 = $1,437.50, Barr's interest
$22,500 (Clark's investment) × .05 = 1,125.00, Clark's interest
                                      $2,562.50, total interest

$2,562.50 — $2,400 (net profit) = $162.50, net loss
$162.50 ÷ 2 = $81.25, each partner's loss after interest is deducted

$1,437.50 — $81.25 = $1,356.25, Barr's share
$1,125.00 — $81.25 = 1,043.75, Clark's share
                     $2,400.00

Practice Drills

1. The partnership agreement of Lund and Fielder provided that each partner should receive an interest credit of 6% on his investment before profits were distributed and that the remaining profits should be divided equally. Lund's investment at the beginning of the year amounted to $24,000 and Fielder's to $14,000. If the profits for the year amounted to $10,200, what was each partner's share of the net profit?

2. Let us suppose that the articles of copartnership in problem 1 provided that profits or losses should be shared in proportion to each partner's investment at the beginning of the year after the total profits were reduced by the interest credit. If the business showed a profit of $1,620 at the end of the year, how should it be distributed?

ANSWERS 1. $1,440 + $3,960 = $5,400, Lund; $840 + $3,960 = $4,800, Fielder
         2. $1,440 — $416.84 = $1,023.16, Lund; $840 — $243.16 = $596.84, Fielder

Arbitrary Distribution with Interest Charge

Under this type of agreement, profits are distributed equally or arbitrarily after an interest charge is made on the difference between the sum agreed upon and the actual investment. If the amount of the investment is greater than that provided by the agreement, interest is credited on the excess.

Example

PROBLEM Folger and Dunn were partners. The partnership agreement provided that profits and losses were to be shared in the ratio of 3 to 2, Folger receiving $\frac{3}{5}$ and Dunn $\frac{2}{5}$. It was further agreed that each partner was to maintain an average investment of $10,000 in the business at all times and that 6% interest was to be charged if the investment was less than the sum agreed upon, or credited if the investment exceeded it. Last year, Folger's investment amounted to $7,200 and Dunn's to $13,500. If the business showed a profit of $8,600 for the year and each partner left his share in the business, how much did each of the capital accounts amount to at the beginning of the next year?

SOLUTION Folger's investment is $2,800 less than the $10,000 required. Folger's account should be charged with 6% of $2,800, or $168 interest. Dunn's investment is $3,500 more than the $10,000 required. Dunn's account should be credited with 6% of $3,500, or $210 interest.

$210 − $168 = $42, net amount of interest deducted from net profits
$8,600 − $42 = $8,558, profits before distribution

$\frac{3}{5}$ of $8,558 = $5,134.80
$5,134.80 − $168 = $4,966.80, Folger's $\frac{3}{5}$ share

$\frac{2}{5}$ of $8,558 = $3,423.20
$3,423.20 + $210 = $3,633.20, Dunn's $\frac{2}{5}$ share

Capital accounts at the beginning of the next year:
  Folger: $ 7,200 + $4,966.80 = $12,166.80
  Dunn: $13,500 + $3,633.20 = $17,133.20

Practice Drill

The partnership agreement of Lyon and Barron provides the following: (1) Profits are to be shared in the ratio of 5 to 3, Lyon receiving $\frac{5}{8}$ and Barron $\frac{3}{8}$. (2) Each partner is to maintain an average investment of $25,000 in the business. (3) Interest at 6% is to be charged against each partner's account if his average investment falls below $25,000 in any year, or credited to his account if his average investment exceeds $25,000. Lyon's investment last year amounted to $20,000 and Barron's to $35,000. If the profits for the year amounted to $16,700, to how much was each partner entitled?

ANSWER $9,950, Lyon; $6,750, Barron

APPLICATION PROBLEMS

1. On July 1, Sargent invested $9,000 and Cushman invested $12,000 in a partnership. They agreed that interest at 5% was to be paid to each partner on the basis of average investment and the remaining profit or

loss divided equally. On October 1, Sargent invested an additional $3,000. At the end of the fiscal year, profits before payment of interest amounted to $4,800. How should the profits be divided?

2. Milton and Drew, partners, invested $18,000 each at the beginning of the year in a men's clothing store. Three months later, Milton invested an additional $6,000 in the business. On June 1 Drew withdrew $5,000, which he replaced on October 1. He invested an additional $9,000 on December 1. The profits for the year amounted to $12,800. The partnership agreement provided for an equal distribution of profits and losses after 6% interest was paid to each partner on the basis of his average capital.
a. To how much interest is each partner entitled?
b. What is each partner's total share of the profits?

3. Bacon and Thomas entered into a partnership, investing $15,000 and $10,000, respectively. The agreement provided for equal sharing of profits after 6% interest is paid each partner on invested capital. The business earned $7,200 for the year. Find each partner's share of the profits, including interest on his investment.

97 CORPORATE DIVIDEND DISTRIBUTION

The earnings of a corporation are divided among the stockholders according to the number of shares owned by each. The amount each stockholder receives at the periodic distribution of profits is called a *dividend.*

Stock that makes no provision for the payment of a specific dividend or for a definite percent of the profits is called *common stock* (the stock usually issued by a corporation).

When a corporation is trying to raise money for expansion purposes or to provide working capital, it often becomes necessary to offer special inducements to prospective stockholders. In such cases, the company will issue stock that guarantees the payment of a specified dividend before any dividend will be paid on the common stock. This stock is called *preferred stock.*

Dividends are computed as a percent of the par, or face, value of the common and preferred stock issued by the company, or as a fixed rate in dollars per share. In the distribution of the dividends, the holders of preferred stock are paid in full before the common stockholders receive anything. Very often, holders of preferred stock also have prior rights, over holders of common stock, to the assets of the corporation in the event of dissolution.

Preferred stock is classified as *cumulative preferred* and *noncumulative preferred.* Unpaid dividends on cumulative preferred stock are accumulated and paid in full before any dividends can be declared on the common stock. Thus, if dividends on a 4%, $50 par-value cumulative preferred stock have not been paid for 2 years, a $6 accumulated dividend would have to be paid to each stockholder at the end of the third year before a dividend could be declared on the common stock.

Unpaid dividends on noncumulative preferred stock do not accumulate. After the payment of an annual dividend on this stock, a dividend can be declared on the common stock. Thus, if dividends on a 4%, $50 par-value noncumulative preferred stock have not been paid for 2 years, the payment of a $2 dividend to each stockholder at the end of the third year would permit the declaration of a dividend on the common stock.

Example

PROBLEM The capital of a corporation consists of 1,000 shares of $100 par-value common stock and 500 shares of 5%, $100 par-value cumulative preferred stock. No dividends were declared during the last 2 years.

a. If a $10,000 dividend is to be distributed this year, to how much is each class of stockholder entitled per share?

b. If a $5,000 dividend is to be distributed, to how much is each common and preferred stockholder entitled per share?

c. If the preferred stock was noncumulative and a $10,000 dividend was to be distributed, how much would the common and preferred stockholders each receive per share?

SOLUTION

a. 500 × $100 = $50,000, par value of 500 shares of preferred stock

5% of $50,000 = $2,500, annual dividends due on preferred stock

3 × $2,500 = $7,500, 3 years' accumulated dividends due on preferred stock

$7,500 ÷ 500 = $15, accumulated dividends per share of preferred stock

$10,000 − $7,500 = $2,500, available for common stockholders

$2,500 ÷ 1,000 = $2.50, dividends per share of common stock

b. $5,000 ÷ 500 = $10, amount each preferred stockholder is entitled to per share

The holders of common stock receive nothing. A balance of $2,500 ($7,500 − $5,000 = $2,500) in dividends remains due on the cumulative preferred stock. This must be paid before a dividend can be paid to the holders of common stock.

c. $2,500 = annual dividend due on preferred stock

$2,500 ÷ 500 = $5, dividend per share of preferred stock

$10,000 − $2,500 = $7,500, available for common stockholders

$7,500 ÷ 1,000 = $7.50, dividend per share of common stock

Practice Drill

The capital stock of Eric-Michaels, Inc., consists of 25,000 shares of $50 par-value common stock and 1,000 shares of $4\frac{1}{2}$%, $100 par-value cumulative preferred stock. No dividends were declared last year. This year the board of directors declared a $17,750 dividend to be distributed out of current earnings. How much is to be paid on each share of preferred stock and common stock?

ANSWER $9, preferred; $.35, common

APPLICATION PROBLEMS

1. The capital of the Roberts Construction Company consists of 1,000 shares of no-par-value common stock and 1,000 shares of 5%, $100 par-value cumulative preferred stock. During the last 3 years, no dividends were declared. This year, a $25,000 dividend is to be distributed out of current earnings. How much is to be paid on each share of preferred stock and on each share of common stock?

2. The directors of Marcia Elizabeth Cosmetics, Inc., announced a dividend of $40,000. The firm had outstanding 500 shares of $100 par-value, 6% cumulative preferred stock and 2,500 shares of no-par-value common stock. If this was the first dividend to be declared in 4 years, to how much would the stockholders be entitled on each share of preferred stock and on each share of common stock?

3. Ronald Gordon Enterprises, Inc., had outstanding 3,750 shares of $6.50 cumulative preferred stock and 15,000 shares of $50 par-value common stock. No dividends had been paid for 4 years. Last year, the directors declared and paid dividends of $245,625. How much was paid on each share of preferred stock and on each share of common stock?

4. The Hudson Drilling Company's capital stock was composed of 2,800 shares of $100 par-value common stock and 1,500 shares of $50 par-value, $5\frac{1}{2}$% noncumulative preferred stock. No dividends were declared for 2 years prior to last year. Last year, the board of directors declared a $14,625 dividend. How much was paid on each share of preferred stock and on each share of common stock?

98 DIVIDING BANKRUPT'S ASSETS

Regardless of the type of organization selected, hundreds of businesses fail each year. There are several reasons: failure to assess the competition accurately, lack of sufficient capital on which to establish and operate the business, bad judgment in buying, inadequate records on which to base intelligent decisions, too-rapid expansion, and so on.

When the owners of a business find their liabilities much greater than their assets so that they cannot meet their obligations or obtain additional credit, they often seek the relief afforded by bankruptcy laws and have themselves declared *bankrupt*. When a person is "discharged in bankruptcy," he is released from his obligations and is enabled to start business anew. Settlement of debts with creditors — that is, dividing a bankrupt's assets among those he owes — is an increasingly important subject in business management.

All the creditors of the bankrupt are assured a settlement in a manner that prevents the possibility of a few creditors taking all the bankrupt's assets, leaving nothing for the rest. Each creditor receives that percentage of the assets that is equivalent to his percentage of the debt. For example, if the total debt is $18,000 and $3,000 is owed to one creditor, that creditor will receive

$$\frac{\$3,000}{\$18,000}$$

or $\frac{1}{6}$ of the assets available for distribution. If $12,000 in assets can be distributed, that creditor will receive $\frac{1}{6}$ x $12,000, or $2,000.

Some debts are not affected by bankruptcy proceedings, and the bankrupt remains liable for them even if he has received a "final discharge in bankruptcy." Such debts include taxes; wages earned within the 3 months before the beginning of bankruptcy proceedings; money deposited by employees; money retained by the employer as security for the faithful performance by employees of the terms of their contracts of employment; alimony or support due, or to become due, for the maintenance of a wife or child; property obtained through fraud; and liabilities incurred by reason of malicious injuries to the person or property of another.

When the assets of the bankrupt are divided, some debts must be paid in full, provided the assets are sufficient, before the ordinary creditors receive anything. These debts include the following, listed in the order of their payment.

1. Secured claims, such as mortgages and liens.
2. Expenses incident to the bankruptcy.
3. Employee wages that have been earned within 3 months prior to the date of filing the bankruptcy petition (not to exceed $600 per employee).
4. Taxes.

Examples | **PROBLEM 1** Thomas Wright had debts totaling $65,000. When he went into bankruptcy, it was found that he had only $26,000 available for his creditors. How much money can Charles Duane, a creditor, expect to receive if he has a claim for $3,108?

SOLUTION

$$\frac{\$26,000}{\$65,000} = .40, \text{ or } 40\%, \text{ rate percent that can be paid of each debt}$$

40% of $3,108 = $1,243.20, Duane's share

PROBLEM 2 A bankrupt's assets amount to $19,333. He owes $608 to the state for taxes and $42,800 to general creditors.
a. How will the assets be distributed?
b. How much will a creditor receive if he is due $12,335?

SOLUTION

a. The taxes take priority in payment and must be paid in full before general creditors can share in the available assets.

$19,333 – $608 = $18,725, assets available to general creditors

b. We need to find the rate percent of the assets available to the creditors and then compute the dollar amounts to be paid to particular creditors.

$$\frac{\$18,725}{\$42,800} = \$18,725 \div \$42,800 = .4375, \text{ or } 43\tfrac{3}{4}\%, \text{ rate percent that can be paid of each debt}$$

$43\tfrac{3}{4}\%$ of $12,335 = $5,396.56, this creditor's share

Practice Drill | A firm went into bankruptcy, owing creditors $19,061.25. Its assets brought $11,730.75. The cost of bankruptcy proceedings was $2\tfrac{1}{2}\%$ of the realized assets.
1. How much can the firm pay on the dollar?
2. How much should a creditor receive if his claim amounts to $6,460?

ANSWERS 1. $.60   2. $3,876

APPLICATION PROBLEMS

1. Each of the following companies was being liquidated because of bankruptcy. Find the rate percent that can be paid of each company's debts and the amounts paid to the creditors whose claims are listed in the table shown at the top of the next page.

Company	Due General Creditors	Assets Available	Rate Percent	Creditor's Claim	Creditor's Share
A	$14,400	$ 5,184	36%	$ 5,200	$ 1872
B	8,890	3,734	_____	975	_____
C	24,750	1,980	_____	3,604	_____
D	68,812	24,084	_____	12,000	_____
E	35,937	24,437	_____	8,286	_____

2. A bankrupt concern paid its creditors 35 cents on the dollar. If a creditor received $429.80, how much did he lose?

3. Bert Davidson's liabilities totaled $85,400. When he filed a petition in bankruptcy, he stated that his assets consisted only of cash amounting to $16,226. If a creditor was owed $4,270, how much would he receive?

4. The creditors of the bankrupt firm of Marchant and Company received 47 cents on the dollar.
a. If the total amount due creditors was $58,226, to how much did the firm's assets amount?
b. How much was owed to a creditor who received $1,880?

PROBLEMS FOR PART THIRTEEN

Distributing Partnership Profits & Corporate Dividends

1. Monserrat and Boone formed a partnership and invested $47,500 and $30,000, respectively, in a men's clothing store. Monserrat worked on a full-time basis and Boone on a half-time basis. The profits for the first year amounted to $16,000. If the partnership agreement made no provision for the distribution of profits, to how much would each partner be entitled?

2. Cahill, Godfrey, and LaMar opened a restaurant in Kentfield. Cahill invested $14,000; Godfrey, $14,000; and LaMar, $7,500. LaMar was to run the restaurant since his two partners had other full-time interests. They made an arbitrary decision to divide the profits as follows: Cahill, 20%, Godfrey, 20%; and LaMar, 60%. The profits of the restaurant for the first year were $17,886.66. How much will each partner receive?

3. Bowman and Hiller entered into a partnership agreement to operate a rent-all business, deciding to divide profits and losses $66\frac{2}{3}\%$ to Bowman and $33\frac{1}{3}\%$ to Hiller. The new business got a very slow start, and in the first year of operation it lost \$3,640.40. How would the losses be divided?

1. Meehand and Howe, partners, invested \$11,500 and \$17,250, respectively, in a nursery business. The partnership agreement provided for profit sharing according to the original investment. To how much is each partner entitled if the profit for the first year amounted to \$7,500?

2. Stewart and Reyholm invested \$5,000 and \$10,000, respectively, in a landscaping business. The partnership agreement provided for the sharing of profits and losses in proportion to the investment of each partner at the beginning of the year. Profits the first year amounted to \$6,000; the second year, to \$8,400. Each year, Stewart withdrew half of his share of the profits and Reyholm withdrew his full share. To how much was each partner entitled the first year and the second year?

3. Lockwood and Sutkowski, partners, share profits in proportion to their share in the average capital invested. Lockwood's investment in the business on January 1 amounted to \$100,000. He invested an additional \$20,000 on June 1 and \$17,500 on September 1. Sutkowski's investment on January 1 amounted to \$85,000. He withdrew \$12,000 on June 1 and invested \$50,000 on October 1. Find each partner's share of a profit of \$37,500 for the year.

1. On March 1, Lowell and Parton entered into an agreement to operate a management-consulting firm. Lowell invested \$20,000 and Parton \$16,000. They agreed that interest at 6% was to be paid to each partner according to his average investment and the remaining profit or loss divided equally. On July 1, Parton invested an additional \$4,000 to finance a nationwide promotion campaign. On September 15, Lowell put an additional \$5,000 in the firm. At the end of the year, profits before payment of interest amounted to \$36,700. How should this amount be divided?

2. Langley and Akoubian formed a partnership at the beginning of the year to operate a carpet store, each investing \$35,000. On April 1, Langley invested an additional \$10,000. On July 1, Akoubian withdrew \$8,000, which he replaced on September 15. On December 1, Akoubian invested an additional \$6,000. The profits for the first year amounted to \$9,400. The partnership agreement provided for an equal distribution of profits and losses after 5% interest was paid to each partner on the basis of average capital.
a. To how much interest is each partner entitled?
b. Find each partner's share of the profits.

3. On July 1, Toshida and Ashamoto entered into a partnership to operate a restaurant. Toshida contributed the building and equipment, which were assessed at $40,000. Ashamoto invested $20,000 in cash. The partnership agreement provided for equal sharing of profits after 8% interest is paid each partner on invested capital. By the end of the year, after only six months of operation, the restaurant had earned $11,460.84. Find each partner's share of profits, including interest on his investment.

97

1. Gordon Brill Dairies had outstanding 3,500 shares of no-par-value common stock and 2,500 shares of $50 par-value, 7% cumulative preferred stock. The company had completed 3 years of operations. During the first 2 years, dividends of $1.25 were paid annually on each share of preferred stock. The third year, the directors declared a dividend of $28,750. How much of this dividend was paid on each share of preferred stock and on each share of common stock?

2. The Maxsad Manufacturing Company had a capital stock of $50,000 consisting of 200 shares of $100 par-value, $4\frac{1}{2}$% noncumulative preferred stock and 600 shares of $50 par-value common stock. No dividends had been paid during the last 2 years. What is the minimum amount that must be declared as a dividend this year to enable the holders of common stock to receive 6% on their holdings?

98

1. A merchant who was in financial straits converted all his assets into cash and paid $13,572 to his creditors. If this sum was 39% of his total debts, how much did he still owe after this payment?

2. A bankrupt has assets valued at $82,908. His liabilities amount to $176,400.
a. What percent of his debts can he pay?
b. How much would a creditor receive to whom he owes $4,036?

3. The creditors of a bankrupt firm received $37\frac{1}{2}$% of their claims.
a. Find the total amount due a creditor who received $10,764.
b. If the amount due this creditor was $18\frac{3}{4}$% of the total liabilities, find the total liabilities.
c. Find the total assets.

4. Vogel, a bankrupt, has an estate of $17,058. He owes $1,475 in wages to employees (earned within 3 months of his bankruptcy) and $1,093 in taxes. His debts to general creditors total $32,813. Assume that no employee is due more than $600.
a. What percent of their claims can the creditors expect to have paid?
b. How much would a creditor receive if he was due $2,272.75?

PART FOURTEEN

Debt Repayment

City governments and large corporations often find it necessary to borrow large sums of money for major expenditures — new buildings, for example. To obtain the money they need, they usually issue bonds. The most popular method employed by these city governments and corporations to give bondholders (or purchasers) definite assurance that the bonds will be paid at maturity is to create a sinking fund. A *sinking fund* is an amount of money that is set aside periodically—for example, annually or semiannually—so that the amount of all the payments into the fund, plus their interest accumulations, equals the amount of the entire issue of bonds to be retired. It is better business policy to place a definite amount each year in a fund (called *annual rent*) than it is to wait until the bonds become due and simply hope that there will be enough money on hand to pay off the bonds. The money that is set aside periodically is usually paid to a trustee who protects the interests of the bondholders. The cash in the sinking fund is used to purchase securities of other corporations or cities that pay a satisfactory rate of interest.

If an issue of bonds amounting to $500,000 is due in ten years, it might seem that $50,000 should be set aside each year to have sufficient cash on hand with which to redeem the bonds at the end of ten years. Such is not the case, however, because each payment into the fund draws interest. The amount to be placed in the fund each year, then, is considerably less than $50,000, depending on the interest that can be secured on the principal of the sinking fund. The principal of the sinking fund is increased by each periodic payment and by the interest on all previous payments.

Often, bonds mature over a period of successive years. To provide for this, an *amortization plan* is established. This plan, starting with any desired year, provides for an increased redemption of bonds year by year as the interest charge decreases. Under this plan, as in the case of the sinking-fund plan, the total amount set aside for principal and interest annually is the same, although the amount applicable to principal and to interest is not equal.

99   SINKING FUNDS

The sinking-fund plan of borrowing money, under which the entire principal must be repaid at one time, involves the following two types of computations.

1. Determining the amount accumulated in the fund at the end of any period of time when the annual or periodic contribution is given.

2. Computing the periodic payments necessary to redeem the bonds at maturity or to accumulate a stated sum when the number of years or periods is stated.

Sinking-fund tables similar to the one on pages 284-285 are used extensively in these computations.

Using a Sinking-Fund Table

FINDING ACCUMULATED AMOUNTS

To find, with the aid of a sinking-fund table, the amount accumulated in a sinking fund, proceed as follows.

1. In the left column under "n" find the number of years or periods for which the sinking fund is to be created.

2. Follow horizontally to the column headed by the interest rate at which the periodic payments are to be invested to find the sum to which $1 yearly will accumulate.

3. Multiply the amount of $1 by the periodic payment to find the total amount accumulated in the sinking fund.

Examples

PROBLEM 1   A corporation in need of funds for expansion floated a 10-year bond issue. The bonds provided for the establishment of a sinking fund. At the end of each year from the date of the issuance of the bonds, the corporation was to contribute an amount sufficient to retire the bonds at maturity. If $12,493.64 was paid into the sinking fund each year and invested at 4% interest, compounded annually, to how much would the fund amount at the end of the 10-year period?

SOLUTION   Find 10 years in the left column of the sinking-fund table, and follow horizontally to the 4% column. This shows that $1 paid into the sinking fund at the end of each year for 10 years at 4% interest will accumulate to $12.0061071.

$12,493.64 × $12.0061071 = $149,999.98, compound amount

The amount of the bond issue is obviously $150,000. The last payment will therefore have to be increased to bring the fund to $150,000. The annual accumulations (contributions and interest) in the fund can best be shown by the sinking-fund schedule of accumulations shown below. This table shows the growth of a sinking fund over a 10-year period, with interest at 4%, when the annual contributions amount to $12,493.64.

SINKING-FUND SCHEDULE OF ACCUMULATIONS

Year	Amount at Beginning of Year	Annual Interest (4%)	Annual Contribution	Total Annual Increase	Amount at End of Year
1	....	....	$ 12,493.64	$ 12,493.64	$ 12,493.64
2	$ 12,493.64	$ 499.75	12,493.64	12,993.39	25,487.03
3	25,487.03	1,019.48	12,493.64	13,513.12	39,000.15
4	39,000.15	1,560.01	12,493.64	14,053.65	53,053.80
5	53,053.80	2,122.15	12,493.64	14,615.79	67,669.59
6	67,669.59	2,706.78	12,493.64	15,200.42	82,870.01
7	82,870.01	3,314.80	12,493.64	15,808.44	98,678.45
8	98,678.45	3,947.14	12,493.64	16,440.78	115,119.23
9	115,119.23	4,604.77	12,493.64	17,098.41	132,217.64
10	132,217.64	5,288.71	12,493.65	17,782.36	150,000.00
Proof		$25,063.59	$124,936.41	$150,000.00	

PROBLEM 2 How much will $750 paid into a sinking fund annually for 12 years amount to if it is invested at 5% interest, compounded semi-annually?

SOLUTION The interest compounded semiannually for 12 years at 5% is the same as for 24 years at 2½%. The sinking-fund table shows that $1 paid annually for 24 years at 2½% interest will accumulate to a sum amounting to $32.3490380.

$750 × $32.3490380 = $24,261.7785, compound amount

Practice Drills

1. A public utility corporation floats a 15-year bond issue. To provide for the redemption of the bonds at maturity, the corporation annually contributes $11,585.57 to a sinking fund. At the end of the 15-year period, this fund should amount to a sum sufficient to retire the bonds. If the money is invested at 5% interest, compounded annually, how much will the fund amount to on the redemption date? Prepare a sinking-fund schedule of accumulations showing the annual accumulations (contributions and interest).

2. A sinking fund is created for the purpose of redeeming a 10-year bond issue. If $2,500 is contributed to the fund semiannually during the 10-year period and invested at 4% interest, compounded semiannually, how much will the fund amount to when the bonds mature?

ANSWERS 1. $249,999.96   2. $60,743.42

SINKING-FUND TABLE: AMOUNT OF $1 PER PERIOD

n	½%	1%	1½%	2%	2½%	3%
1	1.000 0000	1.000 0000	1.000 0000	1.000 0000	1.000 0000	1.000 0000
2	2.005 0000	2.010 0000	2.015 0000	2.020 0000	2.025 0000	2.030 0000
3	3.015 0250	3.030 1000	3.045 2250	3.060 4000	3.075 6250	3.090 9000
4	4.030 1001	4.060 4010	4.090 9034	4.121 6080	4.152 5156	4.183 6270
5	5.050 2506	5.101 0050	5.152 2669	5.204 0402	5.265 3285	5.309 1358
6	6.075 5019	6.152 0151	6.229 5509	6.308 1210	6.387 7367	6.468 4099
7	7.105 8794	7.213 5352	7.322 9942	7.434 2834	7.547 4301	7.662 4622
8	8.141 4088	8.285 6706	8.432 8391	8.582 9691	8.736 1159	8.892 3360
9	9.182 1158	9.368 5273	9.559 3317	9.754 6284	9.954 5188	10.159 1061
10	10.228 0264	10.462 2125	10.702 7217	10.949 7210	11.203 3818	11.463 8793
11	11.279 1665	11.566 8347	11.863 2625	12.168 7154	12.483 4663	12.807 7957
12	12.335 5624	12.682 5030	13.041 2114	13.412 0897	13.795 5530	14.192 0296
13	13.397 2402	13.809 3280	14.236 8296	14.680 3315	15.140 4418	15.617 7904
14	14.464 2264	14.947 4213	15.450 3820	15.973 9382	16.518 9528	17.086 3242
15	15.536 5475	16.096 8955	16.682 1378	17.293 4169	17.931 9267	18.598 9139
16	16.614 2303	17.257 8645	17.932 3698	18.639 2853	19.380 2248	20.156 8813
17	17.697 3014	18.430 4431	19.201 3554	20.012 0710	20.864 7304	21.761 5877
18	18.785 7879	19.614 7476	20.489 3757	21.412 3124	22.386 3487	23.414 4354
19	19.879 7169	20.810 8950	21.796 7164	22.840 5586	23.946 0074	25.116 8684
20	20.979 1154	22.019 0040	23.123 6671	24.297 3698	25.544 6576	26.870 3745
21	22.084 0110	23.239 1940	24.470 5221	25.783 3172	27.183 2741	28.676 4857
22	23.194 4311	24.471 5860	25.837 5799	27.298 9835	28.862 8559	30.536 7803
23	24.310 4032	25.716 3018	27.225 1436	28.844 9632	30.548 4273	32.452 8837
24	25.431 9552	26.973 4649	28.633 5208	30.421 8625	32.349 0380	34.426 4702
25	26.559 1150	28.243 1995	30.063 0236	32.030 2997	34.157 7639	36.459 2643
26	27.691 9106	29.525 6315	31.513 9690	33.670 9057	36.011 7080	38.553 0423
27	28.830 3701	30.820 8878	32.986 6785	35.344 3238	37.912 0007	40.709 6335
28	29.974 5220	32.129 0967	34.481 4787	37.051 2103	39.859 8007	42.930 9225
29	31.124 3946	33.450 3877	35.998 7009	38.792 2345	41.856 2958	45.218 8502
30	32.280 0166	34.784 8915	37.538 6814	40.568 0792	43.902 7032	47.575 4157
31	33.441 4167	36.132 7404	39.101 7616	42.379 4408	46.000 2707	50.002 6782
32	34.608 6237	37.494 0679	40.688 2880	44.227 0296	48.150 2775	52.502 7585
33	35.781 6669	38.869 0085	42.298 6123	46.111 5702	50.354 0344	55.077 8413
34	36.960 5752	40.257 6986	43.933 0915	48.033 8016	52.612 8853	57.730 1765
35	38.145 3781	41.660 2756	45.592 0879	49.994 4776	54.928 2074	60.462 0818
36	39.336 1050	43.076 8784	47.275 9692	51.994 3672	57.301 4126	63.275 9443
37	40.532 7855	44.507 6471	48.985 1087	54.034 2545	59.733 9479	66.174 2226
38	41.735 4494	45.952 7236	50.719 8854	56.114 9396	62.227 2966	69.159 4493
39	42.944 1267	47.412 2509	52.480 6837	58.237 2384	64.782 9791	72.234 2328
40	44.158 8473	48.886 3734	54.267 8939	60.401 9832	67.402 5535	75.401 2597
41	45.379 6415	50.375 2371	56.081 9123	62.610 0228	70.087 6174	78.663 2975
42	46.606 5397	51.878 9895	57.923 1410	64.862 2233	72.839 8078	82.023 1965
43	47.839 5724	53.397 7794	59.791 9881	67.159 4678	75.660 8030	85.483 8923
44	49.078 7703	54.931 7572	61.688 8679	69.502 6751	78.552 3231	89.048 4091
45	50.324 1642	56.481 0747	63.614 2010	71.892 7103	81.516 1312	92.719 8614
46	51.575 7850	58.045 8855	65.568 4140	74.330 5645	84.554 0344	96.501 4572
47	52.833 6639	59.626 3443	67.551 9402	76.817 1758	87.667 8853	100.396 5009
48	54.097 8322	61.222 6078	69.565 2193	79.353 5193	90.859 5824	104.408 3960
49	55.368 3214	62.834 8338	71.608 6976	81.940 5897	94.131 0720	108.540 6479
50	56.645 1630	64.463 1821	73.682 8280	84.579 4015	97.484 3488	112.796 8673

SINKING-FUND TABLE: AMOUNT OF $1 PER PERIOD (CONTINUED)

n	$3\frac{1}{2}$%	4%	$4\frac{1}{2}$%	5%	$5\frac{1}{2}$%	6%
1	1.000 0000	1.000 0000	1.000 0000	1.000 0000	1.000 0000	1.000 0000
2	2.035 0000	2.040 0000	2.045 0000	2.050 0000	2.055 0000	2.060 0000
3	3.106 2250	3.121 6000	3.137 0250	3.152 5000	3.168 0250	3.183 6000
4	4.214 9429	4.246 4640	4.278 1911	4.310 1250	4.342 2664	4.374 6160
5	5.362 4659	5.416 3226	5.470 7097	5.525 6313	5.581 0910	5.637 0930
6	6.550 1522	6.632 9755	6.716 8917	6.801 9128	6.888 0510	6.975 3185
7	7.779 4075	7.898 2945	8.019 1518	8.142 0085	8.266 8938	8.393 8376
8	9.051 6868	9.214 2263	9.380 0136	9.549 1089	9.721 5730	9.897 4679
9	10.368 4958	10.582 7953	10.802 1142	11.026 5643	11.256 2595	11.491 3160
10	11.731 3932	12.006 1071	12.288 2094	12.577 8925	12.875 3538	13.180 7949
11	13.141 9919	13.486 3514	13.841 1788	14.206 7872	14.583 4982	14.971 6426
12	14.601 9616	15.025 8055	15.464 0318	15.917 1265	16.385 5907	16.869 9412
13	16.113 0303	16.626 8377	17.159 9133	17.712 9828	18.286 7981	18.882 1377
14	17.676 9864	18.291 9112	18.932 1094	19.598 6320	20.292 5720	21.015 0659
15	19.295 6809	20.023 5876	20.784 0543	21.578 5636	22.408 6635	23.275 9699
16	20.971 0297	21.824 5311	22.719 3367	23.657 4918	24.641 1400	25.672 5281
17	22.705 0157	23.697 5124	24.741 7069	25.840 3664	26.996 4027	28.212 8798
18	24.499 6913	25.645 4129	26.855 0837	28.132 3847	29.481 2048	30.905 6525
19	26.357 1805	27.671 2294	29.063 5625	30.539 0039	32.102 6711	33.759 9917
20	28.279 6818	29.778 0786	31.371 4228	33.065 9541	34.868 3180	36.785 5912
21	30.269 4707	31.969 2017	33.783 1368	35.719 2518	37.786 0755	39.992 7267
22	32.328 9022	34.247 9698	36.303 3780	38.505 2144	40.864 3097	43.392 2903
23	34.460 4137	36.617 8886	38.937 0300	41.430 4751	44.111 8467	46.995 8277
24	36.666 5282	39.082 6041	41.689 1963	44.501 9989	47.537 9982	50.815 5773
25	38.949 8567	41.645 9083	44.565 2101	47.727 0988	51.152 5882	54.864 5120
26	41.313 1017	44.311 7446	47.570 6446	51.113 4538	54.965 9805	59.156 3827
27	43.759 0602	47.084 2144	50.711 3236	54.669 1264	58.989 1094	63.705 7657
28	46.290 6273	49.967 5830	53.993 3332	58.402 5828	63.233 5105	68.528 1116
29	48.910 7993	52.966 2863	57.423 0332	62.322 7119	67.711 3535	73.639 7983
30	51.622 6773	56.084 9378	61.007 0697	66.438 8475	72.435 4780	79.058 1862
31	54.429 4710	59.328 3353	64.752 3878	70.760 7899	77.419 4293	84.801 6774
32	57.334 5025	62.701 4687	68.666 2452	75.298 8294	82.677 4979	90.889 7780
33	60.341 2101	66.209 5274	72.756 2263	80.063 7708	88.224 7603	97.343 1647
34	63.453 1524	69.857 9085	77.030 2565	85.066 9594	94.077 1221	104.183 7546
35	66.674 0127	73.652 2249	81.496 6180	90.320 3074	100.251 3638	111.434 7799
36	70.007 6032	77.598 3138	86.163 9658	95.836 3227	106.765 1888	119.120 8667
37	73.457 8693	81.702 2464	91.041 3443	101.628 1389	113.637 2742	127.268 1187
38	77.028 8947	85.970 3363	96.138 2048	107.709 5458	120.887 3242	135.904 2058
39	80.724 9060	90.409 1497	101.464 4240	114.095 0231	128.536 1271	145.058 4580
40	84.550 2777	95.025 5157	107.030 3231	120.799 7742	136.605 6141	154.761 9656
41	88.509 5375	99.826 5363	112.846 6876	127.839 7630	145.118 9228	165.047 6836
42	92.607 3713	104.819 5978	118.924 7885	135.231 7511	154.100 4636	175.950 5446
43	96.848 6293	110.012 3817	125.276 4040	142.993 3387	163.575 9891	187.507 5772
44	101.238 3313	115.412 8770	131.913 8422	151.143 0056	173.572 6685	199.758 0319
45	105.781 6729	121.029 3920	138.849 9651	159.700 1559	184.119 1653	212.743 5138
46	110.484 0314	126.870 5677	146.098 2135	168.685 1637	195.245 7194	226.508 1246
47	115.350 9725	132.945 3904	153.672 6331	178.119 4218	206.984 2339	241.098 6121
48	120.388 2566	139.263 2060	161.587 9016	188.025 3929	219.368 3668	256.564 5288
49	125.601 8456	145.833 7343	169.859 3572	198.426 6626	232.433 6270	272.958 4006
50	130.997 9102	152.667 0837	178.503 0283	209.347 9957	246.217 4764	290.335 9046

FINDING AMOUNT OF PERIODIC PAYMENTS

To find the periodic payments necessary to accumulate a stated sum, proceed as follows. Use the sinking-fund table on pages 284-285.

1. In the left column find the number of years or periods for which the sinking fund is to be created.

2. Move horizontally to the column headed by the interest rate at which the periodic payments are to be invested to find the sum to which $1 yearly will accumulate.

3. Divide the sum desired by the amount of $1 to find the periodic payments necessary.

Examples | **PROBLEM 1** A corporation in need of funds borrowed $100,000 by floating a 12-year bond issue. A sinking fund was established for the purpose of retiring the bonds at maturity. To this fund, the corporation contributed annually for 12 years a sum that, when invested at $3\frac{1}{2}$% interest, compounded annually, amounted to $100,000. Find the amount of annual contribution necessary to achieve the purpose of the fund.

SOLUTION $1 contributed annually into a sinking fund for 12 years at $3\frac{1}{2}$% interest will amount to $14.6019616. For the sinking fund to amount to $100,000 at the end of 12 years, as many dollars must be contributed annually as the number of times the accumulation of $1 ($14.6019616) is contained in $100,000.

$100,000 ÷ 14.6019616 = $6,848.39, annual contribution

The annual contribution to the sinking fund will be $6,848.40, with an adjustment made in the last payment for an excess of 7¢.

The schedule of accumulations shows the accuracy of this computation.

SINKING-FUND SCHEDULE OF ACCUMULATIONS

Year	Amount at Beginning of Year	Annual Interest ($3\frac{1}{2}$%)	Annual Contribution	Total Annual Increase	Amount at End of Year
1	. . . . .	. . . . .	$ 6,848.40	$ 6,848.40	$ 6,848.40
2	$ 6,848.40	$ 239.69	6,848.40	7,088.09	13,936.49
3	$13,936.49	487.78	6,848.40	7,336.18	21,272.67
4	21,272.67	744.54	6,848.40	7,592.94	28,865.61
5	28,865.61	1,010.30	6,848.40	7,858.70	36,724.31
6	36,724.31	1,285.35	6,848.40	8,133.75	44,858.06
7	44,858.06	1,570.03	6,848.40	8,418.43	53,276.49
8	53,276.49	1,864.68	6,848.40	8,713.08	61,989.57
9	61,989.57	2,169.63	6,848.40	9,018.03	71,007.60
10	71,007.60	2,485.27	6,848.40	9,333.67	80,341.27
11	80,341.27	2,811.94	6,848.40	9,660.34	90,001.61
12	90,001.61	3,150.06	6,848.33	9,998.39	100,000.00
Proof		$17,819.27	$82,180.73	$100,000.00	

This schedule shows the growth of the sinking fund of $100,000 over a 12-year period with interest at $3\frac{1}{2}$%. (The annual contributions to the fund as determined in the solution are $6,848.40.)

Proof: The sum of the Annual Interest column plus the sum of the Annual Contribution column must equal the sum of the Total Annual Increase column.

PROBLEM 2 What sum set aside quarterly by a corporation and invested at 6% interest, compounded quarterly, will amount to a sum sufficient to meet a $125,000 bond issue maturing in 10 years?

SOLUTION The interest compounded quarterly for 10 years at 6% is the same as the interest compounded annually for 40 years at $1\frac{1}{2}$%. The sinking-fund table shows that $1 paid annually for 40 years at $1\frac{1}{2}$% interest will accumulate to a sum amounting to $54.2678939.

$125,000 ÷ 54.2678939 = $2,303.3877, quarterly payment

Practice Drills

1. To modernize its plant, a corporation sold $150,000 worth of bonds maturing in 20 years. To retire the bonds at maturity, the corporation contributed annually for 20 years a sum that, when invested at $4\frac{1}{2}$% interest, compounded annually, amounted to $150,000. What was the amount of the annual contribution?

2. A corporation must retire a $100,000 bond issue in 12 years when the bonds mature. What sum should be set aside quarterly and invested at 6% interest, compounded quarterly, to meet this debt at maturity?

ANSWERS 1. $4,781.42   2. $1,437.50

APPLICATION PROBLEMS

1. Use the sinking-fund table on pages 284-285 to find the amount accumulated in each of the following problems. Prepare a sinking-fund schedule of accumulations in each case.

	Payments	No. of Payments	Invested At	Compounded	Total Accumulation
a.	$250 annually	10	$4\frac{1}{2}$%	Annually	$_____
b.	750 annually	12	5%	Annually	_____
c.	640 annually	15	$2\frac{1}{4}$% ½	Annually	_____
d.	800 semiannually	8	5%	Semiannually	_____
e.	590 quarterly	4	10%	Quarterly	_____

2. Find the payments necessary to accumulate the sums indicated in each of the following problems. Use the sinking-fund table on pages 284-285.

	Sinking Fund Desired	No. of Years	Invested at	Compounded	Payments
a.	$214,928.70	20	5%	Annually	$_____ annually
b.	33,792.58	10	4¼%	Annually	_____ annually
c.	74,508.16	12	3%	Annually	_____ annually
d.	100,901.40	10	5%	Semiannually	_____ semiannually
e.	172,845.26	4	12%	Quarterly	_____ quarterly

100 AMORTIZATION

The amortization plan of borrowing money, under which a debt is repaid in installments over a period of time, also involves solving the following two types of problems.
1. Computing the amount that can be borrowed if the annual payment to be made on interest and principal is given, and
2. Determining the amount necessary to meet the annual payment on accruals of interest and principal redemption if the amount borrowed is known.

These computations are made with the help of amortization tables. A partial amortization table is illustrated on pages 290-291.

Using an Amortization Table

To find, with the aid of an amortization table, the amount that can be borrowed, proceed as follows.
1. In the left column under *n* find the number of years or periods for which the money is to be borrowed.
2. Move horizontally to the column headed by the interest rate to be paid on the loan to find the amount that can be borrowed and financed by the payment of $1 annually for the number of years and at the rate of interest given.
3. Multiply the amount that can be financed by the payment of $1 yearly by the annual payment to find the total amount that can be borrowed.

Example | **PROBLEM** A corporation pays $25,000 annually on a 10-year, 5% loan on the amortization plan. Find the amount of the loan.

SOLUTION Find 10 years in the left column of the amortization table, and move horizontally to the 5% column. Notice that $1 paid annually for 10 years, with 5% interest, will finance a loan of $7.7217349. An amount of $25,000 instead of $1 paid each year will finance a loan (or provide for payment of interest accrual and principal redemption annually over a 10-year period) 25,000 times as much as $7.7217349.

25,000 × $7.7217349 = $193,043.37, amount of loan

The accuracy of these computations can be checked in the amortization schedule shown below. This table shows the amortization of a debt of $193,043.37, with interest at 5%, in 10 annual payments of $25,000 each. It also shows the annual reduction of principal.

AMORTIZATION SCHEDULE OF DEBT

Year	Debt at Beginning of Year	Annual Interest (5%)	Annual Installment	Reduction of Principal	Debt at End of Yr.
1	$193,043.37	$ 9,652.17	$ 25,000	$ 15,347.83	$177,695.54
2	177,695.54	8,884.78	25,000	16,115.22	161,580.32
3	161,580.32	8,079.02	25,000	16,920.98	144,659.34
4	144,659.34	7,232.97	25,000	17,767.03	126,892.31
5	126,892.31	6,344.62	25,000	18,655.38	108,236.93
6	108,236.93	5,411.85	25,000	19,588.15	88,648.78
7	88,648.78	4,432.44	25,000	20,567.56	68,081.22
8	68,081.22	3,404.06	25,000	21,595.94	46,485.28
9	46,485.28	2,324.26	25,000	22,675.74	23,809.54
10	23,809.54	1.190.46*	25,000	23,809.54	. . . .
Proof		$56,956.63	$250,000	$193,043.37	

*The last interest payment is reduced 2¢ to account for an increase in interest in previous years. This increase was due to the fact that, when interest computations in these years included fractional-cent credit, this credit in each case was changed to a full cent.

Practice | A corporation amortized a loan by making 12 annual payments of
Drill | $12,500 each to cover interest at 5½% and principal redemption. What was the amount of the loan?

ANSWER $107,731.47

AMORTIZATION TABLE: PRESENT VALUE OF $1 PER PERIOD

n	½%	1%	1½%	2%	2½%	3%
1	0.995 0249	0.990 0990	0.985 2217	0.980 3922	0.975 6098	0.970 8738
2	1.985 0994	1.970 3951	1.955 8834	1.941 5609	1.927 4242	1.913 4697
3	2.970 2481	2.940 9852	2.912 2004	2.883 8833	2.856 0236	2.828 6114
4	3.950 4957	3.901 9656	3.854 3846	3.807 7287	3.761 9742	3.717 0984
5	4.925 8663	4.853 4312	4.782 6450	4.713 4595	4.645 8285	4.579 7072
6	5.896 3844	5.795 4765	5.697 1872	5.601 4309	5.508 1254	5.417 1914
7	6.862 0740	6.728 1945	6.598 2140	6.471 9911	6.349 3906	6.230 2830
8	7.822 9592	7.651 6778	7.485 9251	7.325 4814	7.170 1372	7.019 6922
9	8.779 0639	8.566 0176	8.360 5173	8.162 2367	7.970 8655	7.786 1089
10	9.730 4119	9.471 3045	9.222 1846	8.982 5850	8.752 0639	8.530 2028
11	10.677 0267	10.367 6282	10.071 1178	9.786 8480	9.514 2087	9.252 6241
12	11.618 9321	11.255 0775	10.907 5052	10.575 3412	10.257 7646	9.954 0040
13	12.556 1513	12.133 7401	11.731 5322	11.348 3737	10.983 1850	10.634 9553
14	13.488 7078	13.003 7030	12.543 3815	12.106 2488	11.690 9122	11.296 0731
15	14.416 6246	13.865 0525	13.343 2330	12.849 2635	12.381 3777	11.937 9351
16	15.339 9250	14.717 8738	14.131 2640	13.577 7093	13.055 0027	12.561 1020
17	16.258 6311	15.562 2513	14.907 6493	14.291 8719	13.712 1977	13.166 1185
18	17.172 7680	16.398 2686	15.672 5609	14.992 0313	14.353 3636	13.753 5131
19	18.082 3562	17.226 0085	16.426 1684	15.678 4620	14.978 8913	14.323 7991
20	18.987 4191	18.045 5530	17.168 6388	16.351 4333	15.589 1623	14.877 4749
21	19.887 9793	18.856 9831	17.900 1367	17.011 2092	16.184 5486	15.415 0241
22	20.874 0590	19.660 3793	18.620 8244	17.658 0482	16.765 4132	15.936 9166
23	21.675 6806	20.455 8211	19.330 8614	18.292 2041	17.332 1105	16.443 6084
24	22.562 8662	21.243 3873	20.030 4054	18.913 9256	17.884 9858	16.935 5421
25	23.445 6380	22.023 1557	20.719 6112	19.523 4565	18.424 3764	17.413 1477
26	24.324 0179	22.795 2037	21.398 6317	20.121 0358	18.950 6111	17.876 8424
27	25.198 0278	23.559 6076	22.067 6175	20.706 8978	19.464 0109	18.327 0315
28	26.067 6894	24.316 4432	22.726 7167	21.281 2724	19.964 8887	18.764 1082
29	26.933 0242	25.065 7853	23.376 0756	21.844 3847	20.453 5499	19.188 4546
30	27.794 0540	25.807 7082	24.015 8380	22.396 4556	20.930 2926	19.600 4413
31	28.650 8000	26.542 2854	24.646 1458	22.937 7015	21.395 4074	20.000 4285
32	29.503 2835	27.269 5895	25.267 1387	23.468 3348	21.849 1780	20.388 7655
33	30.351 5259	27.989 6925	25.878 9544	23.988 5636	22.291 8809	20.765 7918
34	31.195 5482	28.702 6659	26.481 7285	24.498 5917	22.723 7863	21.131 8367
35	32.035 3713	29.408 5801	27.075 5946	24.998 6193	23.145 1573	21.487 2201
36	32.871 0162	30.107 5050	27.660 6843	25.488 8425	23.556 2511	21.832 2525
37	33.702 5037	30.799 5099	28.237 1274	25.969 4534	23.957 3181	22.167 2354
38	34.529 8544	31.484 6633	28.805 0516	26.440 6406	24.348 6030	22.492 4616
39	35.353 0890	32.163 0330	29.364 5829	26.902 5888	24.730 3444	22.808 2151
40	36.172 2279	32.834 6861	29.915 8452	27.355 4792	25.102 7751	23.114 7720
41	36.987 2914	33.499 6892	30.458 9608	27.799 4894	25.466 1220	23.412 4000
42	37.798 2999	34.158 1081	30.994 0500	28.234 7936	25.820 6068	23.701 3592
43	38.605 2735	34.810 0081	31.521 2316	28.661 5623	26.166 4457	23.981 9021
44	39.408 2324	35.455 4535	32.040 6222	29.079 9631	26.503 8495	24.254 2739
45	40.207 1964	36.094 5084	32.552 3372	29.490 1599	26.833 0239	24.518 7125
46	41.002 1855	36.727 2361	33.056 4898	29.892 3136	27.154 1696	24.775 4491
47	41.793 2194	37.353 6991	33.553 1920	30.286 5820	27.467 4826	25.024 7078
48	42.580 3178	37.973 9595	34.042 5536	30.673 1196	27.773 1537	25.266 7066
49	43.363 5003	38.588 0787	34.524 6834	31.052 0780	28.071 3695	25.501 6569
50	44.142 7863	39.196 1175	34.999 6881	31.423 6059	28.362 3117	25.729 7640

AMORTIZATION TABLE: PRESENT VALUE OF $1 PER PERIOD (CONTINUED)

n	$3\frac{1}{2}$%	4%	$4\frac{1}{2}$%	5%	$5\frac{1}{2}$%	6%
1	0.966 1836	0.961 5385	0.956 9378	0.952 3810	0.947 8673	0.943 3962
2	1.899 6943	1.886 0947	1.872 6678	1.859 4104	1.846 3197	1.833 3927
3	2.801 6370	2.775 0910	2.748 9644	2.723 2480	2.697 9334	2.673 0119
4	3.673 0792	3.629 8952	3.587 5257	3.545 9505	3.505 1501	3.465 1056
5	4.515 0524	4.451 8223	4.389 9767	4.329 4767	4.270 2845	4.212 3638
6	5.328 5530	5.242 1369	5.157 8725	5.075 6921	4.995 5303	4.917 3243
7	6.114 5440	6.002 0547	5.892 7009	5.786 3734	5.682 9671	5.582 3814
8	6.873 9555	6.732 7449	6.595 8861	6.463 2128	6.334 5660	6.209 7938
9	7.607 6865	7.435 3316	7.268 7905	7.107 8217	6.952 1952	6.801 6923
10	8.316 6053	8.110 8958	7.912 7182	7.721 7349	7.537 6258	7.360 0871
11	9.001 5510	8.760 4767	8.528 9169	8.306 4142	8.092 5363	7.886 8746
12	9.663 3343	9.385 0738	9.118 5808	8.863 2516	8.618 5178	8.383 8439
13	10.302 7385	9.985 6478	9.682 8524	9.393 5730	9.117 0785	8.852 6830
14	10.920 5203	10.563 1229	10.222 8253	9.898 6409	9.589 6479	9.294 9839
15	11.517 4109	11.118 3874	10.739 5457	10.379 6580	10.037 5809	9.712 2490
16	12.094 1168	11.652 2956	11.234 0150	10.837 7696	10.462 1620	10.105 8953
17	12.651 3206	12.165 6689	11.707 1914	11.274 0662	10.864 6086	10.477 2597
18	13.189 6817	12.659 2970	12.159 9918	11.689 5869	11.246 0745	10.827 6035
19	13.709 8374	13.133 9394	12.593 2936	12.085 3209	11.607 6539	11.158 1165
20	14.212 4033	13.590 3263	13.007 9365	12.462 2103	11.950 3825	11.469 9212
21	14.697 9742	14.029 1599	13.404 7239	12.821 1527	12.275 2441	11.764 0766
22	15.167 1248	14.451 1153	13.784 4248	13.163 0026	12.583 1697	12.041 5817
23	15.620 4105	14.856 8417	14.147 7749	13.488 5739	12.875 0424	12.303 3790
24	16.058 3676	15.246 9631	14.495 4784	13.798 6418	13.151 6990	12.550 3575
25	16.481 5146	15.622 0799	14.828 2090	14.093 9446	13.413 9327	12.783 3562
26	16.890 3523	15.982 7692	15.146 6114	14.375 1853	13.662 4954	13.003 1662
27	17.285 3645	16.329 5857	15.451 3028	14.643 0336	13.898 0999	13.210 5341
28	17.667 0188	16.663 0632	15.742 8735	14.898 1273	14.121 4217	13.406 1643
29	18.035 7670	16.983 7146	16.021 8885	15.141 0736	14.333 1012	13.590 7210
30	18.392 0454	17.292 0333	16.288 8885	15.372 4510	14.533 7452	13.764 8312
31	18.736 2758	17.588 4936	16.544 3910	15.592 8105	14.723 9291	13.929 0860
32	19.068 8655	17.873 5515	16.788 8909	15.802 6767	14.904 1982	14.084 0434
33	19.390 2082	18.147 6457	17.022 8621	16.002 5492	15.075 0694	14.230 2296
34	19.700 6842	18.411 1978	17.246 7580	16.192 9040	15.237 0326	14.368 1411
35	20.000 6611	18.664 6132	17.461 0124	16.374 1943	15.390 5522	14.498 2463
36	20.290 4938	18.908 2820	17.666 0406	16.546 8517	15.536 0684	14.620 9871
37	20.570 5254	19.142 5788	17.862 2398	16.711 2873	15.673 9985	14.736 7803
38	20.841 0874	19.367 8642	18.049 9902	16.867 8927	15.804 7379	14.846 0192
39	21.102 4999	19.584 4848	18.229 6557	17.017 0407	15.928 6615	14.949 0747
40	21.355 0723	19.792 7739	18.401 5844	17.159 0864	16.046 1247	15.046 2969
41	21.599 1037	19.993 0518	18.566 1095	17.294 3680	16.157 4642	15.138 0159
42	21.834 8828	20.185 6267	18.723 5498	17.423 2076	16.262 9992	15.224 5433
43	22.062 6887	20.370 7949	18.874 2103	17.545 9120	16.363 0324	15.306 1729
44	22.282 7910	20.548 8413	19.018 3831	17.662 7733	16.457 8506	15.383 1820
45	22.495 4503	20.720 0397	19.156 3474	17.774 0698	16.547 7257	15.455 8321
46	22.700 9181	20.884 6536	19.288 3707	17.880 0665	16.632 9154	15.524 3699
47	22.899 4378	21.042 9361	19.414 7088	17.981 0157	16.713 6639	15.589 0282
48	23.091 2443	21.195 1309	19.535 6065	18.077 1578	16.790 2027	15.650 0266
49	23.276 5645	21.341 4720	19.651 2981	18.168 7217	16.862 7514	15.707 5723
50	23.455 6179	21.482 1846	19.762 0078	18.255 9255	16.931 5179	15.761 8606

Finding Annual Rent or Installment

To find the amount of the annual rent (installment) necessary to meet interest and principal payments, proceed as follows. Use the amortization table on pages 290-291.

1. In the left column find the number of years or periods in the amortization period.
2. Move horizontally to the column headed by the interest rate to be paid on the loan to find the amount that $1 paid annually will repay in the time indicated.
3. Divide the total amount borrowed by the present value of $1 per period for the time and rate given to find the annual rent or installment.

Example

PROBLEM A city floated a $250,000 bond issue for the purpose of constructing a school. The bonds were to be amortized over a 10-year period at $3\frac{1}{2}$% interest, with principal and interest to be paid in 10 equal annual installments. Find the amount of the annual installment. Construct the amortization schedule.

SOLUTION In the amortization table, the present value of $1 per period for 10 periods at $3\frac{1}{2}$% is $8.3166053. Thus, $8.3166053 can be borrowed for 10 years at $3\frac{1}{2}$% interest and repaid on the amortization plan in 10 annual installments of $1 each. If $250,000 is borrowed for the same period at the same rate on the amortization plan, as many dollars must be paid each year as the number of times $8.3166053 is contained in $250,000.

$$\$250,000 \div 8.3166053 = \$30,060.342$$

Therefore, $30,060.34, known as the annual rent, must be paid annually for 10 years to provide for interest due and principal redemption.

Remember that bonds can be redeemed in full denominations only, such as $100, $500, $1,000, and so on. Thus, if the annual installment is $30,060.34 and the first year's interest ($3\frac{1}{2}$% of $250,000) is $8,750, then $21,310.34 ($30,060.34 − $8,750) will be available for bond redemption. If $1,000 bonds were issued, only 21 bonds worth $21,000 can be redeemed the first year. Interest the second year would be paid on the outstanding debt: $250,000 − $21,000, or $229,000.

$$3\frac{1}{2}\% \text{ of } \$229,000 = \$8,015$$
$$\$30,060.34 - \$8,015 = \$22,045.34$$

The amount of $22,045.34 plus the unredeemed portion of the first year, $310.34, or $22,355.68, would be available for bond redemption the second year. Twenty-two bonds worth $22,000 would be redeemed. This procedure would be followed annually during the 10-year period. The annual rent, $30,060.34, is used as a basis for determining the number of bonds that can be redeemed each year.

The following amortization schedule is presented to prove the accuracy of these computations. This table shows the amortization of a debt of $250,000 by annual installments applied to the payment of interest and the reduction of principal.

AMORTIZATION SCHEDULE OF DEBT

Year	Debt at Beginning of Year	Annual Interest ($3\frac{1}{2}$%)	Annual Installment	Reduction of Principal	Debt at End of Year
1	$250,000.00	$8,750.00	$30,060.34	$21,310.34	$228,689.66
2	228,689.66	8,004.14	30,060.34	22,056.20	206,633.46
3	206,633.46	7,232.17	30,060.34	22,828.17	183,805.29
4	183,805.29	6,433.19	30,060.34	23,627.15	160,178.14
5	160,178.14	5,606.23	30,060.34	24,454.11	135,724.03
6	135,724.03	4,750.34	30,060.34	25,310.00	110,414.03
7	110,414.03	3,864.49	30,060.34	26,195.85	84,218.18
8	84,218.18	2,947.64	30,060.34	27,112.70	57,105.48
9	57,105.48	1,998.69	30,060.34	28,061.65	29,043.83
10	29,043.83	1,016.53	30,060.36	29,043.83	. . . . .

Practice Drill

A businessman borrowed $50,000 at $5\frac{1}{2}$% interest on the amortization plan. He was to repay the loan by making principal and interest payments in 12 equal annual installments. Find the amount of each installment.

ANSWER $5,801.46

APPLICATION PROBLEMS

1. Using the amortization table on pages 290-291, find the amount that can be borrowed in each of the following problems. In each case, prepare a schedule of amortization showing the repayment of the debt.

Payments	No. of Payments	Interest Compounded at	Amount Borrowed
a. $ 750 quarterly	5	6%	$_____
b. 10,000 annually	10	5%	_____
c. 5,000 annually	15	4%	_____
d. 1,250 annually	12	$5\frac{1}{2}$%	_____
e. 2,500 semiannually	10	3%	_____

2. Using the amortization table on pages 290-291, find the installments necessary to meet interest and principal payments in each of the following problems. Prepare an amortization schedule of each debt.

Amount of Debt	No. of Years	Interest Compounded At	Installments
a. $ 25,000	5	5%	$_____ semiannually
b. 150,000	12	6%	_____ annually
c. 80,000	10	$3\frac{1}{2}$%	_____ annually
d. 200,000	10	3%	_____ semiannually
e. 7,500	4	2%	_____ quarterly

PROBLEMS FOR PART FOURTEEN

Debt Repayment

1 47 45. 85

99

1. How much will $1,200 paid into a sinking fund each year and invested at $4\frac{1}{2}$% interest, compounded annually, amount to at the end of 10 years?

2. A corporation contributed annually for 12 years a sum that, when invested at 3%, compounded annually, amounted to $150,000. Find the amount of the annual contribution.

3. A man opened a $360 savings account into which he made 4 semi-annual deposits of $360 each. If the bank paid 4% interest, compounded semiannually, how much would be accumulated in the account when a fifth deposit was made? Prepare a schedule of accumulations. Use the sinking-fund table on pages 284-285.

100

1. $20,000 is paid annually on a 12-year, 6% loan on the amortization plan. Find the amount of the loan.

2. Five semiannual payments of $500 each are made on a 4% loan. Each installment is applied to the payment of interest first; then the balance is applied to reduction of principal. Find the amount of the loan. Use the amortization table on pages 290-1. Check the accuracy of the computations by preparing a schedule of amortization.

PART FIFTEEN

Preparing Statistical Data & Graphs

Many people use the term "statistics" as a synonym for mathematics when, strictly speaking, it is only one branch of mathematics. *Statistics* specializes in recording, classifying, and interpreting numeric data items. These activities lay a basis for effective decision-making in both business and government.

The businessman is constantly required to determine trends that will affect the future of his business. He must, therefore, be able to describe the *population* with which he is dealing. The person responsible for television programming is concerned with the total population of television viewers. He may survey a *sample* of 5,000 television viewers in the hope that their responses are indicative of the preferences of the total viewing population.

Statistical *data,* or the numeric items themselves, can take many forms. Those of special significance to decision-makers in business and government are *measures of central tendency*, or measures that tend to represent a population, and *graphs,* which show relationships between sets of numeric data items.

Below are some terms commonly used in statistics.

Mean	The sum of a set of numeric data items divided by the number of data items.
Deviation	The difference between the mean and a particular data item.
Median	The midpoint, or middle number, of a set of numeric data items arranged in order of size. This arrangement is sometimes called *rank order*.
Mode	The number that occurs most frequently in a set of numeric data items, or the number having the greatest *frequency*.
Frequency distribution	The classification of a large number of numeric data items into *groups* of data. Such data can also be called *grouped data*.
Class interval	Numeric data items arranged in rank order and then grouped to show a particular range (for example, 25-30). The upper and lower numbers of each such range are called the *class limits*.
Graph	A visual device used to show relationships between numeric data items.

101 MEASURES OF CENTRAL TENDENCY

A measure of central tendency is a single measure that tends to represent an entire group of data. The several measures of central tendency include the mean, the median, and the mode. Most references to an *average* imply one of these three measures. You will learn the importance of selecting the measure that is most suited to a particular application.

Finding the Mean

The arithmetic mean, or sum of a set of numeric data items divided by the number of data items, is the most common average. Thus, when the weather bureau reports that the mean temperature yesterday was 65, it is saying, in effect, that the average of all the temperature readings taken yesterday was 65. When we are told that the mean score of the class on a mathematics examination was 79, it means that the average of all the examination scores was 79.

To find the mean, or the arithmetic mean, of several scores or other measures, add the scores and divide the sum by the number of scores. Each mean should be rounded off so that it is in line with the numeric data items you started with. That is, test scores should be rounded to the nearest unit, monetary values to the nearest cent, and so on.

Example | **PROBLEM** Liberty Distributing Corporation pays the following annual salaries to the 8 regional managers: $22,500, $19,700, $21,600, $24,200, $17,960, $23,840, $20,690, and $19,400. What is the mean salary?

SOLUTION The total salaries paid to the regional managers come to $169,890.

$$\frac{\$21,236.25, \text{ mean annual salary}}{8)\$169,890.00}$$

Practice | 1. Neighborhood volunteers for a local charity drive made the follow-
Drills | ing collections: $108.60, $211.50, $98.15, $128.90, $264.35, $182.25, $166.50, and $93.45. What was the mean amount collected?

2. On a qualifying test for apprenticeship training, a group of high school graduates made the following scores. Find the mean test score.

No. of Graduates	Test Score
3	95
2	92
1	89
5	85
8	83
10	81
7	76
6	74
3	70
2	68
1	65
1	55

ANSWERS 1. $148.62+   2. 79+

One of the prerequisites of a measure of central tendency is that all the numbers in the group be dispersed evenly about this number. The mean is not always a good average to use because sometimes it does not represent the entire group of data adequately: it can lead to a mistaken impression of some data if a few very high or very low numbers shift the mean out of line. For example, if 7 stores in a retail chain reported sales during a recent week of $28,100, $24,900, $26,500, $28,400, $27,300, $29,600, and $78,800, respectively, the mean would be $34,800 ($243,600 ÷ 7). The sales of the seventh store ($78,800) make it appear that the sales average for the group is more than one-fourth larger than the mean of the first 6 stores ($164,800 ÷ 6 = $27,467).

In this case the mean is obviously a poor measure of central tendency because the data includes one sales figure that is seriously out of line with the others. True, the sales are balanced about the mean: the sum of the deviations of the sales below the mean is equal to the deviation of the one sale above the mean. However, the mean found here is not a representative average of the sales of the several stores. The sales in all stores but one are under $30,000, yet the mean found is over $34,000. This example illustrates that when numbers, scores, or other measures are widely scattered, or a few numbers differ greatly from the main group in the data, the mean may not be a fair measure of the central tendency of the data.

Finding the Median

Sometimes the *median,* or middle number, would be a more adequate measure of the central tendency. The median is the middle number of a group of numbers arranged in rank order—that is, arranged in order from highest to lowest or from lowest to highest.

Examples

PROBLEM 1 During a recent week seven retail stores reported sales of $28,100, $24,900, $26,500, $28,400, $27,300, $29,600, and $78,800, respectively. Find the median sales.

SOLUTION The rank order of the sales figures of the 7 retail stores is as follows.

$$\begin{array}{r} \$78,800 \\ 29,600 \\ 28,400 \\ 28,100 \\ 27,300 \\ 26,500 \\ 24,900 \end{array}$$

The middle number is the fourth from each end, which is $28,100, the median sales. For this example, the median is considered a better average than the mean because it more nearly describes most of the sales figures.

PROBLEM 2 Referring to problem 1, suppose the store that reported sales of $78,800 was sold, leaving 6 stores—an even number. Find the median.

SOLUTION In this case, there is no number at the exact middle; therefore, the median is found by adding the two middle numbers (28,100 and 27,300) and dividing by 2.

$$\$28,100 + \$27,300 = \$55,400$$
$$\$55,400 \div 2 = \$27,700, \text{ the median}$$

The median in this case may also be reported as the interval $27,300–$28,100.

Practice Drill

During a recent week, 9 employees of LePage and Company produced the following number of units: 88, 140, 97, 96, 72, 95, 119, 136, and 83. Find the median and the mean.

ANSWERS 96, median; 102+, mean

Finding the Mode

The *mode,* or *modal measure,* is the number or measure that occurs the greatest number of times, or most frequently, in a collection of data.

If two or more numbers or measures occur an equal number of times in a group of data and these are the most frequently occurring measures, each one is considered a mode, or average. In many sets of numbers there is no one measure that appears with greater frequency than any other measure. In such a case, there is no mode.

Example

PROBLEM The scores on a civil service test given to 15 job applicants were as follows: 92, 88, 64, 73, 77, 73, 83, 90, 61, 85, 66, 75, 88, 73, and 83. Find the mode, or modal score.

SOLUTION The test scores are listed in rank order as follows.

92
90
88
88
85
83
83
77
75
73
73
73
66
64
61

The most frequently occurring score is 73. This is the modal score. If there were only two scores of 73 on the tests, then the two 88 scores, the two 83 scores, and the two 73 scores, respectively, would each be considered a mode. If each of the 15 scores were different, there would be no modal score.

Practice Drill

The following table shows the frequency of contributions to a community fund by the employees of a local firm. Find the mean amount contributed, the median of the group, and the mode of the group.

No. of Employees	Amount of Contribution
15	$ 1.00
35	5.00
24	10.00
3	20.00
7	25.00
2	50.00
1	100.00

ANSWERS $9.94+, mean; $20, median; $5, mode

Finding Average from Grouped Data

When we have a large number of data items, it can be useful to combine them into a relatively small number of *class intervals*, or *ranges* of data items. Two guidelines for establishing class intervals are

1. to set up only a small number of intervals, usually between 10 and 20 but sometimes even fewer, and

2. to set up appropriate class intervals—often with a range of 3, 5, 6, or 10 data items.

Once these intervals have been established, the frequency and the midpoint of the data items in each class interval can be specified. A listing of such information is called a *frequency distribution,* or *frequency table.* The data items themselves are called *grouped data.*

Because the data items are not actually listed in the frequency distribution, it is not possible to compute the mean in the usual way—that is, by adding all of the data items and then dividing by the number of data items. And, because the actual value of the middle number is not given under these conditions, the median cannot be found by counting to the middle data item.

To find the mean of the data items listed in a frequency distribution, it must first be assumed that all the items of each class interval are concentrated at the midpoint and that all have the middle value of the interval. That is, if the class interval for some data items is 60 to 66, all data items falling in that interval are assumed to have a middle value of 63 (60 + 66 = 126; 126 ÷ 2 = 63). To find the median for the data items of a frequency distribution, first determine the mean; then use the total number of data items to find the median, or middle-ranking data item.

Examples | **PROBLEM 1** The students in a banking course made the following scores on a test. (The scores are listed in rank order in the frequency table.) Convert the table by giving each class interval its midpoint value or score and then find the mean and median score.

Frequency	Class Interval	Midpoint Score	Total Score
2	95-99	97	2 × 97 = 194
1	90-94	92	1 × 92 = 92
6	85-89	87	6 × 87 = 522
7	80-84	{82	7 × 82 = 574
6	75-79	{77	6 × 77 = 462
4	70-74	72	4 × 72 = 288
3	60-64	62	3 × 62 = 186
2	55-59	57	2 × 57 = 114
1	35-39	37	1 × 37 = 37
			32 scores = 2,469

SOLUTION   2,469 ÷ 32 = 77.15, mean score

The median score falls between the 16th and 17th scores, which fall, respectively, in the class intervals of 80-84 and 75-79 (with midpoints of 82 and 77, respectively).

82 + 77 = 159; 159 ÷ 2 = 79.5, median score

PROBLEM 2 Sometimes the median score falls in a class interval but not at its exact midpoint. The frequency distribution for another examination listed the scores as below. Here the *proportional distance* from the class limits must be computed to obtain the median score.

Frequency	Class Interval
2	95-99
4	90-94
5	85-89
8	80-84
7	75-79
3	70-74
2	60-64
31	

SOLUTION Since the total number of scores is 31, the median is the middle score, or 16th score, listed in rank order, counting from either highest to lowest or lowest to highest. Adding down, we find 2, 6, 11 (or 2 + 4 + 5), so we need five more scores out of the eight in the fourth class interval. This means that the median lies within the 80-84 class interval, and that $\frac{5}{8}$ of the range of this interval must be computed to determine the median.

$\frac{5}{8}$ × 5 = $3\frac{1}{8}$, or 3, the nearest whole-number value

This value is subtracted from the lower value in the next-higher, or preceding, interval.   85 – 3 = 82, median

Practice Drill The following scores achieved by a group taking a general-information test for employment in a large consulting firm are shown in rank order. Using this information, prepare a table, giving each interval its midpoint value. Then, find the mean score and the median score.

Frequency	Class Interval
5	90-99
19	80-89
27	70-79
9	60-69
4	50-59
4	40-49
2	30-39

ANSWERS 73.36 +, mean; 76, median

APPLICATION PROBLEMS

1. The commissions paid during the year to 7 salesmen of Atlantic Wholesale Novelty Company were as follows: $8,900, $11,700, $9,975, $12,350, $8,600, $10,100, and $11,080. Find the mean commission paid.

2. Advertising expenditures for six branch stores of Giant King Stores during the past year were as follows: $13,650, $14,050, $13,250, $14,800, $14,200, and $39,400.
a. Find the mean advertising cost.
b. Find the median.

3. During a 3-week period a salesman for Bountiful Garden Supplies made the following purchases of gasoline: 15 gallons at 33.9¢, 18 gallons at 34.9¢, 12 gallons at 32.9¢, 10 gallons at 35¢, 16 gallons at 35.9¢, 15 gallons at 36.9¢, 15 gallons at 34.9¢, and 18 gallons at 35.9¢.
a. Find the mean price per gallon to the nearest tenth of a cent.
b. Find the median price per gallon.
c. Find the modal price.

4. The weights of the 32 members of the Pound Wise Club are shown in the following frequency table. Find the mean weight of the group and the median weight.

Frequency	Class Interval
1	110-119
3	130-139
2	140-149
3	150-159
6	160-169
8	170-179
5	180-189
4	190-199

102 ILLUSTRATING STATISTICAL DATA

Various kinds of visual devices are used to show the relationships existing between quantities or between various kinds of other information. Among the more common devices are the horizontal bar graph, the vertical bar graph, the single-line graph, the rectangle graph, the broken-line graph, and the circle graph.

Horizontal Bar and Vertical Bar Graphs

Bar graphs are used to show the relationships between sets of data. They should be drawn as follows.

1. Assemble the data to be shown.
2. Use graph paper if possible. If graph paper is not available, on plain paper draw lines an equal distance from one another.
3. Choose a scale that will make the graph easy to interpret.
4. Label the graph at equal intervals according to the scale you have established.
5. Use dots to show where the bars should be drawn. This is called *plotting* the data. Draw the bars.
6. Give the graph an informative title.

Examples | **PROBLEM 1** The following contributions were made to the United Fund of Hartsdale for each of the 12 years indicated. Present this information in the form of a vertical bar graph.

Year	Amount		Year	Amount
19X9	$57,000		19X5	$79,000
19X0	46,000		19X6	97,000
19X1	77,000		19X7	42,000
19X2	94,000		19X8	80,000
19X3	36,000		19X9	63,000
19X4	90,000		19X0	79,000

SOLUTION

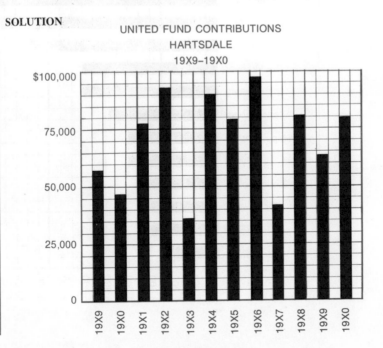

UNITED FUND CONTRIBUTIONS
HARTSDALE
19X9–19X0

PROBLEM 2   The Intercontinental Export Company is studying the average salaries paid to its office workers in various foreign countries. It has decided to put this information for each branch office in horizontal bar graph form. The following salaries are paid by the New Delhi branch. Present the amounts in a horizontal bar graph.

Position	Salary
Office manager	$12,000
Accountant	10,000
Supervisor	8,400
Bookkeeper	6,000
Secretary	6,000
Stenographer	4,800
Shipping clerk	4,000
Typist	4,000
Ledger clerk	3,600
File clerk	3,000
Receptionist	3,000
Messenger	2,400

SOLUTION

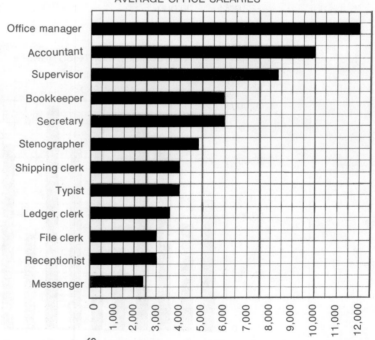

NEW DELHI BRANCH
AVERAGE OFFICE SALARIES

1. Make a vertical bar graph of the sales volume of the Randolph Equipment Company for the years 19X3 to 19X2.

Year	Sales
19X3	$ 84,000
19X4	96,000
19X5	103,000
19X6	77,000
19X7	94,000
19X8	103,000
19X9	120,000
19X0	132,000
19X1	134,000
19X2	140,000

2. Prepare a horizontal bar graph showing the total dollar value of major contracts awarded the construction industry during one year.

Company	Contract
Algozini & Morris	$7,500,000
Curtis Industries	9,250,000
Levy Brothers Construction	3,000,000
Milgrim Company	5,750,000
Prentiss Construction Corp.	6,500,000

3. Prepare a vertical bar graph showing the percentage of funds borrowed by Cities A through H based on the assessed valuation of their taxable property.

City	Long-Term Debt Burden %
A	6.5
B	2.5
C	3.5
D	13.75
E	5.0
F	9.5
G	5.75
H	7.0

Broken-Line Graphs

Broken-line graphs are used to show (*1*) the relationships between three or more data items and (*2*) the change over a period of time. *Multiple broken-line graphs* include two or more broken-line graphs, so that they also convey similar information. In addition, for each year they show the relationships among all the data items and, when applicable, to the sum of the data items.

Broken-line graphs are drawn as follows.
1. Assemble the data to be shown.
2. Use graph paper if possible. Otherwise, prepare a substitute.
3. Choose a scale that will make the graph easy to interpret.
4. Label the graph at equal intervals according to the scale you have established.
5. Plot the points at which the data items and the years intersect. That is, move along the horizontal scale to the year needed; then move straight up to the point representing the data item. This is the *point of intersection.*
6. Connect the dots.
7. Give the graph an informative title.

In the examples below, problem 1 shows a broken-line graph, and problem 2 shows a multiple broken-line graph. Notice that each broken-line graph in a multiple broken-line graph should look unique. The illustration in problem 2 provides a key for each of the three broken-line graphs represented so that the reader knows for what it stands.

Examples

PROBLEM 1 The following profits were made by the Robert Mays Manufacturing Company for a 10-year period. Present these amounts in a broken-line graph.

Year	Profits
19X3	$ 94,000
19X4	112,000
19X5	168,000
19X6	126,000
19X7	78,000
19X8	56,000
19X9	62,000
19X0	74,000
19X1	92,000

SOLUTION

PROFITS OF THE ROBERT MAYS MANUFACTURING COMPANY
19X3—19X2

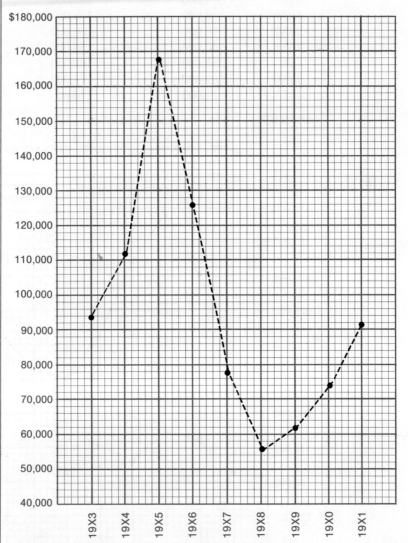

PROBLEM 2 The accounting records of Lyle Lumpkin, Inc., showed the following sales, cost of goods sold, and expenses for the 10-year period ending December 31, 19X2. Present these amounts in a multiple broken-line graph. (As its name implies, a multiple broken-line graph combines several broken-line graphs in one statistical report.) Note that each small block in the vertical scale represents $6,000.

Year	Sales	Cost of Goods Sold	Expenses
19X3	$270,000	$156,000	$18,000
19X4	330,000	186,000	24,000
19X5	384,000	192,000	18,000
19X6	342,000	168,000	48,000
19X7	276,000	180,000	12,000
19X8	240,000	156,000	24,000
19X9	246,000	162,000	24,000
19X0	282,000	174,000	30,000
19X1	312,000	186,000	36,000

SOLUTION

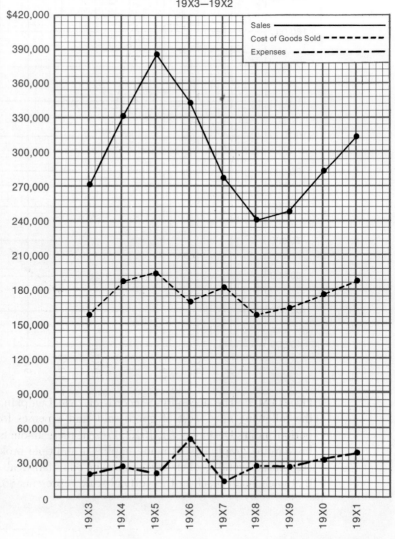

LYLE LUMPKIN, INC.
SALES, COST OF GOODS SOLD, AND EXPENSES
19X3—19X2

Practice
Drill

The records of the Hancock Trading Company showed the following information. Draw a multiple broken-line graph representing these amounts.

Year	Net Sales	Cost of Goods Sold	Operating Expenses	Net Profit (or Loss)
19X3	$186,000	$102,000	$16,000	$ 68,000
19X4	209,000	118,000	18,000	73,000
19X5	175,000	119,000	22,000	34,000
19X6	236,000	124,000	21,000	91,000
19X7	242,000	126,000	23,000	93,000
19X8	285,000	140,000	28,000	117,000
19X9	220,000	137,000	26,000	57,000
19X0	192,000	146,000	31,000	15,000
19X1	164,000	129,000	48,000	13,000 (loss)
19X2	147,000	102,000	53,000	8,000 (loss)

Single-Line and Rectangle Graphs

Single-line and *rectangle graphs* are used to show the relationships of several data items to one another and to the sum of the items. The larger the section of the graph allowed for a data item, the closer the relationship between that data item and the sum of all the data items, or the whole graph.

Single-line and rectangle graphs are drawn as follows.
1. Use either a single vertical line or a rectangle.
2. Determine the number of items or values and the percent each item is of the total sum.
3. Indicate the relationships among the items or values on the single line or rectangle by the distance taken up by each item.

Example

PROBLEM The following table shows a budget prepared by a bank for the use of a $15,000 income by a family of four. Present these numeric amounts in a single-line graph and then in a rectangle graph.

Use	Percent of Income	Use	Percent of Income
Food	25%	Recreation	10%
Rent	25%	Health	5%
Savings	15%	Charity	5%
Clothing	10%	Miscellaneous	5%

SOLUTION

SINGLE-LINE GRAPH		RECTANGLE GRAPH	

SINGLE-LINE GRAPH

25%	Food $3,750
25%	Rent $3,750
15%	Savings $2,250
10%	Clothing $1,500
10%	Recreation $1,500
5%	Health, $750
5%	Charity, $750
5%	Miscellaneous, $750

RECTANGLE GRAPH

25%	Food	$3,750
25%	Rent	$3,750
15%	Savings	$2,250
10%	Clothing	$1,500
10%	Recreation	$1,500
5%	Health	$750
5%	Charity	$750
5%	Miscellaneous	$750

Practice   In a recent year there were approximately 75,000 accidental deaths in the United States. These fatalities were due to the causes listed in the following table. Convert all amounts to percents, and present these percents and their corresponding amounts in a single-line graph and in a rectangle graph.

Cause	Amount
Automobiles	33,750
Falls	16,500
Fires	6,000
Drowning	6,000
Public transportation	2,250
Firearms	1,875
Other causes	8,625

ANSWERS   (percents only)   automobiles, 45%; falls, 22%; fires, 8%; drowning, 8%; public transportation, 3%; firearms, $2\frac{1}{2}$%; other causes, $11\frac{1}{2}$%

Circle Graph

Circle graphs are used to show the relationship between data items on a percentage or dollar basis. They should be drawn as follows.
1. Draw a circle with the aid of a compass.
2. When a relationship on a percentage basis is to be shown, 100% is represented by a 360° circle. Change each percent to its degree equivalent. When trying to show dollar values, use the same technique.

Example

PROBLEM Prepare a circle graph from the budget given in the example on page 309.

SOLUTION

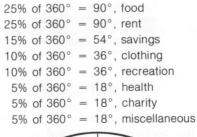

25% of 360° = 90°, food
25% of 360° = 90°, rent
15% of 360° = 54°, savings
10% of 360° = 36°, clothing
10% of 360° = 36°, recreation
 5% of 360° = 18°, health
 5% of 360° = 18°, charity
 5% of 360° = 18°, miscellaneous

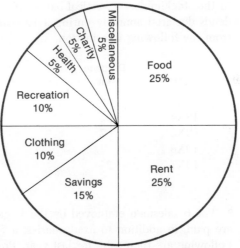

Practice Drill

The operating expenses of the Andover Manufacturing Company last year amounted to $138,000, divided among the items shown in the following table. Find what percent each expenditure is of the total amount of expenditures for the year, and change each percent to the corresponding number of degrees. Then, using a compass and a protractor, construct a circle graph to represent these amounts.

Expense	Amount
Salaries	$ 75,900
Rent	20,700
Light, heat, power	6,900
Insurance	2,760
Depreciation	4,140
Taxes	5,520
Selling	12,420
Supplies	4,140
Miscellaneous	+ 5,520
Totals	$138,000

ANSWERS   (percents and degrees only)   (percents) salaries, 55%; rent, 15%; light, heat, power, 5%; insurance, 2%; depreciation, 3%; taxes, 4%; selling, 9%; supplies, 3%; miscellaneous, 4%;   (degrees) salaries, 198°; rent, 54°; light, heat, power, 18°; insurance, 7.2°; depreciation, 10.8°; taxes, 14.4°; selling, 32.4°; supplies, 10.8°; miscellaneous, 14.4°

APPLICATION PROBLEMS

1. The board of directors of a surgical instrument company distributed to the stockholders a vertical bar graph showing the percent of dividends declared annually during a 10-year period. Prepare this graph from the following information.

Year	Dividend Rate	Year	Dividend Rate
19X3	8%	19X8	$3\frac{1}{2}$%
19X4	$10\frac{1}{2}$	19X9	4
19X5	7	19X0	$6\frac{1}{2}$
19X6	4	19X1	7
19X7	$2\frac{1}{2}$	19X2	6

2. The 6 salesmen employed by the Regal Floor Covering Company are paid, in addition to fixed salaries, a $7\frac{1}{2}$% commission on all sales. Following are their sales for last year. Prepare a horizontal bar graph comparing the sales and the commission of each salesman.

Salesman	Sales	Salesman	Sales
Louis Barr	$85,000	Horace Dow	$82,500
Sidney Clark	75,000	William Tull	81,000
Ray Mann	86,000	John Keegan	89,000

3. The monthly sales, the cost of goods sold, and the expenses of the Precision Automotive Equipment Company for the year ending December 31, 19X4, are given in the following table. Show these facts in comparative form on a broken-line graph.

Month	Sales	Cost of Goods Sold	Expenses
January	$209,000	$152,200	$16,800
February	175,600	119,400	9,200
March	186,800	124,800	11,800
April	223,400	155,600	14,600
May	217,000	144,800	12,800
June	248,600	167,000	16,600
July	192,400	129,200	11,600
August	169,000	106,800	9,800
September	199,400	118,800	13,400
October	273,000	173,400	16,400
November	225,800	150,600	14,200
December	292,600	186,200	19,600

4. The expenses of the Provident Oil Company were distributed as shown in the following table. Present these facts on a single-line graph.

Expense	Percent of Total Expenses
Salaries and wages	58%
Rent, light, and heat	18
Sales and promotion	10
Administrative	5
Taxes	4
Employee benefits	3
Insurance	2

5. An eastern city reported the following expenditures during a recent fiscal period. Out of every dollar, 39¢ was spent for schools, 18¢ for the police department, 12¢ for the fire department, 7¢ for the street cleaning department, 4¢ for interest on the public debt, 6¢ for parks and public buildings, 3¢ for administration, and 11¢ for other city activities. Represent these amounts on a circle graph.

PROBLEMS FOR PART FIFTEEN

Preparing Statistical Data & Graphs

101

1. The number of units produced in 1 week by the 11 employees in the plastics manufacturing section of a business were as follows: 312, 218, 296, 281, 309, 326, 330, 316, 292, 263, and 296.
a. What was the mean production to the nearest hundredth?
b. What was the median?
c. What was the mode?

2. A class of 32 students made the following scores on a mid-term examination in business mathematics: two received 95, two received 55, one received 35, six received 75, one received 90, six received 85, three received 60, four received 70, and seven received 80. Find the mean score, the median score, and the modal score.

3. The monthly sales of the Plaython Corporation for a 3-year period are given below. Find the mean and median for each year.

Month	19X4	19X5	19X6
January	$270,000	$305,000	$360,000
February	240,000	280,000	300,000
March	250,000	290,000	320,000
April	230,000	310,000	400,000
May	210,000	290,000	290,000
June	160,000	220,000	240,000
July	170,000	210,000	230,000
August	110,000	200,000	220,000
September	180,000	250,000	280,000
October	220,000	290,000	340,000
November	300,000	350,000	410,000
December	320,000	380,000	510,000

102

1. The following sales, totaling $656,000, were made last year by the Lone Star Home Products Company. Draw a rectangle graph representing these amounts.

Sales	Amount
Cash	$225,000
C.O.D.	93,600
Installment	136,800
On approval	23,200
Monthly charge	177,400

2. The annual report of the Mayflower Department Store showed that the following departments made a profit for the year of $480,000. Show the earnings by departments to the nearest thousand on a horizontal bar graph and to the nearest percent on a rectangle graph.

Department	Profits
Clothing	$168,000
Cosmetics	48,000
Furniture	96,000
Hardware	57,600
Miscellaneous	110,400

3. Draw a circle graph to represent the percentages given in the following budget of expenses for a family of four. Change each percent making up the 100% to the corresponding number of degrees as represented by the 360° of a circle.

Expense	Percent of Total Expenses
Food	25
Rent	20
Insurance and savings	15
Clothing	10
Health	3
Charity	7
Recreation	5
Miscellaneous	15

PART SIXTEEN
Denominate Numbers

The word "denominate" comes from the Latin *"denominare,"* to name. A *denominate number* is one that specifically names something. That is, the number 5 is merely an abstract number, but "5 bushels" is a denominate number since it names, or denominates, bushels.

All of us use denominate numbers in our daily personal and business affairs. We say a 9- by 12-foot carpet, a pint of cream, a pound of tomatoes, a mile, a ream of paper, a dollar, and an 8-ounce glass of milk. Denominate numbers are extremely important in business. A sand and gravel distributor deals in cubic yards; a coal dealer, in long tons; a silversmith, in pennyweights and grains; a pharmacist, in drams; and so on.

There are two systems of denominate numbers: the *English system* and the *metric system.* The English system is used in the United States for most business and consumer transactions. However, nearly all other nations of the world use the metric system. Indeed, England, the father of the English system, is now converting to the metric system. The reason is that most of the nations with which England trades are on this system, and it is complicated and costly to convert transactions involving weights and measures from the English to the metric system. The United States, virtually the only nation committed to the English system, is now considering converting to the metric system so that international business can be transacted more smoothly and easily; and a study is under way by the Federal government to explore the problems of conversion.

Even in the United States, the metric system is used in chemistry, physics, and other scientific fields. The metric system of weights and measures has a distinct advantage over the English system in that all the metric tables use a scale of 10; 10 of one denomination is equal to 1 of the next higher denomination. In linear measure, the scale is 10; in square measure, 100; and in cubic measure, 1,000. When a change is made from one measure to another, it is necessary only to move the decimal point either to the right or to the left.

If you are employed in a firm or organization that transacts business with foreign countries, you are quite likely to work with the metric system of denominate numbers.

103 ENGLISH SYSTEM

Tables of weights and measures have been established by law and custom. The following units of weights and measures are used under the English system of measurements.

Linear Measure

Linear (line or long) measure is used in measuring distances and lengths, widths, or thicknesses.

$$
\begin{aligned}
12 \text{ inches (in. or ")} &= 1 \text{ foot (ft. or ')} \\
3 \text{ feet} &= 1 \text{ yard (yd.)} \\
5\tfrac{1}{2} \text{ yards, or } 16\tfrac{1}{2} \text{ feet} &= 1 \text{ rod (rd.)} \\
40 \text{ rods} &= 1 \text{ furlong (fur.)} \\
8 \text{ furlongs, or } 320 \text{ rods} &= 1 \text{ mile (mi.)} \\
1{,}760 \text{ yards} &= 1 \text{ mile} \\
5{,}280 \text{ feet} &= 1 \text{ mile}
\end{aligned}
$$

The unit of length is the yard.
1 hand = 4 inches (used in measuring the height of horses)
1 fathom (marine measure) = 6 feet (used in measuring depths at sea)
1 knot = $1.152\tfrac{2}{3}$ miles (nautical or geographical mile)
1 league = 3 knots (3 × 1.15 miles)

Square Measure

Square measure is used in measuring areas of surfaces.

$$
\begin{aligned}
144 \text{ square inches (sq. in.)} &= 1 \text{ square foot (sq. ft.)} \\
9 \text{ square feet} &= 1 \text{ square yard (sq. yd.)} \\
30\tfrac{1}{4} \text{ square yards} &= 1 \text{ square rod (sq. rd.)} \\
160 \text{ square rods} &= 1 \text{ acre (A.)} \\
4{,}840 \text{ square yards} &= 1 \text{ acre} \\
43{,}560 \text{ square feet} &= 1 \text{ acre} \\
640 \text{ acres} &= 1 \text{ square mile (sq. mi.)}
\end{aligned}
$$

The unit used in measuring land is the acre, except for city lots.
A square, used in roofing, is 100 square feet.
The unit used in measuring other surfaces is the square yard.

Solid or Cubic Measure

Solid or cubic measure is used in measuring the volume of a body or a solid as well as the contents or capacity of hollow bodies.

$$
\begin{aligned}
1{,}728 \text{ cubic inches (cu. in.)} &= 1 \text{ cubic foot (cu. ft.)} \\
27 \text{ cubic feet} &= 1 \text{ cubic yard (cu. yd.)} \\
231 \text{ cubic inches} &= 1 \text{ gallon (gal.)} \\
24\tfrac{3}{4} \text{ cubic feet} &= 1 \text{ perch (P.) of stone} \\
128 \text{ cubic feet} &= 1 \text{ cord (cd.) of wood} \\
1 \text{ cubic foot} &= 7\tfrac{1}{2} \text{ gallons}
\end{aligned}
$$

A cord of wood (128 cubic feet) is a pile 8 feet long, 4 feet wide, and 4 feet high.

1 cubic yard of earth = 1 load.

1 cubic foot of water weighs 62½ pounds (avoirdupois).

Circular or Angular Measure

Circular or angular measure is used in measuring angles or the parts of circles.

$$60 \text{ seconds } ('') = 1 \text{ minute } (')$$
$$60 \text{ minutes } = 1 \text{ degree } (°)$$
$$360 \text{ degrees } = 1 \text{ circle (cir.)}$$
$$30 \text{ degrees } = 1 \text{ sign } (\tfrac{1}{12} \text{ of a circle})$$
$$60 \text{ degrees } = 1 \text{ sextant } (\tfrac{1}{6} \text{ of a circle})$$
$$90 \text{ degrees } = 1 \text{ quadrant } (\tfrac{1}{4} \text{ of a circle})$$

A 90° angle is a right angle.

Liquid Measure

Liquid measure is used in measuring the liquid capacity of vessels or containers for all liquids except medicine.

$$4 \text{ gills (gi.)} = 1 \text{ pint (pt.)}$$
$$2 \text{ pints } = 1 \text{ quart (qt.)}$$
$$4 \text{ quarts } = 1 \text{ gallon (gal.)}$$
$$31\tfrac{1}{2} \text{ gallons } = 1 \text{ barrel (bbl.)}$$
$$63 \text{ gallons } = 1 \text{ hogshead (hhd.)}$$
$$2 \text{ barrels } = 1 \text{ hogshead}$$
$$7\tfrac{1}{2} \text{ gallons } = 1 \text{ cubic foot (cu. ft.)}$$

The unit of liquid measure is the United States gallon of 231 cubic inches.

1 gallon of water weighs 8⅓ pounds (avoirdupois).

Dry Measure

Dry measure is used in measuring the volume of containers of solids, such as produce, seed, fruits, and so on, that are not sold by weight.

$$2 \text{ pints (pt.)} = 1 \text{ quart (qt.)}$$
$$8 \text{ quarts } = 1 \text{ peck (pk.)}$$
$$4 \text{ pecks } = 1 \text{ bushel (bu.)}$$
$$2\tfrac{3}{4} \text{ bushels } = 1 \text{ barrel (bbl.)}$$

Advoirdupois Weight

Avoirdupois weight is used in weighing heavy or coarse articles, such as coal, iron, grain, hay, and so on.

$$27\tfrac{11}{32}\text{ grains (gr.)} = 1\text{ dram (dr.)}$$
$$16\text{ drams} = 1\text{ ounce (oz.)}$$
$$16\text{ ounces} = 1\text{ pound (lb.)}$$
$$100\text{ pounds} = 1\text{ hundredweight (cwt.)}$$
$$20\text{ hundredweights} = 1\text{ ton (T.)}$$
$$2{,}000\text{ pounds} = 1\text{ ton}$$
$$2{,}240\text{ pounds} = 1\text{ long, or gross, ton}$$
$$7{,}000\text{ grains} = 1\text{ pound avoirdupois}$$

The United States government uses the long ton of 2,240 pounds in fixing the duty on merchandise taxed by the ton.
Coal and iron sold at the mine are also weighed by the long ton.

Troy Weight

Troy weight is used in weighing precious minerals, and by the United States government in weighing coins.

$$24\text{ grains} = 1\text{ pennyweight (pwt.)}$$
$$20\text{ pennyweights} = 1\text{ ounce (oz.)}$$
$$12\text{ ounces} = 1\text{ pound (lb.)}$$
$$240\text{ pennyweights} = 1\text{ pound}$$
$$5{,}760\text{ grains} = 1\text{ pound troy}$$

The unit of weight in the United States is the troy pound.
Pure gold is 24 carats fine. Gold marked 14 carats is $\tfrac{14}{24}$ pure gold by weight and $\tfrac{10}{24}$ alloy by weight.

Apothecaries' Dry Weight and Liquid Measure

Apothecaries' dry weight and liquid measure is used in weighing and measuring drugs and chemicals and in compounding dry and liquid medicines. Avoirdupois weight, however, is used when drugs and chemicals are bought and sold wholesale.

Apothecaries' Dry Weight
$$20\text{ grains (gr.)} = 1\text{ scruple (sc.)}$$
$$3\text{ scruples} = 1\text{ dram (dr.)}$$
$$8\text{ drams} = 1\text{ ounce (oz.)}$$
$$12\text{ ounces} = 1\text{ pound (lb.)}$$

Apothecaries' Liquid Measure
$$60\text{ minims (m., min.)} = 1\text{ fluid dram (fl. dr. or f}\mathrecipe\text{)}$$
$$8\text{ fluid drams} = 1\text{ fluid ounce (fl. oz. or }\mathrecipe\text{)}$$
$$16\text{ fluid ounces} = 1\text{ pint (pt.)}$$
$$8\text{ pints} = 1\text{ gallon (gal.)}$$

Mariner's Measure

$$6 \text{ feet} = 1 \text{ fathom (f.)}$$
$$120 \text{ fathoms} = 1 \text{ cable length}$$
$$7\tfrac{1}{2} \text{ cable lengths} = 1 \text{ marine mile}$$
$$5,280 \text{ feet} = 1 \text{ statute mile (st. mi.)}$$
$$6,080 \text{ feet} = 1 \text{ nautical mile (n. mi.)}$$
$$3 \text{ marine miles} = 1 \text{ marine league}$$

Time Table

$$60 \text{ seconds (sec.)} = 1 \text{ minute (min.)}$$
$$60 \text{ minutes} = 1 \text{ hour (hr.)}$$
$$24 \text{ hours} = 1 \text{ day (da.)}$$
$$7 \text{ days} = 1 \text{ week (wk.)}$$
$$30 \text{ days} = 1 \text{ month (mo.)}*$$
$$52 \text{ weeks} = 1 \text{ year (yr.)}$$
$$12 \text{ months} = 1 \text{ year}$$
$$365 \text{ days} = 1 \text{ year}*$$
$$100 \text{ years} = 1 \text{ century (cen.)}$$

Counting Table

$$20 \text{ units} = 1 \text{ score}$$
$$12 \text{ units} = 1 \text{ dozen (doz.)}$$
$$12 \text{ dozen} = 1 \text{ gross (gro., or gr.)}$$
$$12 \text{ gross} = 1 \text{ great gross (g. gr.)}$$

Paper Measure

$$24 \text{ (or sometimes 25) sheets} = 1 \text{ quire (qr.)}$$
$$20 \text{ quires} = 1 \text{ ream (rm.)}$$
$$2 \text{ reams} = 1 \text{ bundle (bdl.)}$$
$$5 \text{ bundles} = 1 \text{ bale (bl.)}$$

Monetary Value

United States Money
$$10 \text{ mills} = 1 \text{ cent (¢)}$$
$$10 \text{ cents} = 1 \text{ dime}$$
$$10 \text{ dimes} = 1 \text{ dollar (\$)}$$
$$10 \text{ dollars} = 1 \text{ eagle}$$

The unit of measure is the dollar.

English Money
$$5 \text{ pence} = 1 \text{ shilling (s.)}$$
$$20 \text{ shillings} = 1 \text{ pound (£)}$$

The unit of measure is the pound.

*January, 31 days; February, 28 days (29 days in February in a leap year of 366 days); March, 31 days; April, 30 days; May, 31 days; June, 30 days; July, 31 days; August, 31 days; September, 30 days; October, 31 days; November, 30 days; December, 31 days.

French Money

10 millimes (m.) = 1 centime (c.)
10 centimes = 1 decime (dc.)
10 decimes = 1 franc (Fr.)

The unit of measure is the franc.

Commodity Weights

Beef, barrel	200 lb.	Nails, keg	100 lb.
Butter, firkin	56 lb.	Pork, barrel	200 lb.
Flour, barrel	196 lb.	Salt, barrel	280 lb.

Bushel Weights

The following bushel weights are used in most of the states.

Apples	50 lb.	Oats	32 lb.
Barley	48 lb.	Onions	57 lb.
Beans	60 lb.	Peas	60 lb.
Buckwheat	48 lb.	Potatoes	60 lb.
Clover seed	60 lb.	Rye	56 lb.
Corn (ear)	70 lb.	Sweet potatoes	54 lb.
Corn (shelled)	56 lb.	Timothy seed	45 lb.
Corn meal	48 lb.	Wheat	60 lb.
Flaxseed	56 lb.		

1 U.S. Standard bushel occupies 2,150.42 cubic inches.
1 heaped bushel (apples, beans, potatoes, and so on) occupies about 2,747.41 cubic inches.

APPLICATION PROBLEMS

1. Express 360 square rods as acres.
2. Find the number of gallons in 462 cubic inches.
3. A sterling silver knife weighs 3 ounces 6 pennyweights 12 grains. Find the weight of a dozen knives.
4. Rename 79 rods 3 yards $1\frac{1}{4}$ feet and 5 inches in inches.
5. Express 24 square yards and 15 square feet in square inches.
6. How many yards are there in $7\frac{5}{8}$ miles?
7. Find the number of acres in a plot of ground that measures 600 feet by 1,080 feet.
8. How many sheets of paper, costing $1.54 a ream, must a stationer sell for 2.5¢ each in order to make a profit of 30% of the selling price?
9. A gold bar weighs 5 pounds 9 ounces 3 pennyweights 7 grains. What is it worth at $35 an ounce?
10. 72 gallons of grape juice are purchased at $1.72 a gallon and sold at 20¢ a glass. If each glass contains 2 gills, find the total gain.
11. Garden apartments are to be constructed on a plot of ground measuring 38 rods by 16 rods. How many acres are in the plot?

104 METRIC SYSTEM

The metric system of weights and measures is a decimal system, or a system based on ten. The three principal units of measurement are the following.

1. The meter (the unit of linear measurement)
2. The liter (the unit of capacity measurement)
3. The gram (the unit of weight or mass measurement)

The basic unit of the metric system is the meter, upon which the other units are based. The length of the meter, which is 39.37 inches, was originally determined by taking one ten-millionth of the distance from the equator to one of the poles.

The following units of weights and measures are used under the metric system of measurements.

Linear Measure

10 millimeters (mm.)	= 1 centimeter (cm.)
10 centimeters	= 1 decimeter (dm.)
10 decimeters	= 1 meter (m.)
10 meters	= 1 decameter (dcm.)
10 decameters	= 1 hectometer (hm.)
10 hectometers	= 1 kilometer (km.)
10 kilometers	= 1 myriameter (mym.)

The basic unit of linear measures is the meter.

Square Measure

100 square millimeters (sq. mm.)	= 1 square centimeter (sq. cm.)
100 square centimeters	= 1 square decimeter (sq. dm.)
100 square decimeters	= 1 square meter (sq. m.)
100 square meters	= 1 square decameter (sq. dcm.)
100 square decameters	= 1 square hectometer (sq. hm.)
100 square hectometers	= 1 square kilometer (sq. km.)
100 square kilometers	= 1 square myriameter (sq. mym.)

The basic unit of square measures is the square meter.

Cubic Measure

1,000 cubic millimeters (cu. mm.)	= 1 cubic centimeter (cu. cm., c.c.)
1,000 cubic centimeters	= 1 cubic decimeter (cu. dm.)
1,000 cubic decimeters	= 1 cubic meter (cu. m.)
1,000 cubic meters	= 1 cubic decameter (cu. dcm.)
1,000 cubic decameters	= 1 cubic hectometer (cu. hm.)
1,000 cubic hectometers	= 1 cubic kilometer (cu. km.)
1,000 cubic kilometers	= 1 cubic myriameter (cu. mym.)

The basic unit of measures of volume is the cubic meter.

Liquid and Dry Measure

$$10 \text{ milliliters (ml.)} = 1 \text{ centiliter (cl.)}$$
$$10 \text{ centiliters} = 1 \text{ deciliter (dl.)}$$
$$10 \text{ deciliters} = 1 \text{ liter (l.)}$$
$$10 \text{ liters} = 1 \text{ decaliter (dcl.)}$$
$$10 \text{ decaliters} = 1 \text{ hectoliter (hl.)}$$
$$10 \text{ hectoliters} = 1 \text{ kiloliter (kl.)}$$
$$10 \text{ kiloliters} = 1 \text{ myrialiter (myl.)}$$

The unit of capacity measurement for liquids and solids is the liter.

Weight Measure

$$10 \text{ milligrams (mg.)} = 1 \text{ centigram (cg.)}$$
$$10 \text{ centigrams} = 1 \text{ decigram (dg.)}$$
$$10 \text{ decigrams} = 1 \text{ gram (g.)}$$
$$10 \text{ grams} = 1 \text{ decagram (dcg.)}$$
$$10 \text{ decagrams} = 1 \text{ hectogram (hg.)}$$
$$10 \text{ hectograms} = 1 \text{ kilogram (kg.)}$$
$$10 \text{ kilograms} = 1 \text{ myriagram (myg.)}$$
$$10 \text{ myriagrams} = 1 \text{ quintal (q.)}$$
$$10 \text{ quintals} = 1 \text{ tonneau (T.)}$$

The unit of weight measurement is the gram.

Metric and English Equivalents

The following are the metric and English system equivalents.

Linear Measure

1 in. = 2.54 cm.	1 mm. = .03937 in.
1 ft. = .3048 m.	1 cm. = .3937 in.
1 yd. = .9144 m.	1 dm. = .3281 ft.
1 rd. = 5.029 m.	1 m. = 39.37 in.
1 mi. = 1.6093 km.	1 m. = 3.281 ft.
	1 m. = 1.0936 yd.
	1 dcm. = 1.9884 rd.
	1 km. = .6214 mi.

Square Measure

1 sq. in. = 6.452 sq.cm.	1 sq. mm. = .00155 sq. in.
1 sq. ft. = .0929 sq. m.	1 sq. cm. = .155 sq. in.
1 sq. yd. = .8361 sq. m.	1 sq. dm. = .1076 sq. ft.
1 sq. rd. = 25.293 sq. m.	1 sq. m. = 1.196 sq. yd.
1 A. = 40.47 ares (a.) or .4047 hectares (ha.)	1 a. = 3.954 sq. rd.
	1 ha. = 2.471 A.
1 sq. mi. = 259 ha. or 2.589 sq. km.	1 sq. km. = .3861 sq. mi.

Solid or Cubic Measure

1 cu. in. = 16.3872 cu. cm. (c.c.)
1 cu. ft. = 28.317 cu. dm. or .02832 cu. m.
1 cu. yd. = .7646 cu. m.
1 cd. = 3.624 steres (st.)
1 cu. cm. (c.c.) = .06102 cu. in.
1 cu. dm. = .0353 cu. ft.
1 cu. m. = 1.308 cu. yd.
1 st. = .2759 cd.

Liquid and Dry Measure

1 dry qt. = 1.101 l.   1 l. = .908 dry qt.
1 liquid qt. = .9463 l.   1 l. = 1.0567 liquid qt.
1 liquid gal. = .3785 dcl. or 3.785 l. 1 dcl. = 2.6417 liquid gal.
1 pk. = .881 dcl. or 8.81 l.   1 dcl. = 1.135 pk.
1 bu. = .3524 hl.   1 hl. = 2.8377 bu.

Weight Measure

1 gr. troy = .0648 g.   1 g. = 15.432 gr. troy
1 oz. troy = 31.104 g.   1 g. = .03215 oz. troy
1 oz. avoir. = 28.35 g.   1 g. = .03527 oz. avoir.
1 lb. troy = .3732 kg.   1 kg. = 2.679 lb. troy
1 lb. avoir. = .4536 kg.   1 kg. = 2.2046 lb. avoir.
1 T. (short) = .9072 met. t.   1 met. t. = 1.1023 T. (short)

APPLICATION PROBLEMS

1. Find the number of inches in 877.56 centimeters.
2. How many millimeters are there in 317 meters?
3. Change 7 gallons 3 quarts and 1 pint to liters.
4. The distance between two cities is 892 miles. Express this in metric measurement.
5. How many grams are in 1 pound avoirdupois? In 1 pound troy?
6. One square meter is equal to how many square inches? Square feet?
7. Express 7 decaliters as pecks and as liquid gallons.
8. How many square centimeters are there in a room 21 feet by 14 feet?
9. How much is gained on 350 meters of material that costs 89 cents per meter and sells for $1.15 a yard?
10. Butter is purchased at 64 cents a pound. How many kilograms can be bought for $9.75?
11. The dimensions of a bulletin board are 12 centimeters by 16 centimeters. What are its dimensions in inches?

PROBLEMS FOR PART SIXTEEN
Denominate Numbers

103

1. Describe each phrase as suggestive of a linear, a square, or a cubic measure.
a. The height of the tallest building in the world
b. The area of a room that measures 9 ft. x 12 ft.
c. The distance between the post office and the bank
d. The size of a crate measuring 3 ft. x 2 ft. x 4 ft.
e. A calendar measuring $3\frac{1}{2}$ in. x 2 in.

2. Match each description with its equivalent.
a. 6 quarts   (1) $\frac{1}{2}$ bushel
b. $\frac{1}{6}$ of a circle graph   (2) 160 sq. ft.
c. 16 quarts   (3) 60 degrees
d. A 10 ft. x 16 ft. area   (4) $1\frac{1}{2}$ gallons
e. 180 degrees   (5) A semicircle

3. Compute as indicated. Be sure to label your answers.
a. If Mr. Andrews earns $292.50 semimonthly, what are his weekly earnings?
b. At the end of a day, a group of parking meters contained a total of 205 dimes. How many dollars is this?
c. Mrs. Rodriguez earns $220 a week. What are her monthly earnings?
d. How many square yards of linoleum would be needed to cover a floor that measures 6 ft. x 9 ft?
e. Dan's average lunch delivery takes him 250 yards from the store. If he makes 10 deliveries, how many miles does he travel? (Hint: Count his travel to and from the store.)

104

1. Describe each phrase as suggestive of a linear, a square, or a cubic measure.
a. A road sign labeled 75 km.
b. A garden that measures 10 m. x 5 m.
c. A shoebox measuring 25 cm. x 10 cm. x 10 cm.
d. The distance between New York and Brussels
e. The surface of a table

2. Match each description with its equivalent.

a. 12,500 ml.   (1) 8.5 cm.

b. 85 mm.   (2) 5 g.

c. A hallway having a width of 2½ m.   (3) 12.5 1.

d. 5 trips to a store 200 m. away   (4) 250 cm.

e. 5,000 mg.   (5) 2 km.

3. Give the English equivalent for each metric measure and the metric equivalent for each English measure.

a. 96.558 km.   d. 25 cu. cm.   g. 9 yd.

b. 10 lb. troy   e. 800 km.   h. 9.463 1.

c. 50.8 cm.   f. 30 sq. in.   i. 220.46 lb. avoir.

STANDARD BUSINESS SYMBOLS

+	addition; plus
&	and
. . .	and so on
@	at; each
¢	cent(s)
✓	correct; check mark
°	degree(s), as 90°
÷	division; divided by
$	dollar(s)
=	equals; is equal to
′	foot; feet; minute(s)
>	is greater than
″	inch(es); second(s)
<	is less than
×	multiplication; times; by, as 3′ × 5′
#	number (when written before a figure); pound(s) (when written after a figure)
1¹, 1², 1³	one and one-fourth; one and one-half; one and three-fourths (used in dry goods business)
( )	parentheses; used to indicate that the quantities enclosed by them are to be taken together
%	percent; hundredths
s	percent, as 3s interest; shilling
£	pounds sterling
:	ratio; is to; compared with
‾	repeating decimal fraction, as $\frac{1}{3}$ = .333... or $.\overline{3}$
∵	since; because
√	square root of
—	subtraction; minus
∴	therefore

STANDARD BUSINESS ABBREVIATIONS

A. acre(s)
a/c account
ADP automated data processing
agt. agent
amt. amount
AMW average monthly wage
ans. answer
a/o account of
approx. approximately
art. article
a/s account sales
av., avg. average
bal. balance
bbl. barrel(s)
B/D bank draft
bdl. bundle
b.f.c. bill for collection
bg. bag
bkt. basket
B/L bill of lading
B/O back order
bot. bought
bu. bushel(s)
bx. box
C hundred
cal. calendar
car. carton
c.c., cu. cm. cubic centimeter
cd. cord; card
cg. centigram
ch. chain; chest
chg. charge

cht. chart
c.i.f. cost, insurance, and freight
ck. cask; check
cl. centiliter
CL carload; car lots
CM credit memo
cm. centimeter
cml., coml. commercial
c/o care of
Co. Company; county
COBOL COmmon Business Oriented Language
COD collect, or cash, on delivery
coll. collection
comm. commission
cons., consg't consignment
Corp. Corporation
CPU central processing unit
cr. credit; creditor
crt. crate
cs. case
ctn. carton
cu. cubic
cwt. hundredweight
d. penny; pence
da. day(s)
dept. department
dft. draft
disc. discount
div. dividend

DM debit memo
doz., dz. dozen(s)
dr. debtor; debit; dram
ea. each
EAM electrical accounting machine
EDP electronic data processing
e.g. for example (L., *exempli gratia*)
enc. enclosure
e.o.e. errors and omissions excepted
EOJ end of job
EOM end of month
etc. and so on (L., *et cetera*)
ex. example; express
exch. exchange
exp. expense(s); express
FAD full amount due
far. farthing
FDIC Federal Deposit Insurance Corporation
FICA Federal Insurance Contributions Act
ff. following
FOB free on board
FORTRAN FORmula TRANslation
Fr. franc
frt. freight
ft. foot; feet
fwd. forward

g. gram
g. gr. great gross
gal. gallon(s)
gi. gill(s)
gr. grain; gram; gross
gro. gross
guar. guarantee
hf. half
hhd. hogshead
hp horsepower
hr. hour(s)
hund. hundred
i.e. that is (L., *id est*)
in. inch(es)
Inc. Incorporated
inc. increase
ins. insurance
inst. instant; the current month
int. interest
inv. invoice
invt. inventory
I/O input/output
IRS Internal Revenue Service
j/a joint account
K karat, or carat
kg. kilogram
km. kilometer
kwh, kw.hr. kilowatt-hour
l. liter(s)
lb. pound(s)
L/C letter of credit
l.c.d. lowest common denominator
LCL less-than-carload lots
l.p. list price
LS place of the seal (L., *locus sigilli*)
Ltd. Limited (liability)
m. mill; meter
M thousand
max. maximum
mdse. merchandise

mem., memo memorandum
mfd. manufactured
mfg. manufacturing
mfr. manufacturer
mg. milligram
mgr. manager
mgt. management
mi. mile(s)
min. minute(s)
misc. miscellaneous
ml. milliliter
mm. millimeter
mo. month
mph miles per hour
no. number
NSF not sufficient funds
OASDI Old-Age, Survivors, and Disability Insurance
o/c overcharge; over-the-counter
o/d on demand
o/s out of stock
oz. ounce(s)
p. page
payt. payment
p/c petty cash
pc. piece
pd. paid
per by, by the
perp. perpetual (bonds)
pf., pfd., pref. preferred
pgm. program
pk. peck
pkg. package
PL/1 Programming Language 1
PO purchase order
p.p. parcel post
pp. pages
pr. pair; price
prem. premium
prox. the following month

pt. pint(s)
pwt. pennyweight
qr. quire; quarter; quarterly
qt. quart; quantity
quot. quotation
rect., rec. receipt
rd. rod(s)
recd. received
ref. reference
reg. registered
retd. returned
rm. ream; room
ROG receipt of goods
s percent; shilling
S/D sight draft
S/D-B/L sight draft, bill of lading attached
sec. second(s); secretary
SEC Securities and Exchange Commission
secy. secretary
set. settlement
ship. shipped
shpt., shipt. shipment
shtg. shortage
sig. signed; signature
sq. square
stk. stock
T ton(s)
tb. tub
tr. transfer
treas. treasurer
TSS time-sharing system
ult. last month (L., *ultimo*)
via by way of
viz. namely; to wit (L., *videlicet*)
vol. volume
vs. against (L., *versus*)
wk. week(s)
wt. weight
yd. yard(s)
yr. year(s)

KEY TO ODD-NUMBERED PROBLEMS

Part One

APPLICATION PROBLEMS

Unit 1 (p. 4) 1. 130 3. 162
5. 148 7. 259 9. 241
11. 318 13. 377 15. 413
17. 318 19. 35 21. 37
23. 33 25. 53 27. 4,760
29. $3,540.24

Unit 2 (p. 6) 1. 4,502 3. 515,943
5. $47,461.95 7. $43.80
9. $43.85 11. $50.55 13. $64.45
15. $67.80 17. $73.75

Unit 3 (p. 7) 1. 2,364 3. 1,806
5. 4,957 7. 3,499 9. 1,877
11. 2,582 13. 5,873 15. 2,909

Unit 4 (p. 10) 1. $66,150
3. 4,180,000 5. $348
7. 144,720 9. 397,600
11. $45,999 13. $24,487.50
15. 268,950 17. 1,458
19. 2,088

Unit 5 (p. 11) 1. 113,278
3. 86,592 5. 8,562,684
7. 15,306,489 9. 298,650
11. 1,480,829 13. 452,340
15. 140,684,148 17. 186,365,490
19. $100,292.84

Unit 6 (p. 13) 1. $2.335 3. 1.55
5. 63.67 7. $1.575 9. 11.925
11. $4.34 13. 291.2 15. 2.4

Unit 7 (p. 14) 1. $361\frac{63}{89}$ 3. $987\frac{84}{93}$
5. $174\frac{18}{109}$

Unit 8 (p. 16)

1.		3.		5.	
360		500		6.5	
60		3,300		39.0	
870		1,000		8.1	
10		12,700		219.9	
80		500		.0	

7.		9.	
40		90	
90		50	
100		60	
50		80	
30		80	
310, estimated		360, estimated	
299, actual		355, actual	

11.		13.	
400		6,000	
600		8,000	
800		3,000	
700		8,000	
900		10,000	
3,400, estimated		35,000, estimated	
3,511, actual		34,844, actual	

15. 3,000
3,000
6,000
6,000
9,000
27,000, estimated
27,136, actual

PROBLEMS FOR PART ONE   (p. 17)

1 1. 65   3. 176   5. 189
7. 299   9. 292   11. 326   13. 35
15. 337   17. 5,450
19. $112,554.19

2 1. 42,019   3. 435,255
5. $28,592.46   7. $13,941
9. $7,725   11. $11,078
13. $17,236   15. $12,505
17. $29,847   19. $110,107

3 1. 2,629   3. 2,289   5. 3,527
7. 3,999   9. 4,913   11. +$1,845
13. −$1,815   15. $41,240
17. $6,755

4 1. 4,760   3. 80,000
5. 172,200   7. 324,000
9. 1,632,000   11. 36,000

5 1. 99,462   3. 19,733,868
5. 2,436,168   7. 477,690,780
9. 298,650   11. 10,615,608
13. 1,151,829   15. 353,434,746

6 1. 437   3. 97   5. 12.89
7. 46.3   9. 131.2   11. $.80

7 1. $171\frac{107}{141}$ 3. $102\frac{670}{681}$ 5. $732\frac{121}{467}$
7. $222\frac{91}{199}$

8

1.a. 40   b. 20   3.a. 27,000
b. 78,000   5.a. 27.07   b. 447.33

7. 80   9.   5,000
    40   9,000
    30   6,000
    80   7,000
    70   1,000
    ___   _____
    300, estimated   28,000, estimated
    294, actual   28,385, actual

Part Two

APPLICATION PROBLEMS

Unit 9   (p. 22)   1. $8\frac{3}{7}$ 3. $62\frac{1}{4}$
5. $48\frac{2}{5}$ 7. $19\frac{18}{25}$ 9. $6\frac{2}{5}$

Unit 10   (p. 23)   1. $\frac{103}{3}$ 3. $\frac{331}{4}$
5. $\frac{203}{3}$ 7. $\frac{344}{5}$ 9. $\frac{747}{8}$

Unit 11   (p. 25)   1. 4   3. $1\frac{1}{2}$
5. $\frac{24}{205}$ 7. $\frac{1}{10}$ 9. $1\frac{5}{19}$

Unit 12   (p. 25)   1. $\frac{35}{42}$ 3. $\frac{56}{64}$
5. $\frac{20}{32}$ 7. $\frac{25}{35}$ 9. $\frac{21}{27}$

Unit 13   (p. 26)   1. $16\frac{2}{3}$, or $.16\overline{666}$°
3. $.08\frac{1}{3}$, or $.08\overline{333}$
5. $.83\frac{1}{3}$, or $.83\overline{333}$ 7. $.37\frac{1}{2}$, or $.375$
9. $.18\frac{3}{4}$, or $.1875$ 11. $44\frac{4}{9}$, or $.44\overline{444}$
13. $.58\frac{1}{3}$, or $.58\overline{333}$ 15. $.53\frac{1}{3}$, or $.53\overline{333}$

Unit 14   (p. 27)   1. $\frac{13}{20}$ 3. $\frac{9}{100}$
5. $\frac{21}{2000}$ 7. $\frac{1}{800}$ 9. $\frac{1}{12}$

Unit 15   (p. 28)   1. $\frac{19}{20}$ 3. $\frac{19}{24}$
5. $2\frac{79}{120}$ 7. $2\frac{17}{48}$ 9. $34\frac{3}{20}$ 11. $246\frac{5}{12}$

Unit 16   (p. 30)   1. $\frac{11}{12}$ 3. $\frac{7}{10}$
5. $1\frac{5}{24}$ 7. $1\frac{55}{72}$ 9. $1\frac{23}{35}$

Unit 17   (p. 30)   1. $24\frac{7}{12}$ 3. $43\frac{23}{24}$
5. $17\frac{9}{10}$ 7. $193\frac{13}{24}$ 9. $88\frac{23}{48}$

Unit 18   (p. 31)   1. $\frac{1}{6}$ 3. $\frac{17}{48}$ 5. $\frac{1}{36}$
7. $\frac{15}{56}$ 9. $1\frac{11}{24}$

Unit 19   (p. 32)   1. $46.81\frac{1}{4}$
3. $11.78\frac{11}{12}$ 5. $80.97\frac{11}{12}$ 7. $22.18\frac{1}{4}$
9. $138.81\frac{19}{24}$

Unit 20   (p. 33)   1. $\frac{1}{8}$ 3. $\frac{7}{10}$ 5. $\frac{2}{5}$
7. $\frac{2}{7}$ 9. $\frac{15}{28}$

°The bar over a digit(s) means that the digit(s) repeats
without limit.

Unit 21 (p. 34)   1. $8.81\frac{1}{12}$
3. $3,973\frac{1}{12}$ 5. $2,719\frac{3}{4}$
7. $9,681\frac{77}{108}$ 9. $155\frac{5}{18}$

Unit 22 (p. 35)   1. 291.06
3. 48,129.48   5. 670.53
7. 1,879.412   9. 172,360,689

Unit 23 (p. 36)   1. 4   3. $1\frac{1}{5}$ 5. $\frac{2}{3}$
7. $\frac{25}{64}$ 9. $\frac{5}{6}$

Unit 24 (p. 36)   1. $3\frac{1}{75}$ 3. $1\frac{403}{957}$
5. $2\frac{58}{2155}$ 7. $2\frac{577}{874}$ 9. $1\frac{2533}{3344}$

Unit 25 (p. 37)
1. $1,983\frac{13}{19}$, or 1,983.6842+
3. $940\frac{35}{43}$, or 940.8139+
5. $.28\frac{265}{342}$, or .2877+
7. $64,193\frac{11}{13}$, or 64,193.8461+
9. $3,595\frac{35}{67}$, or 3,595.5223+

PROBLEMS FOR PART TWO   (p. 37)

9 1. $10\frac{3}{4}$ 3. $9\frac{4}{7}$ 5. 19   7. $51\frac{4}{5}$
9. $24\frac{16}{25}$ 11. $75\frac{11}{12}$ 13. $19\frac{12}{25}$ 15. $102\frac{3}{7}$

10 1. $\frac{86}{3}$ 3. $\frac{397}{5}$ 5. $\frac{799}{8}$ 7. $\frac{257}{4}$
9. $\frac{217}{6}$ 11. $\frac{109}{5}$ 13. $\frac{411}{8}$ 15. $\frac{362}{5}$

11 1. $1\frac{1}{9}$ 3. $\frac{4}{9}$ 5. $\frac{6}{65}$ 7. $\frac{10}{13}$
9. $\frac{28}{31}$ 11. $\frac{291}{452}$

12 1. $\frac{36}{48}$ 3. $\frac{35}{56}$ 5. $\frac{77}{84}$ 7. $\frac{20}{36}$
9. $\frac{18}{21}$ 11. $\frac{7}{8}$

13 1. $.66\frac{2}{3}$, or $.66\overline{666}$°   3. $.91\frac{2}{3}$,
or $.91\overline{666}$ 5. $.85\frac{5}{7}$, or $.85\overline{714285}$
7. $.13\frac{1}{3}$, or $.13\overline{333}$ 9. $.62\frac{1}{2}$, or .625
11. $.37\frac{1}{2}$, or .375   13. $.56\frac{1}{4}$, or .5625
15. $.31\frac{1}{4}$, or .3125   17. $.42\frac{6}{7}$,
or $.42\overline{857142}$ 19. $.44\frac{4}{9}$, or $.44\overline{444}$
21. $.58\frac{1}{3}$, or $.58\overline{333}$ 23. $.7\frac{1}{7}$,
or $.7\overline{142857}$

°The bar over a digit(s) means that the digit(s) repeats
without limit.

14 1. $\frac{83}{100}$ 3. $\frac{101}{10,000}$ 5. $\frac{15}{16}$ 7. $\frac{5}{16}$
9. $\frac{2}{7}$ 11. $\frac{1}{16}$ 13. $\frac{3}{16}$ 15. $\frac{4}{15}$

15 1. $1\frac{1}{12}$ 3. $2\frac{1}{4}$ 5. $1\frac{29}{30}$ 7. $1\frac{5}{7}$
9. $1\frac{5}{12}$ 11. $3\frac{53}{120}$ 13. $3\frac{5}{16}$
15. $2\frac{7}{30}$

16 1. $1\frac{7}{15}$ 3. $1\frac{1}{12}$ 5. $1\frac{5}{16}$ 7. $9\frac{5}{8}$

17 1. $14\frac{5}{6}$ 3. $58\frac{5}{12}$ 5. $39\frac{33}{35}$
7. $35\frac{13}{18}$ 9. $14\frac{17}{24}$ 11. $223\frac{5}{16}$
13. $298\frac{31}{40}$ 15. $510\frac{52}{63}$

18 1. $\frac{7}{24}$ 3. $\frac{17}{30}$ 5. $\frac{11}{30}$ 7. $6\frac{11}{12}$

19 1. $8.88\frac{5}{6}$ 3. $715\frac{9}{16}$ 5. $125\frac{47}{48}$
7. $6\frac{5}{24}$ 9. $\frac{25}{48}$

20 1. $\frac{7}{12}$ 3. $\frac{1}{4}$ 5. $\frac{55}{96}$ 7. $\frac{10}{21}$

21 1. $1,584\frac{3}{8}$ 3. 3,616
5. $3,957\frac{5}{18}$ 7. $29,941\frac{5}{32}$
9. $18,291.910\frac{5}{16}$ 11. $15,794\frac{2}{15}$

22 1. 393.648   3. 3,851.92
5. 4.846035   7. 4.32762

23 1. $\frac{25}{48}$ 3. $\frac{11}{18}$ 5. $1\frac{1}{8}$ 7. $1\frac{1}{4}$

24 1. $1\frac{7}{10}$ 3. $1\frac{191}{597}$ 5. $2\frac{58}{2155}$
7. $1\frac{1087}{2208}$ 9. $2\frac{605}{812}$ 11. $1\frac{13}{158}$

25 1. $1,523.77\frac{19}{53}$ 3. $1,251\frac{1}{8}$
5. $.01\frac{461}{1233}$ 7. 7.4414, or $7.44\frac{92}{807}$

Part Three

APPLICATION PROBLEMS

Unit 26 (p. 42)   1. $\frac{1}{16}$ 3. $\frac{1}{8}$ 5. $\frac{5}{6}$
7. $\frac{5}{16}$ 9. $\frac{7}{12}$ 11. $\frac{5}{12}$ 13. $\frac{7}{8}$
15. $\frac{7}{16}$

Unit 27 (p. 43) 1. $.37$\frac{1}{2}$ 3. $.18$\frac{3}{4}$
5. $.41$\frac{2}{3}$ 7. $.91$\frac{2}{3}$ 9. $.68$\frac{3}{4}$
11. $.45$\frac{5}{11}$ 13. $.58$\frac{1}{3}$ 15. $.44$\frac{4}{9}$

Unit 28 (p. 44) 1.a. $26.50 b. $25.25
c. $129.50 d. $161.33 e. $490.75
f. $833.33

Unit 29 (p. 45) 1. 1,344 3. 456
5. 288 7. 640 9. 516

Unit 30 (p. 46)

1. $\frac{2}{5} = \frac{40}{100} = .40 = 40\%$

3. $\frac{3}{8} = \frac{37\frac{1}{2}}{100} = .37\frac{1}{2} = 37\frac{1}{2}\%$

5. $\frac{5}{12} = \frac{41\frac{2}{3}}{100} = .41\frac{2}{3} = 41\frac{2}{3}\%$

7. $\frac{5}{6} = \frac{83\frac{1}{3}}{100} = .83\frac{1}{3} = 83\frac{1}{3}\%$

9. $\frac{3}{16} = \frac{18\frac{3}{4}}{100} = .18\frac{3}{4} = 18\frac{3}{4}\%$

11. $\frac{11}{12} = \frac{91\frac{2}{3}}{100} = .91\frac{2}{3} = 91\frac{2}{3}\%$

Unit 31 (p. 47) 1.a. $322 b. $70.50
c. $261.36 d. $1,066 e. $170
f. $59.80 g. $10.995 h. $4.35
3.a. $110,024.60 b. $518,687.40
5. $3,964

Unit 32 (p. 48) 1.a. 18% b. 13%
c. 17% d. 75% e. 67% f. 42%
3. 52 + % 5. 83%, 9.5%, 7.5%
(all rounded off)

Unit 33 (p. 49) 1.a. $504 b. $792
c. $576 d. $190 e. $7,900 f. $504
g. $250 h. $900 i. $300 j. $2,400
3. $132.67

PROBLEMS FOR PART THREE (p. 50)

26 1. $\frac{1}{4}$ 3. $\frac{5}{8}$ 5. $\frac{11}{12}$ 7. $\frac{1}{15}$
9. $\frac{2}{7}$

27 1. $.40 3. $.75 5. $.33
7. $.09 9. $.64 11. $.89

28
1.a. $(\frac{1}{12})$ = $ 22
b. $(\frac{5}{12})$ = 220
c. $(\frac{1}{6})$ = 125
d. $(\frac{1}{3})$ = 198
e. $(\frac{11}{12})$ = 319
f. Total $884

3.a. $(\frac{1}{12})$ = $ 11
b. $(\frac{1}{3})$ = 124
c. $(\frac{1}{6})$ = 105
d. $(\frac{11}{12})$ = 154
e. $(\frac{5}{12})$ = 140
f. Total $534

29 1. 832 3. 1,328 5. 805
7. 544 9. 2,509

30 1. .5 3. .8 5. 1
7. .0016 9. .005 11. $\frac{3}{8}$ 13. $\frac{7}{8}$
15. $\frac{1}{8}$ 17. $\frac{1}{7}$ 19. $7\frac{1}{2}$ 21. 75%
23. $62\frac{1}{2}\%$ 25. $112\frac{1}{2}\%$ 27. $66\frac{2}{3}\%$
29. .3%

31 1. 75 3. 61 5. 31 7. 43
9. 57 11. 235 13. $181.50
15. $114.75 17. 285 19. $.75
21. $216

32 1. $16\frac{2}{3}\%$ 3. $16\frac{2}{3}\%$ 5. 75%
7. 20%

33 1. $560 3. $24 5. $216 7. $208

Part Four

APPLICATION PROBLEMS

Unit 34 (p. 53) 1. $360

Unit 35   (p. 56)

	Trade Discount	Net Price
1.a.	$224.00	$336.00
b.	90.16	105.84
c.	241.67	483.33
d.	159.60	182.40
e.	201.60	470.40
f.	58.50	175.50
g.	103.02	222.98
h.	214.00	321.00

3. The offer from the Executive Office Equipment Company is better by $9.52.

Unit 36   (p. 58)   1.a. 48%   b. 50%
c. 31.6%   d. 46%   e. 46%   f. 27.1%

3.a.	$181.44
b.	87.36
c.	168.48
d.	339.12
e.	96.39
	$872.79

Unit 37   (p. 59)

	Single-Discount Equivalent	Trade Discount	Net Price
1.	14.5%	$ 47.12	$277.88
3.	27.32%	127.82	340.03
5.	46%	242.10	284.20
7.	16.64%	149.88	750.87
9.	46.56%	40.69	46.71

Unit 38   (p. 61)

	Cash Discount	Net Amount Paid
1.	$ 29.32	$1,436.68
3.	147.48	3,539.52
5.	250.15	4,752.85
7.	213.45	4,055.55
9.	11.84	1,172.16

Unit 39   (p. 62)
1.a. $8.025, discount; $152.47, due
  b. $16.70, discount; $539.93, due
  c. $21.58, discount; $697.80, due
  d. $21.92, discount; $1,069.03, due

Unit 40   (p. 63)
1. $3.75, discount; $90, due
3. $249.10, discount; $5,978.30, due

Unit 41   (p. 64)
1. $23.63, discount; $763.87, due
3. $3.75, discount; $371.53, due

Unit 42   (p. 66)   1. $1,405.79
3. $4,073   5.a. $10,683.22   b. 1,243
c. $5.23

Unit 43   (p. 67)   1. $6,104.68
3. $4,145   5. $4,738.13

373.06

PROBLEMS FOR PART FOUR   (p. 68)

34 1. $186.25, discount; $558.75, net price
3. $222, discount; $888, net price
5. $435, discount; $1,305, net price

35 1. $487.20, discount; $1,252.80, net price
3. $315, discount; $560, net price
5. $205.90, discount; $1,214.10, net price
7. $345, discount; $405, net price
9. $346.50

36 1. 28%   3. 19%   5. 37%
7. 25%   9. 40%

37 1. $524.16   3. $99.79
5. $369.33   7. $104.25
9. $173.54   11. $593.18

38

	Cash Discount	Net Amount Paid
1.	$123.00	$2,337.00
3.	—	3,674.00
5.	41.16	1,330.84
7.	31.86	3,154.14

39

1. $31.50, discount; $755.90, due
3. $73.22, discount; $1,147.18, due

40

1. $41.01, discount; $779.19, due

41

1. $0, discount; $12.78, due

42

	Collection and Guaranty		Commission	
1.	2% =	$ 7.20	4% =	$14.40
3.	$1\frac{1}{2}$% =	4.80	3% =	9.60
5.	$1\frac{1}{4}$% =	5.79	4% =	18.52

	Total Charges	Net Proceeds
1.	$ 44.09	$ 315.91
3.	30.54	289.46
5.	58.65	404.35

43

	Guaranty	Commission
1.	$23.55	$ 47.10
3.	5.88	20.58
5.	4.89	14.67

	Total Charges	Gross Cost
1.	$149.20	$934.20
3.	67.37	655.37
5.	91.02	417.02

Part Five

APPLICATION PROBLEMS

Unit 44 (p. 75) 1. $7; 13%
3. $7; 39%

Unit 45 (p. 77) 1. $60   3. $108.70

Unit 46 (p. 79) 1. $4.80   3. $5.40

Unit 47 (p. 81) 1. $129
3.a. $206.08   b. $247.30

Unit 48 (p. 85)

	Net Cost	Selling Price
1.a.	$165	$235.71
b.	390	780.00
c.	265	387.57
d.	552	736.00
e.	162	249.23

Unit 49 (p. 88) 1. $31,500 (value of average inventory based on cost price); 3.94 (merchandise inventory rate)
3. 6.75

PROBLEMS FOR PART FIVE   (p. 88)

44 1.a. $0.98; 38.88, or approximately 39%   b. $0.98; 28%

45 1.a. $30.41   b. $32.80

46 1.a. $118.08   b. $123

47 1. $50; $12\frac{1}{4}$%   3. $68

48 1.a. 100%   b. 50%

49 1. $72,220; 4.37
3.a. $49,824
b. (1) 7.04   (2) 7.04

Part Six

APPLICATION PROBLEMS

Unit 50   (p. 93)

Interest
1. $12.30
3. $11.40
5. $6.70
7. $6.25

Unit 51   (p. 96)   1. $815   3. $3.39
5. $3.89   7. $6.04   9. $6.48
11. $3.16   13. $8.22   15. $3.03

Unit 52   (p. 98)

Interest
1. $13.44
3. $5.50
5. $57.11

Unit 53   (p. 99)   1.a. 207   b. 74
c. 379   d. 126   e. 140   3. $191.88

Unit 54   (p. 103)   1.a. 264   b. 255
c. 195   d. 545   e. 145   f. 21   g. 125

Unit 55   (p. 106)   1. $54,000
3. $25,000   5. $22\frac{1}{2}$ (or 23) days
7. 15%   9. $4\frac{1}{2}$%

PROBLEMS FOR PART SIX   (p. 107)

50 1. $6.42   3. $6.60   5. $1.38
7. $8.28   9. $4.86   11. $3.06

51 1. $3.75   3. $24.00
5. $3.33   7. $8.58   9. $2.04

52
Interest
1. $ 9.61
3.   8.09
5.   5.50

53 1. $4.62   3. $9.94   5. $8.43
7. $14.25   9. $10.34

54 1. 173   3. 216   5. 545

	Time in Days	Accurate Interest	Amount Due
7.	117	8.31	440.31
9.	420	9.67	177.67
11.	297	30.82	535.82

55 1. $9,600   3. $113,760
5. 246 days   7. $2\frac{1}{2}$%   9. $4\frac{1}{4}$%
11. $2,820

Part Seven

APPLICATION PROBLEMS

Unit 56 (p. 112)

1. July 10; 39 days.
3. January 17; 77 days.

Unit 57 (p. 115)

1. $2,369.33

3.

	Note A	Note B
Interest on note	$ 63.00	$ 53.50
Value at maturity	$4,263.00	$5,403.50
Date of maturity	Nov. 3	Aug. 15
Term of discount	81 days	43 days
Bank discount	$ 57.55	$ 32.27
Collection fee	$ 5.33	$ 5.40
Total charges	$ 62.88	$ 37.67
Proceeds	$4,200.12	$5,365.83

	Note C	Note D
Interest on note	$ 24.75	$ 23.70
Value at maturity	$2,499.75	$1,603.70
Date of maturity	April 1	May 16
Term of discount	58 days	59 days
Bank discount	$ 28.19	$ 21.03
Collection fee	$ 6.25	$ 2.00
Total charges	$ 34.44	$ 23.03
Proceeds	$2,465.31	$1,580.67

Unit 58 (p. 119)
1. $1,651.81
3. $1,154.62

Unit 59 (p. 121)
1. $369.75
3. $300.50

Unit 60 (p. 124)

	Date of Maturity	Term of Discount
1.a.	Oct. 1	48 days
b.	Feb. 1	76 days
c.	Mar. 4	112 days
d.	Apr. 27	24 days
e.	July 10	65 days
f.	Oct. 5	39 days

PROBLEMS FOR PART SEVEN (p. 125)

56

	Date of Maturity	Term of Discount
1.	Aug. 20	73 days
3.	Mar. 14	80 days
5.	May 9	38 days
7.	June 22	20 days
9.	May 6	55 days

57

	Note A	Note B
1. Date of maturity	July 12	June 28
Term of discount	131 days	57 days
Bank discount	$ 9.55	$ 60.81
Collection fee	$ .62½	$ 10.67
Total charges	$ 10.18	$ 71.48
Proceeds	$364.82	$8,463.52

	Note C	Note D
Date of maturity	July 7	Nov. 15
Term of discount	31 days	105 days
Bank discount	$ 5.65	$ 23.92
Collection fee	$ 4.38	$ 1.64
Total charges	$ 10.03	$ 25.56
Proceeds	$864.97	$1,614.44

3. $1,200.35

58   1. $912.21   3. $1,315.29

59   1. $415.36   3. $459.12

60   1.a. $7,386.87   b. $7,421.67
c. $7,407.81   3. $837.48
5. $1,470.25

Part Eight

APPLICATION PROBLEMS

Unit 61   (p. 133)

	Compound Interest	Compound Amount
1.a.	$225.66	$1,085.66
b.	105.80	855.80
c.	243.60	4,243.60
d.	141.40	3,641.40
e.	101.25	2,101.25
f.	489.20	4,989.20

	Compound Interest	Compound Amount
3.a.	$292.49	$1,152.49
b.	68.03	494.03
c.	127.02	477.02
d.	248.15	478.15
e.	230.00	680.00
f.	159.04	752.04
g.	97.58	705.58
h.	210.90	994.90
i.	122.07	1,087.07
j.	193.64	915.64

5. $10,617.29

Unit 62   (p. 138)

	Present Worth	True Discount
1.a.	$1,188.12	$ 11.88
b.	872.55	17.45
c.	728.93	21.87
d.	3,064.36	30.64
e.	464.69	5.81
f.	641.28	9.62
g.	4,807.69	192.31
h.	938.88	21.12

3. $58.12

Unit 63   (p. 142)

	Installment Price	Carrying Charge
1.a.	$ 64.00	$ 4.00
b.	99.0C	5.00
c.	106.50	10.00
d.	157.00	7.50
e.	151.20	16.20
f.	201.60	21.60
g.	254.70	39.70

3. $90.00

	Install. Price	Interest (Carrying Charge)	Total Period (in Mos.)	Rate of Int. (%)
5.a.	$ 990	$ 60	105	12.3
b.	285	60	171	36.1
c.	450	60	36	53.3
d.	405	45	28	50.0
e.	1,050	150	78	36.9
f.	148	16	136	20.2
g.	360	46	10	80.6
h.	330	30	78	21.5
i.	74	8	36	38.1
j.	165	15	78	21.5

Unit 64   (p. 145)

	Carrying Charge	Monthly Payment	Monthly Principal
1.a.	$144.00	$212.00	$200.00
b.	60.00	58.89	55.56
c.	300.00	90.00	80.00
d.	270.00	181.67	166.67
e.	100.00	45.83	41.67
f.	166.67	108.33	100.00

	Time (in Mos.)	Rate of Interest (%)
1.a.	78	11.1
b.	171	7.6
c.	465	9.7
d.	171	11.4
e.	300	9.6
f.	210	9.5

3. 12.18 + %

Unit 65   (p. 148)

	No. of Payments	Total Interest Paid	Payments Plus Interest
1.a.	4	$7.50	$757.50
b.	4	5.00	555.00
c.	5	4.50	364.50
d.	3	2.26	272.26
e.	5	9.00	759.00

3. $719.56

Unit 66   (p. 150)   1. $84.80; 32.3%
3. $50.74; 32.0 + %   5. $42.25; 31.7%

PROBLEMS FOR PART EIGHT   (p. 151)

61   1. $629.88   3. $19,293.75
5. $1,384.82, compound interest;
$4,234.82, compound amount

62   1. $3,883.50   3. $7,093.60
5. $771.43; $68.57, gain

63   1. 10.6%   3. 20 months
5. 32.57%

64   1. $15, interest; $26.50, monthly
payment   3. $107.87; 8.6 + %

65

	No. of Payments	Total Int. Paid	Payments Plus Int.
1.a.	16	$34.00	$834.00
b.	3	.76	75.76
c.	6	6.30	366.30
d.	5	6.00	406.00
e.	5	5.25	355.25
f.	6	5.25	305.25

3. $791.76

66   1. $88.90; 26.7%
3. $63.45; 31.7%   5. $106.42; 26.9%

Part Nine

APPLICATION PROBLEMS

Unit 67   (p. 157)

	Tax
1.a.	$35.20
b.	42.60
c.	28.40
d.	35.20

Unit 68   (p. 164)

	Reg. Hours	Total Earnings
1.a.	39	$136.50
b.	37	114.70
c.	32	123.52
d.	$36\frac{1}{2}$	124.10
e.	$35\frac{3}{4}$	112.97
f.	29	94.25
		Total $706.04

Unit 69   (p. 166)   1.a. $120.00
b. $111.80   c. $143.75   d. $102.35
e. $84.00   f. $125.44   g. $148.40
h. $123.05   i. $97.50   j. $115.20

Unit 70   (p. 169)

	Employee	Weekly Gross Earnings
1.	A.H.	$ 165.29
	B.J.	196.81
	F.T.	187.74
	L.M.	207.60
	P.K.	195.06
	V.B.	252.08
	Total	$1,204.58

Daily totals, $245.11; $247.41; $250.65;
$237.60; $223.81

Employ.	Work Hours Acc.	Minimum Weekly Wage	Premium	Total Weekly Wage
3. C.T.	45	$152.00	$ 7.60	$159.60
H.B.	45	140.00	7.00	147.00
M.M.	$52\frac{1}{2}$	136.00	17.00	153.00
O.S.	40	126.00		126.00
C.H.	36	130.00		130.00
I.L.	50	150.00	15.00	165.00
		$834.00	$46.60	$880.60

Unit 71 (p. 173)

1. $16,000

	Bonus	Total Earnings
3.a.	$13,680 (200 x $68.40)	$48,680
b.	3,420 (50 x $68.40)	32,920
c.	3,078 (45 x $68.40)	29,078
d.	2,394 (35 x $68.40)	27,894
e.	2,736 (40 x $68.40)	31,736
f.	1,710 (25 x $68.40)	25,210
g.	2,394 (40 x $68.40)	26,394

PROBLEMS FOR PART NINE (p. 175)

67 1. Riggs, $42.20; Kane, $19.90; Ganges, $57.80; Potts, $29.80

68

	Gross Earnings		Gross Earnings
a.1.	$126.75	b.1.	$126.75
3.	144.00	3.	144.00
5.	164.50	5.	176.75
7.	123.50	7.	123.50
9.	151.70	9.	151.70

	Gross Earnings
c.1.	$131.63
3.	144.00
5.	176.75
7.	133.61
9.	161.95

69

Employee	Weekly Gross Earnings
1. Cardozo	$ 150.00
Phelps	183.12
Potter	155.52
Pucci	162.64
Rogoff	138.84
Ruh	157.65
Swift	168.00
Taussig	213.51
Zweig	175.54
Total	$1,504.82

Daily totals, $292.52; $297.30; $308.85; $310.92; $295.23

70

Employee	Weekly Gross Earnings
1. Cripps	$ 231.05
Long	192.96
Mays	188.72
Hawkins	222.40
Dakin	186.32
Maestro	171.34
Total	$1,192.79

Daily totals, $207.64; $245.21; $261.18; $257.36; $221.40

Employee	Work Hours Accomplished	Minimum Weekly Wage
3. Glaser	44	$114.00
Frome	46	120.00
Lysander	$46\frac{2}{3}$	121.00
Crump	$43\frac{1}{13}$	128.00
Kroft	$48\frac{8}{9}$	128.00
Hunsiker	44.8	122.00
Total		$733.00

Employee	Premium	Total Weekly Wage
Glaser	$ 4.56	$118.56
Frome	7.20	127.20
Lysander	8.27	129.27
Crump	3.84	131.84
Kroft	11.38	139.38
Hunsiker	5.86	127.86
Totals	$41.11	$774.11

71 1. Cartright, $1,511.21; Dooley, $1,222.92; Brinkman, $944.44
3.a. $22.93 b. Ketcham, $2,293; Melrose, $2,293; Lanier, $2,063.70; Grossman, $2,063.70; Fabrizzi, $1,949.05; Arnold, $1,719.75; Youngquist, $1,719.75; Bellman, $1,719.75; Poteet, $1,605.10; Quito, $1,605.10; Cable, $1,605.10; Troseth, $1,375.80; Hicks, $1,146.50; Turner, $1,146.50; Garcia, $1,031.85; Thornton, $1,031.85; Lequeux, $917.20; Baroody, $917.20; Doblier, $917.20; Klein, $687.90

Part Ten

APPLICATION PROBLEMS

Unit 72 (p. 179) 1. $10,285

Unit 73 (p. 181) 1. Class A, $496.87; Class B, $585; Class C, $736.25
3. Collating machine, $1,523.25; office furniture, $2,045.70

Unit 74 (p. 182) 1. $4,816.07

Unit 75 (p. 183)

	Depreciation Charge
1.a.	$ 500.00
b.	1,300.00
c.	198.90

Unit 76 (p. 185)

	Depreciation Amount
1.a.	$ 28.57
b.	72.53
c.	10.73
d.	15.98
e.	118.10
. f.	12.87
g.	15.79

Unit 77 (p. 188) 1. $18,304

	Depreciation	Book Value
3. First year	$1,493.33	$1,706.67
Second year	568.89	1,137.78
Third year	379.26	758.52
Fourth year	252.84	505.68
Fifth year	168.56	337.12
Sixth year	112.37	224.75

5. $2,799.50, straight-line method; $3,956, declining-balance method; $3,402.89, sum-of-the-years-digits method

PROBLEMS FOR PART TEN (p. 189)

72 1. $6.77%; $1,995, first year; $1,850, second year; $1,705, third year; $1,560, fourth year; $1,415, fifth year; $1,270, sixth year; $1,125, seventh year; $980, eighth year; $835, ninth year; $690, tenth year; $545, eleventh year; $400, twelfth year

73

	Annual Deprec. Charge	Book Value
1. First yr.	$2,820	$6,030
Second yr.	2,115	3,915
Third yr.	1,410	2,505
Fourth yr.	705	1,800, trade-in
	$7,050	value

74   1. $1,555.27

75   1. $264

76   1. $109.71, first year; $91.43, second year; $73.14, third year; $54.86, fourth year; $36.57, fifth year; $18.29, sixth year

77   1. $1,025.15   3. $1,783.25, first year; $565.25, each year, second to eighth years

Part Eleven

APPLICATION PROBLEMS

Unit 78   (p. 195)

	Percent of Overhead
1. Raw Materials	12%
Parts Manufacturing	$42\frac{2}{3}\%$
Assembling	$21\frac{1}{3}\%$
Finished Goods	$16\frac{2}{3}\%$
Offices	$7\frac{1}{3}\%$

3.a. $44\frac{4}{9}\%$ b. $24,000

Unit 79   (p. 199)   1. $24,648.39, net sales; $12,716.34, cost of goods sold; $11,932.05, gross profit on sales; $141.02, net loss

Unit 80   (p. 203)

1.

Amounts		Amount of Increase or Decrease
Current	Last	During Current Year
$186,545	$180,986	$5,559
18,819	21,008	(2,189)
157,312	163,912	(6,600)
176,131	184,920	(8,789)
23,409	31,176	(7,767)
152,722	153,744	(1,022)
33,823	27,242	6,581
9,709	8,815	894
24,114	18,427	5,687

3. 3.7%, rent; 2.3%, advertising; 9.5%, salaries; 1.4%, insurance; 1.9%, taxes

Unit 81   (p. 209)   1. 3.75 to 1
3. 2.98, 19X2; 3.44, 19X3

Unit 82   (p. 213)   1.a. $95,333.33
b. $213,333.33   3. $109,776
5. $332,742.50

Unit 83   (p. 216)

	Adjusted Bank and Checkbook Balance
1.a.	$ 989.50
b.	$ 610.93
c.	$4,917.43
d.	$1,873.42

	Adjusted Bank and Checkbook Balance
e.	$1,490.86
f.	$7,525.94
g.	$1,150.10
h.	$ 920.98

3. $1,457.94

PROBLEMS FOR PART ELEVEN
(p. 217)

78

1.

Expenses	Dress Dept. 40%	Shoe Dept. 15%	Access. Dept. 10%
Taxes	$ 9,856.00	$ 3,696.00	$ 2,464.00
Light	1,150.00	431.25	287.50
Insurance	2,567.20	962.70	641.80
Delivery	3,185.60	1,194.60	796.40
Clerical	7,460.80	2,797.80	1,865.20
Admin.	16,847.60	6,317.85	4,211.90
Totals	$41,067.20	$15,400.20	$10,266.80

Area Occupied

Expenses	Cosmetics Dept. 11%	Lingerie Dept. 24%
Taxes	$ 2,710.40	$ 5,913.60
Light	316.25	690.00
Insurance	705.98	1,540.32
Delivery	876.04	1,911.36
Clerical	2,051.72	4,476.48
Admin.	4,633.09	10,108.56
Totals	$11,293.48	$24,640.32

Grand Total: $102,668

3.

Month	Raw Materials (12%)	Parts Mfg. (42⅚%)	Assembling (21⅓%)
January	$762.00	$2,709.33	$1,354.67
February	681.00	2,421.33	1,210.67
March	874.80	3,110.40	1,555.20
April	830.16	2,951.68	1,475.84
May	524.04	1,863.25	931.63
June	718.32	2,554.03	1,277.01

Month	Finished Goods (16⅔%)	Offices (7⅓%)
January	$1,058.33	$465.67
February	945.83	416.17
March	1,215.00	534.60
April	1,153.00	507.32
May	727.83	320.25
June	997.67	438.97

79
1.a. $51,440   b. $8,750

80
1. $176,000, Net Sales;
$145,505,
Cost of Goods Available for Sale;
$127,925,
Cost of Goods Sold; $48,075, Gross
Profit; $21,085, Total Operating
Expenses;
$26,990, Net Income from Operations

81
1.a. 14.3%, cash; 1.9%, notes
receivable; 26.5%, accounts receivable;
35.2%, stock on hand; 4.4%, supplies on
hand; 9.5%, furniture; 8.3%, equipment
b. 3.7%, notes payable; 12.8%,
accounts payable; .2%, interest
payable; 83.2%, owner's equity
3. 11.5% = ($3,979 ÷ $34,600)
5. 1.25 to 1

82

1.

	Goodwill at Beginning of Year	Average Net Annual Profit
First	$38,000	$26,712
Second	30,488	26,712
Third	22,976	26,712
Fourth	15,464	26,712
Fifth	7,952	26,712
Sixth	440	26,712

	Normal Net Profit Rate, 12%	Excess Profit Earned	Goodwill at End of Year
First	$19,200	$7,512	$30,488
Second	19,200	7,512	22,976
Third	19,200	7,512	15,464
Fourth	19,200	7,512	7,952
Fifth	19,200	7,512	440
Sixth	19,200	440	......

3.a. $32,400 (12% of $270,000)
b. $11,100   c. $111,000

83 1. $2,941.38   3. $493.40

Part Twelve

APPLICATION PROBLEMS

Unit 84   (p. 230)   1a. $1.39   b. $.75
c. $42.25   d. $.10   e. $6.22   f. $.03
g. $.12   h. $.33

	Tax Rate Levied on:	
$1	$100	$1000
3.a. .012	$1.20	$12.00
b. .021	2.10	21.00
c. .012	1.20	12.00
d. .065	6.50	65.00
e. .05	5.00	50.00
f. .06765	6.77	67.65

Unit 85   (p. 233)   1.a. $121.50   b. $196
c. $3.28   3. $89.39

Unit 86   (p. 235)   1. $23,000. The
actual loss will be reduced, since the
amount is less than the insurance
carried.

Unit 87   (p. 237)

	Amount Paid by Insurance Company
1.a.	$10,000
b.	20,000
c.	18,000
d.	7,000
e.	4,800
f.	15,000
g.	35,000
h.	12,500

Unit 88   (p. 239)

Premium Amount	Days in Force	Premium Returned	Premium Retained
1. $600.00	59	$503.01	$ 96.99
3. $675.00	147	403.15	271.85
5. $138.75	189	66.90	71.85

Unit 89   (p. 241)

	Percent of Premium Returned	Amount of Premium Returned
1.a.	73%	$212.92
b.	69%	144.90
c.	65%	364.00
d.	46%	138.00
e.	63%	85.05
f.	68%	57.38
g.	17%	61.09
h.	40%	41.28

3. $41.22

Unit 90   (p. 247)   1.a. $88.15
b. $66.00   c. $54.60   d. $124.60
e. $122.40

Unit 91   (p. 250)   1.a. $149.40
b. $141.10   c. $69.00   d. $94.55

Unit 92   (p. 252)

1.a. $36.19	$72.38	$19.00
b. 16.27	162.70	83.79
c. 32.15	192.90	17.04

3. $33.34, annually; $85.85,
semiannually; $43.76, quarterly;
$14.73, monthly

Unit 93   (p. 256)   1. $182.95
3.a. $3,603   b. $369   5. $37.70

PROBLEMS FOR PART TWELVE
(p. 258)

84 1.a. $16.12 b. $.02 c. $.22
d. $.95 + $2.46 = $3.41 e. $2.24 +
$5.83 = $8.07 f. $.33 g. $.58
h. $64.09
3. $2,019.22

85

	Premium Paid
1.a.	$ 59.76
b.	29.03
c.	96.00
d.	481.25
e.	58.67
f.	9.45
g.	268.65

86 1. $100,000. The actual loss would
be recovered since the amount is less
than the insurance carried.

3. $7,312.50, Company A; $3,656.25,
Company B; $2,193.75, Company C

87

1. $24,000

3. $27,000, Company A; $36,000,
Company B; $54,000, Company C;
$18,000, Company D

88

	Annual Premium Amount	Days in Force	Amount of Premium Returned	Retained
1.a.	$280.00	90 (365-90 = 275, days canceled)	$210.96	$69.04
b.	45.00	95 (365-95 = 270, days canceled)	33.28	11.72
c.	105.00	75 (365-75 = 290, days canceled)	83.43	21.57
d.	150.00	160 (365-160 = 205, days canceled)	84.24	65.76
e.	148.83	60 (365-60 = 305, days canceled)	121.86	23.97

3.a. 1.60% b. $88.80 c. $158.95

89

	Annual Premium Amount	Days in Force	Premium Returned
1.a.	$ 750.00	65	$616.44 ($750 − $133.56)
b.	1,593.75	210	676.80 ($1,593 − $916.95)
c.	281.25	125	184.93 ($281.25 − $96.32)
d.	305.63	132	195.10 ($305.63 − $110.53)
e.	880.00	245	289.32 ($880 − $590.68)

90 1. $5,000; $3,500 bodily-injury

	Basic Premium B.I.	P.D.	Operator Factor	Accident Factor
3.a.	$43	–	1.50	.70
b.	–	$21	1.80	.00
c.	$37	–	1.75	.30
d.	23	–	1.40	.00
e.	–	$22	.75	.70

	Total Factor	B. I. Premium	P. D. Premium	Total Premium
a.	2.20	$94.60	–	$94.60
b.	1.80	–	$37.80	37.80
c.	2.05	$75.85	–	75.85
d.	1.40	32.20	–	32.20
e.	1.45	–	$31.90	31.90

91 1. $1,209.20 3.a. $126.10
b. $16.50 c. $39.10 d. $197.40
e. $166.60

92 1.a. $76.98 b. $456.40
c. $152.85 d. $545.72
3. $79.36

93 1. $12,600 3. $66.77

Part Thirteen

APPLICATION PROBLEMS

Unit 94 (p. 266) 1. $1,900
3. Meagher's share: $14,519.07;
McGrath's share: $7,259.53

Unit 95 (p. 269) 1. Wallace's share:
$1,100, first year, and $12,550, second
year; Wright's share: $1,650, first
year, and $18,000, second year
3. $6,240.89, Hopkins' share; $6,059.11,
Smith's share

Unit 96 (p. 272) 1. $2,381.25,
Sargent's total share; $2,418.75,
Cushman's total share   3. $3,750,
Bacon's share; $3,450, Thomas's share

Unit 97 (p. 275) 1. $20, preferred;
$5, common   3. $26, preferred;
$9.88, common

Unit 98 (p. 277)

	Rate Percent (%)	Creditor's Share
1.a.	36	$1,872.00
b.	42	409.50
c.	8	288.32
d.	35	4,200.00
e.	68	5,634.48

3. $811.30

PROBLEMS FOR PART THIRTEEN
(p. 278)

94 1. $8,000   3. $2,426.93,
Bowman's share of loss; $1,213.47,
Hiller's share of loss

95 1. $3,000, Meehan's share;
$4,500, Howe's share   3. $21,187.50,
Lockwood's share; $16,312.50,
Sutkowski's share

96 1. $18,433.75, Lowell's share;
$18,266.25, Parton's share

3. $6,130.42, Toshida's share; $5,330.42,
Ashamoto's share

97 1. $8, preferred; $2.50, common

98 1. $21,228   3.a. $28,704
b. $153,088   c. $54,408

Part Fourteen

APPLICATION PROBLEMS

Unit 99 (p. 287)

	Total Accumulation
1.a.	$ 3,072.05
b.	11,937.84
c.	11,476.43
d.	6,988.89
e.	2,449.98

Unit 100 (p. 293)

	Amount Borrowed
1.a.	$ 3,586.98
b.	77,217.35
c.	55,591.94
d.	10,773.15
e.	23,055.46

PROBLEMS FOR PART FOURTEEN
(p. 294)

99 1. $14,745.85   3. $1,873.45

100 1. $167,676.88

Part Fifteen

APPLICATION PROBLEMS

Unit 101 (p. 302) 1. $10,386+
3.a. 35.1¢   b. 34.95¢   c. Both 35.9¢
and 34.9¢

Unit 102 Practice Drills

Plotted graphs for the odd-numbered problems in Unit 102 Practice Drills have been included here as a further aid to understanding and exercising the concepts of illustrating statistical data. The Application Problems for Unit 102 follow on page 352.

(p. 305) 1.

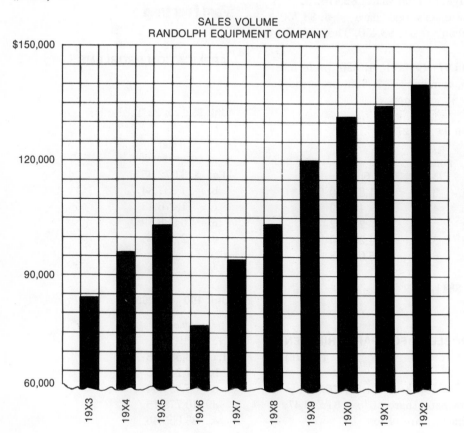

SALES VOLUME
RANDOLPH EQUIPMENT COMPANY

(p. 305) 3.

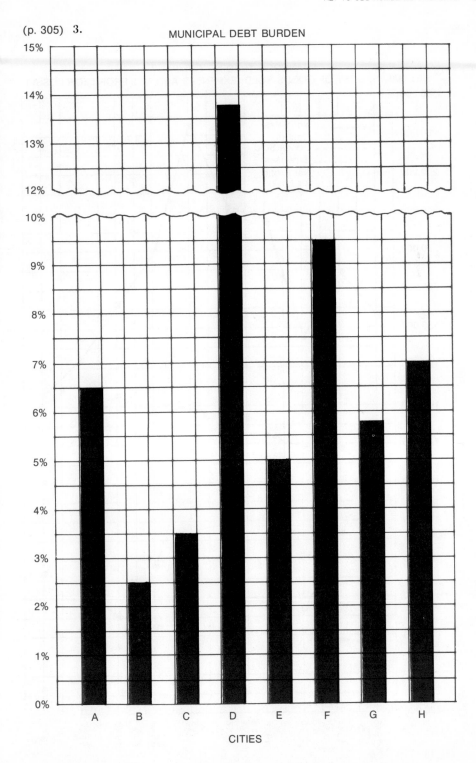

MUNICIPAL DEBT BURDEN

CITIES

(p. 309)

HANCOCK TRADING COMPANY
NET SALES, COST OF GOODS SOLD, EXPENSES AND NET PROFIT (OR LOSS)

(p. 310)

SINGLE-LINE GRAPH	RECTANGLE GRAPH

45%	Automobiles 33,750		45%	Automobiles 33,750
22%	Falls 16,500		22%	Falls 16,500
8%	Fires 6,000		8%	Fires 6,000
8%	Drowning 6,000		8%	Drowning 6,000
3%	Public Transportation, 2,250		3%	Public Transportation 2,250
2½%	Firearms, 1,875		2½%	Firearms 1,875
11½%	Other Causes 8,625		11½%	Other Causes 8,625

(p. 311)

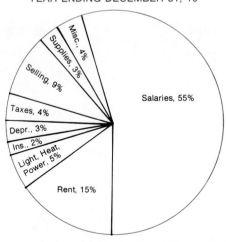

ANDOVER MANUFACTURING COMPANY
OPERATING EXPENSES
YEAR ENDING DECEMBER 31, 19--

Unit 102   (p. 312)

1.

PRECISION SURGICAL INSTRUMENT COMPANY
ANNUAL DIVIDENDS
19X3 - 19X2

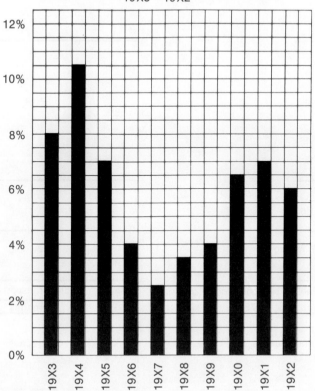

3. Ideally, a graph showing amounts of $100 would be divided into sections of $100. Because each unit of this graph is based on $10,000, the points plotted are approximations.

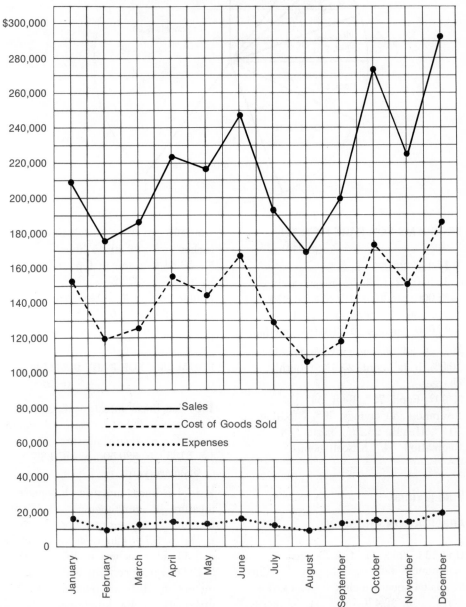

PRECISION AUTOMOTIVE EQUIPMENT COMPANY
SALES, COST OF GOODS SOLD, AND EXPENSES
YEAR ENDING DECEMBER 31, 19--

——— Sales
- - - - - Cost of Goods Sold
· · · · · · · · Expenses

5.

ANY CITY, U.S.A.
EXPENDITURES PER DOLLAR

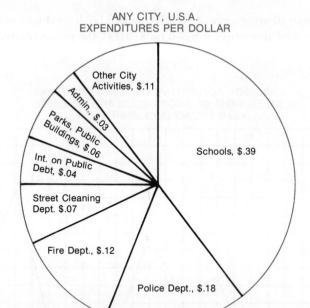

PROBLEMS FOR PART FIFTEEN
(p. 314)

101 1.a. 303.55   b. 309
3. 19×4: $221,666.67, mean, and
$225,000, median; 19×5: $281,250,
mean, and $295,000, median; 19×6:
$325,000, mean, and $310,000, median

102 1. 34.3%, cash; 14.3%, C.O.D.;
20.9%, installment; 27.0%, monthly
charge
3. 90°, Food; 72°, Rent; 54°,
Insurance and savings; 36°, Clothing;
10.8°, Health; 25.2°, Charity; 18°,
Recreation; 54°, Miscellaneous

Part Sixteen

APPLICATION PROBLEMS

Unit 103 (p. 321) 1. 2.25 acres
3. 3 pounds 3 ounces   18 pennyweights
5. 33,264 square inches   7. 14.87+
acres   9. $2,420.76   11. 3.8 acres

Unit 104 (p. 324) 1. 345.49+
inches   3. 29.80845 liters
5. 453.64+ grams in 1 pound
avoirdupois; 373.25+ grams in 1
pound troy   7. 7.9455 pecks; 18.494
liquid gallons   9. $128.67
11. 4.72+ inches × 6.29+ inches

PROBLEMS FOR PART SIXTEEN
(p. 325)

103 1.a. linear measure   b. square
measure   c. linear measure   d. cubic
measure   e. square measure
3.a. $135   b. $20.50   c. $953.33
d. 6 square yards   e. 2.84+ miles

104 1.a. linear measure   b. square
measure   c. cubic measure   d. linear
measure   e. square measure 3.a. 60
miles   b. 3.7+ kilograms   c. 20 inches
d. 1.53 cubic inches   e. 497+ miles
f. 193.6 square centimeters   g. 8.2
meters   h. 10 liquid quarts; 420.4
dry quarts   i. 100 kilograms

INDEX